T5-AFE-336

Thomas Friedli, Michael Kickuth, Frank Stieneker,
Peter Thaler, and Jürgen Werani

Operational Excellence in the Pharmaceutical Industry

Operational Excellence

in the Pharmaceutical Industry

Edited by
Thomas Friedli, Michael Kickuth, Frank Stieneker,
Peter Thaler, and Jürgen Werani

With contributions from
Bart Bastoen, Stephen E. Chick, Thomas Friedli, Keith Goffin, David Hampton,
Michael Kickuth, Christoph H. Loch, Hermann Osterwald, Bruce Ramsay, Gerrit Reepmeyer,
Marek Szwejczewski, Daniel Tykal, Malcolm Wheatley, Jürgen Werani, and Bart Dewolf

Editio Cantor Verlag Aulendorf (Germany)

Der Pharmazeutische Betrieb · Band/Volume 50

Bibliographic data available from the National Library of Germany ("Deutsche Bibliothek")

This publication is catalogued and indexed in "Deutsche Nationalbibliographie" of the National Library of Germany; detailed bibliographic data is available on the Internet at http://dnb.ddb.de.

Operational Excellence in the Pharmaceutical Industry

ISBN 3-87193-350-3

Typeset by Texdo, Stuttgart (Germany); printed and bound by VeBu Druck + Medien GmbH, Bad Schussenried (Germany)

ECV · Editio Cantor Verlag on the Internet: www.ecv.de

Contents

Preface 9

Editors, Authors, and Acknowledgements 10

Introduction 12

List of Abbreviations 14

I Challenges in the Pharmaceutical Industry 17

Gerrit Reepmeyer and Michael Kickuth

I.1 Declining R&D Productivity 17

I.2 Changing Market Conditions 21

I.3 Increasing Competition 23

I.4 Increasing Costs and Low Operating Efficiency 24

I.5 Implications for Manufacturing 26

II A Reference Model for Operational Excellence 30

Michael Kickuth, Thomas Friedli, Christoph H. Loch, and Stephen E. Chick

II.1 Introduction 30

II.2 Management Quality and Factory Performance 32

II.3 Developing the Operational Excellence Reference Model for the OPEX project 40

III The Status of the Pharmaceutical Industry 53

Michael Kickuth, Thomas Friedli, Peter Thaler, Daniel Tykal, and Hermann Osterwald

III.1 How Do Pharmaceutical Companies Respond to the Changing Environment? 55

III.2 Cost Savings Potential - What is the Main Leverage for Streamlining Operations? 56

III.3 Linking Practice to Performance: Testing the Operational Excellence Model 58

III.4 Linking Operational Excellence to Overall Plant Performance 68

III.5 Does Operational Excellence Matter from a Corporate Perspective? 69

III.6 Insights from the Plant Audits 70

III.7 Special Insights from a Contract Manufacturer – The Case of NextPharma 77

IV Operational Excellence in the Pharmaceutical Industry: Case Studies from the Field 82

Michael Kickuth, Thomas Friedli, Daniel Tykal, Marek Szwejczewski, Keith Goffin, Malcolm Wheatley, Bart Bastoen, Bart Dewolf, David Hampton, Christian Ewers, Christoph H. Loch, Stephen E. Chick, and Bruce Ramsay

IV.1 Case Study: Launching an Operational Excellence Initiative in a Global Pharmaceutical Company - The Case of Pfizer Inc. 82

IV.2 Case Study: The Capsugel Way to Operational Excellence 95

IV.3 Case Study: Maximizing Equipment Effectiveness at Reckitt Benckiser 102

IV.4 Case Study: Achieving 6-Sigma Levels at a Pharmaceutical Plant 110

IV.5 Lean Compliance: Implementing Just-in-Time (JIT) in a Regulated Environment 124

IV.6 The Role of Management Quality in the Context of Operational Excellence 131

IV.7 Stages of Operational Excellence 138

V The Pharmaceutical Plant of the Future 147

Michael Kickuth and Thomas Friedli

V.1 The Pharmaceutical Industry in 2010 147

V.2 Implications for Manufacturing 150

V.3 How To Respond? 153

V.4 The Plant of the Future 164

Appendices 171

References 187

Preface

More than 20 years have gone since we established the expression "lean production" for a set of Japanese techniques which changed the whole competitive landscape of the automotive industry in the 1980s giving way to fundamental changes how production is done in industry after industry.

The concepts described in our book "The Machine that Changed the World" and further elaborated in our later publications have been widely copied throughout the world. But there remains healthy debate regarding the extent to which the philosophy behind these techniques is applicable.

The results of the benchmarking study in the pharmaceutical industry that is described in this book are a further proof that "lean thinking" knows no industry barriers. If pharmaceutical companies want to stay ahead of competition they should have a look at the evidence presented in this book an draw their conclusions!

Prof. Dr. Daniel T. Jones
The Lean Enterprise Academy
Ross-on-Wye, Herefordshire (UK)

Prof. Dr. Daniel T. Jones is author of „The Machine that Changed the World: the Story of Lean Production", „Lean Thinking: Banish Waste and Create Value in Your Corporation" and "Lean Solutions: How Companies and Costumers can Create Value and Wealth together", all of them together with James P. Womack.

Editors, Authors, and Acknowledgements

Editors

Prof. Dr. Thomas Friedli, University of St. Gallen (Switzerland)
Dr. Michael Kickuth, University of St. Gallen (Switzerland)
Dr. Frank Stieneker, International Association for Pharmaceutical Technology (APV – Arbeitsgemeinschaft für Pharmazeutische Verfahrenstechnik), Mainz (Germany)
Peter Thaler, Institut für angewandte Prozeßoptimierung AG (IFAP), Kaisten (Switzerland)
Dr. Jürgen Werani, Pfizer Europe, Karlsruhe (Germany)

Authors

Bart Bastoen, Pfizer (Belgium)
Dr. Stephen E. Chick, INSEAD (France)
Prof. Dr. Thomas Friedli, University of St. Gallen (Switzerland)
Prof. Dr. Keith Goffin, Cranfield School of Management, Cranfield University (UK)
David Hampton, Rath & Strong (UK)
Dr. Michael Kickuth, University of St. Gallen (Switzerland)
Prof. Dr. Christoph H. Loch, INSEAD (France)
Dr. Hermann Osterwald, NextPharma (Germany)
Bruce Ramsay, WPI Group (UK)
Dr. Gerrit Reepmeyer, University of St. Gallen (Switzerland)
Dr. Marek Szwejczewski, Cranfield School of Management, Cranfield University (UK)
Daniel Tykal, University of St. Gallen (Switzerland)
Dr. Malcolm Wheatley, Cranfield School of Management (UK)
Bart Dewolf, Pfizer (Belgium)

Special thanks for making valuable contributions to:

Dr. Hermann Allgaier, CEO, Merckle Biotec (Germany)
Harald Doerenbach, Babenhausen Plant, Siemens VDO Automotive (Germany)
Dr. Christian Ewers, Schering (Germany)
Ron Millender, Vice President & General Manager, Americas, Capsugel (USA)
Dr. G. K. Raju, Massachusetts Institute of Technology (MIT) (USA)
Dr. Daniel Vasella, Chairman & CEO, Novartis (Switzerland)

The editors and authors would further like to thank all companies that participated in the Operational Excellence project and the following persons that have supported the project and the editing of the book: Michael Kamber, Stefan Krieger, Christoph Müller, and Daniel Tykal.

Introduction

When we came together in mid 2003 we had a vision in mind: the vision of a pharmaceutical company operating like Toyota, reducing every kind of waste, steadily optimizing the way how things are done and systematically nurturing a culture of continuous improvement. For us there were clear signs that a radical rethinking of pharmaceutical manufacturing would be necessary in order to ensure a sustainable future. Based on this understanding we started the biggest benchmarking project ever seen in pharmaceutical manufacturing; being well aware that at the beginning of the transformation of the U.S. and German car manufacturing industry was also a benchmarking study that had been documented in the famous book "The machine that changed the world" by James Womack and Daniel Jones. The results of our study and an outlook on the future of pharmaceutical manufacturing are described in this book.

We start with a look on the changing environment for pharmaceutical companies by working out the challenges they are facing. Then we develop the model we used for our study. This model shows our understanding of "Operational Excellence". We go on with a description of what we found in plants all over Europe and draw a conclusion concerning the importance of Operational Excellence for overall sustainable superior performance of a pharmaceutical company. In chapter IV we refer to a sample of different case studies. Each of them highlights a particular aspect of successfully striving for Operational Excellence. We end chapter IV with a stage model for launching an Operational Excellence program derived from the study of the cases. Lastly, in chapter V we develop the picture of the pharmaceutical plant of the future.

The way to Operational Excellence is a journey. This journey is long and often hard but it is quite clear that all companies that hesitate to take this journey, that are hiding themselves behind regulations, are risking their future. We hope that with this book we give some valuable advice on starters of how to make things happen; whilst also offering to all the others already on the road some guidance on the way.

We would like to thank all the people that helped to make this project happen and to all of the authors who provided us with their know-how. Especially we would like to thank

- Prof. Dr. Fritz Fahrni who supported the initialization from the side of the University of St. Gallen (Switzerland)

- Prof. Dr. Peter Kleinebudde, President International Association for Pharmaceutical Technology (APV – Arbeitsgemeinschaft für Pharmazeutische Verfahrenstechnik), Mainz (Germany), who did the same in his organization
- And the Authors for their contribution

Thomas Friedli, Michael Kickuth,
Frank Stieneker, Peter Thaler,
and Jürgen Werani

February 2006

List of Abbreviations

APV	International Association for Pharmaceutical Technology
ADMET	Analytical, Distribution, Metabolism, Excretion and Toxicology
AMT	Advanced Manufacturing Technologies
ANOG	Analysis of Goodness
API	Active Pharmaceutical Ingredient
APS	Advanced Planning Software
BPR	Business Process Reengineering
C&E	Cause-and-Effect
CAQ	Computer Aided Quality
CEO	Chief Executive Officer
CFO	Chief Financial Officer
cGMP	Current Good Manufacturing Process
CMO	Contract Manufacturer Organization
CP	Combination Pack Line
CTQ	Critical to Quality
DMAIC	Define, Measure, Analyze, Improve, Control
DOE	Design of Experiments
DPMO	Defects Per Million Opportunities
DS	Drug Substance
EAI	Enterprise Application Integration
EM	Efficient Manufacture
ERP	Enterprise Resource Planning
FDA	Food and Drug Administration
FIFO	First-In-First-Out
FMEA	Failure Mode and Effect Analysis
GFT	Gelatin Filled Tanks
GMP	Good Manufacturing Process
HCM	Hard Capsule Machine
IEA	Industrial Excellence Award
JIT	Just-in-Time
KPI	Key Performance Indicator
MIT	Massachusetts Institute of Technology

Mn	Manganese
MRP	Material Requirements Planning
NCE	New Chemical Entities
NDA	New Drug Application
NHS	National Health System
NPS	NextPharma Production System
NVA	Non-Value Adding
OEE	Overall Equipment Effectiveness
OPEX	Operational Excellence in the Pharmaceutical Industry
ou	output units
PAT	Process Analytical Technology
PGM	Pfizer Global Manufacturing
PhRMA	Pharmaceutical Research and Manufacturers of America
POMA	Pharmaceutical Outsourcing Management Association
PTS	Production Technology Support
QA	Quality Assurance
QC	Quality Control
QFD	Quality Function Deployment
R&D	Research and Development
RFID	Radio Frequency Identification
RFT	Right First Time
RFT LT	Right First Time Leadership Team
SIPOC	Supplier-Input-Process-Output-Customer
SME	Small and Medium-sized Enterprises
SMED	Single Minute Exchange of Die
SOP	Standard Operating Procedure
SPC	Statistical Process Control
TPM	Total Productive Maintenance
TPS	Toyota Production System
TQC	Total Quality Control
TQM	Total Quality Management
VA	Value Adding
VOC	Voice of the Customer
WIP	Work-in-progress

I Challenges in the Pharmaceutical Industry

Gerrit Reepmeyer and Michael Kickuth

"Today, there are few people that are not aware about the future challenges of the [pharmaceutical] industry: In the fundamental research sciences – molecular biology, genomics, chemical sciences and computer sciences there are interesting technical advancements – however the development of the institutional, regulatory and social political environment will put the future earnings potentials of this industry to the test."

Gary P. Pisano
Harvard Business School

In this chapter we describe the current industry environment for pharmaceutical companies to understand the role of manufacturing in this context. At the end of the chapter, we derive explicit requirements for manufacturing in the pharmaceutical industry.

I.1 Declining R&D Productivity

By definition, research and development (R&D) productivity is the ratio of input in R&D versus its output. The black-box in between consists of the drug development pipeline, new screening and research technologies, worldwide cooperation networks in clinical research and testing, and a whole new armada of licensing and cooperation agreements with competitors and biotechnology start-ups. Still, as a recent Reuters study shows, R&D performance of the major pharmaceutical companies is sub-optimal (Reuters 2003):

- Pipeline output is low and declining;
- Costs of R&D are rising rapidly, driven by larger and more complex clinical studies and expensive new enabling technologies;

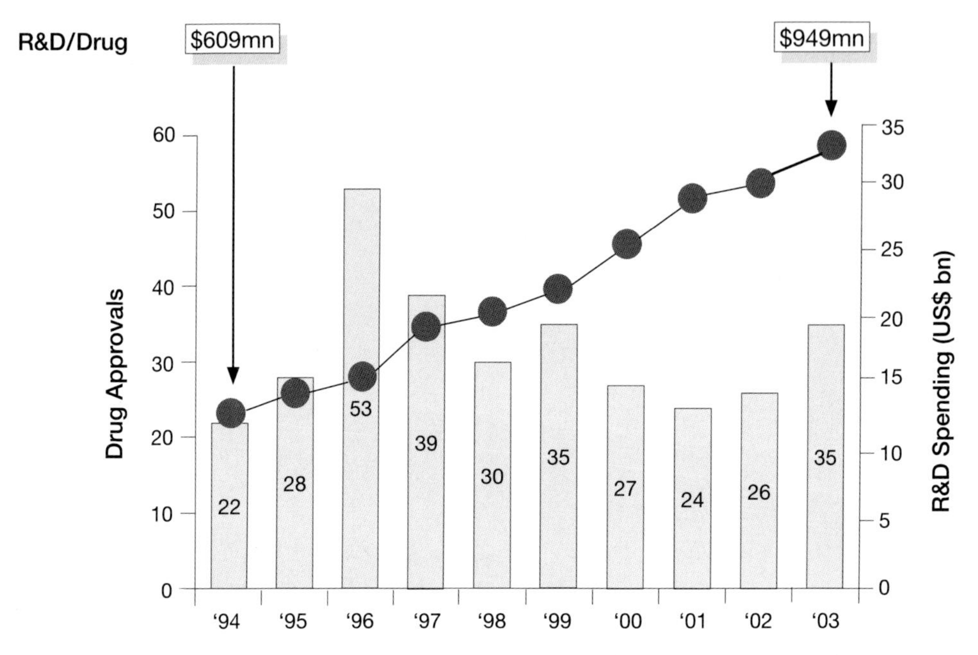

Figure 1: The widening productivity gap in drug discovery (Source: PhRMA 2004).

- Heavy competition from follow-on drugs, a decrease of the period of market exclusivity and falling numbers of new product launches make it difficult to replace revenues lost through patent expiry;
- Protracted clinical trials and administrative procedures reduce the marketed shelf life of patented products.

In addition, R&D expenditures of the pharmaceutical companies worldwide have grown constantly over the last decades (in relative terms, from 11.4% of sales in 1970 to 18.5% in 2001), and – according to PhRMA – the major US and European companies invested more than USD 33 billion in R&D in 2003 alone (PhRMA 2004). But since the mid-1990s, the launch of new molecular entities on the market has declined or has been constant at best (Figure 1). The number of new drugs approved by the Food and Drug Administration (FDA) in the United States fell to just 24 in 2001, although this number slightly improved in 2002 and 2003. The long average lead time in pharmaceutical R&D cannot be used as an excuse because, firstly, the greatest R&D expenses are in the final phases of drug development (within just a few years of market introduction) and, secondly, because the observed trends in the 1990s were already present in the decades before.

Consequently, drug development costs per new drug approval are constantly increasing. In 1976, it cost USD 54 million to develop a new drug, USD 231 million in 1987, and about USD 280 million in 1991 (DiMasi 2001). This number has grown to close to USD 1 billion by now. Even though it is not legitimate to make a direct comparison between R&D spending and R&D productivity, the tendency of increasing R&D costs per drug is certainly a concern for the top management in pharmaceutical companies.

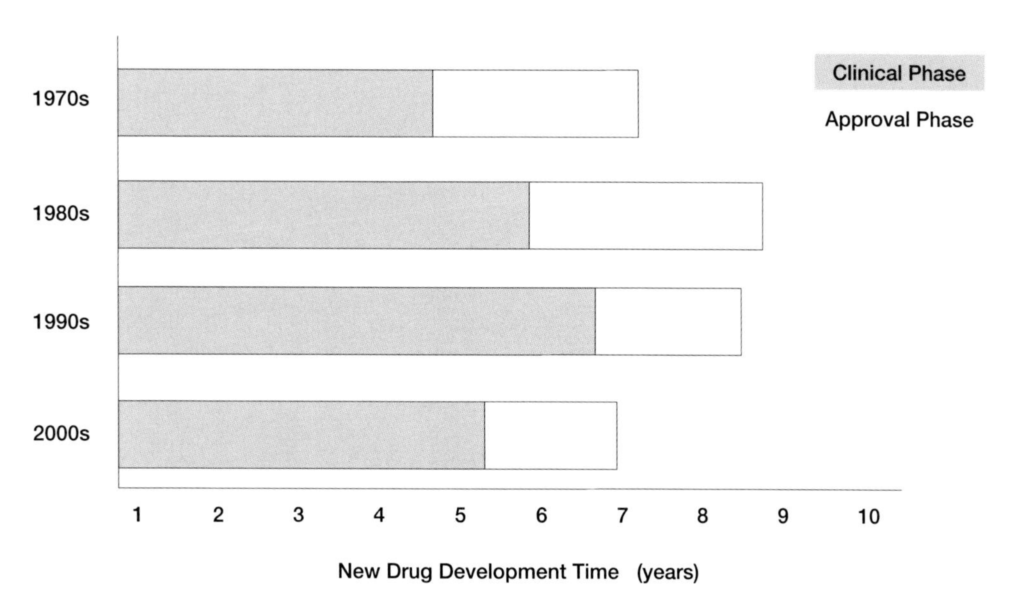

Figure 2: Time spent by a drug candidate in the clinical and approval phases (Source: PhRMA 2004).

The increase in average R&D costs per new drug approval is based on two general developments. On the one hand, the costs of clinical trials have grown due to the increased need of differentiating new drugs in the market, which is only possible by proving the drugs' profile in more comprehensive clinical studies. On the other hand growing safety and efficacy requirements have triggered a continuous increase of the complexity, duration and size of clinical trials. Increased R&D expenditures are therefore the price for increased product safety and reduced likelihood of severe health issues connected to the introduction of a new drug.

The situation has been exceptionally precarious for most large pharmaceutical companies for many years, where R&D productivity expressed as the number of launched new chemical entities (NCEs) has been particularly low. According to research by KPMG and Lehman Brothers, the companies Roche and Novartis spent on average about USD 1.7 billion in R&D per year from 1992 until 1998, but launched an average of just 2 or 1.2 NCEs per year between 1996 and 1999, respectively[1]. However, Novartis' R&D performance improved significantly making the company the most successful firm in terms of launched NCEs over the most recent past.

Furthermore the average duration of drug development has increased since the 1970s, although it seems to have improved recently. Compared to the 1980s and 1990s, modest time-gains seem to have been made during the drug approval stage (i.e., after most R&D has actually been completed) and where the cooperation, speed and involvement of regulatory authorities are paramount. The average time a drug candidate spends in clinical trials has been reduced from almost seven years in the 1990s to a little more than five years in the early 2000s (Figure 2). The still long average development times are partly due to relatively

1 KPMG and Lehmann Brothers (2002).

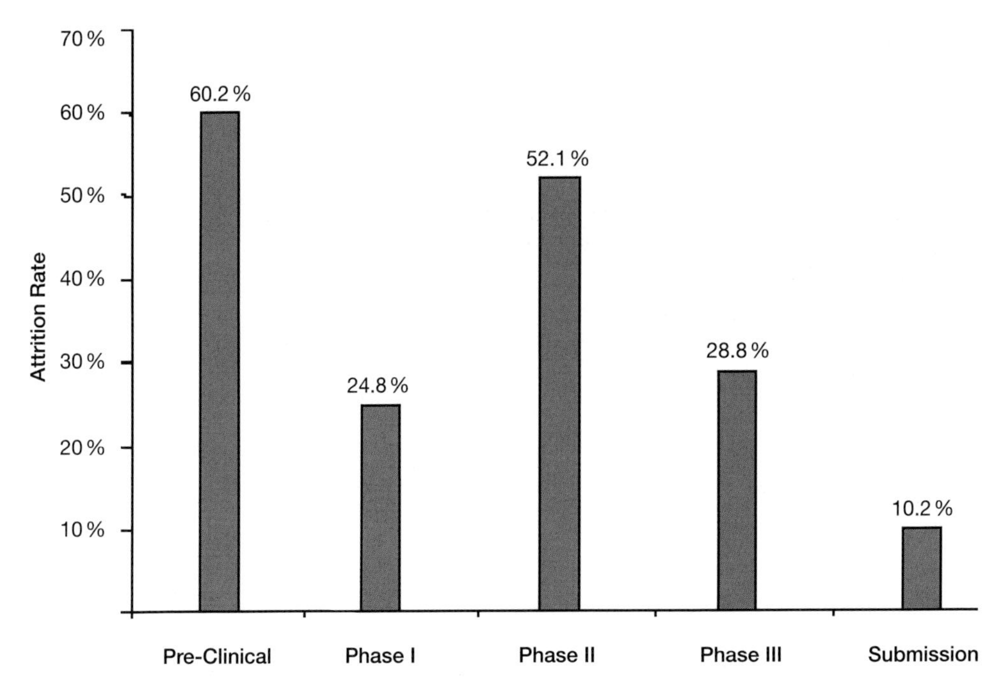

Figure 3: Attrition rates in pharmaceutical R&D by phase (Source: Buchanan 2002, based on the Tufts Center for Drug Development Data).

high attrition rates in later stages of the development process. Drug development attrition rates – the percentage of NCEs that drop out during a phase of testing – are highest in the pre-clinical phase (60.2 %) and still very high in the clinical phase II (52.1 %), that is, after several years of development. Once a new drug candidate has been submitted to the regulatory authorities for approval, the attrition rate decreases to around 10 % (Figure 3).

Here is where the pharmaceutical industry is unique: in most other industries, the decision to terminate a project is made on the basis of economic/financial considerations, and not on technical or scientific ones (e. g., a lack of efficacy or safety which might only become visible at the clinical phase II). Translating the attrition rates into success rates provides an overview on the probability of success for a compound in the R&D pipeline. While a compound in the pre-clinical phase only has a probability of success of around 10 %, this rate increases significantly once the compound passes the clinical phase II and reaches clinical phase III (65.8 %). Considering and comparing attrition rates and probabilities of success, the greatest potential for improvement in productivity seems to be in clinical phase II, as well as just before the pre-clinical phase (i.e. lead identification and lead optimization).

I.2 Changing Market Conditions

From 2001 to 2004, pharmaceutical sales increased worldwide by about 28% to USD 550 billion (VFA 2005). For the past decades, most pharmaceutical companies relied on blockbuster drugs – a drug with at least USD 1 billion in annual sales – as the market strategy to achieve these growth rates (Figure 4).

In 2002, fifty-eight ethical pharmaceutical products with aggregated sales of USD 120 billion have been qualified as blockbuster drugs. Only two companies – GlaxoSmithKline and Pfizer – owned eight blockbuster products. The majority of companies owned only between one and three blockbusters. However, analysis conducted by Reuters shows that blockbuster drugs worth about USD 30 billion in revenues were due to lose their US patent protection by the end of 2002 (Reuters 2003). Furthermore, the blockbuster market in 2008 will be worth only 1.4 times that of the blockbuster market during 2000, and will therefore not be able to keep up with the 10%+ annual revenue growth expectation (Reuters 2003). In addition, the traditional blockbuster markets are crowded with competing products launched at increasingly close intervals targeting similar therapeutic areas. This raises the question of whether blockbusters can or should remain a focus of future growth. Most pharmaceutical companies have now started to question the traditional blockbuster strategy and have started to offer 'multi-buster' drugs: a series of personalized therapies that are able to dominate a certain targeted disease area. Consequently, the new 'multi-buster' strategy requires targeting increasingly differentiated markets with specialized therapies. However, specialty markets

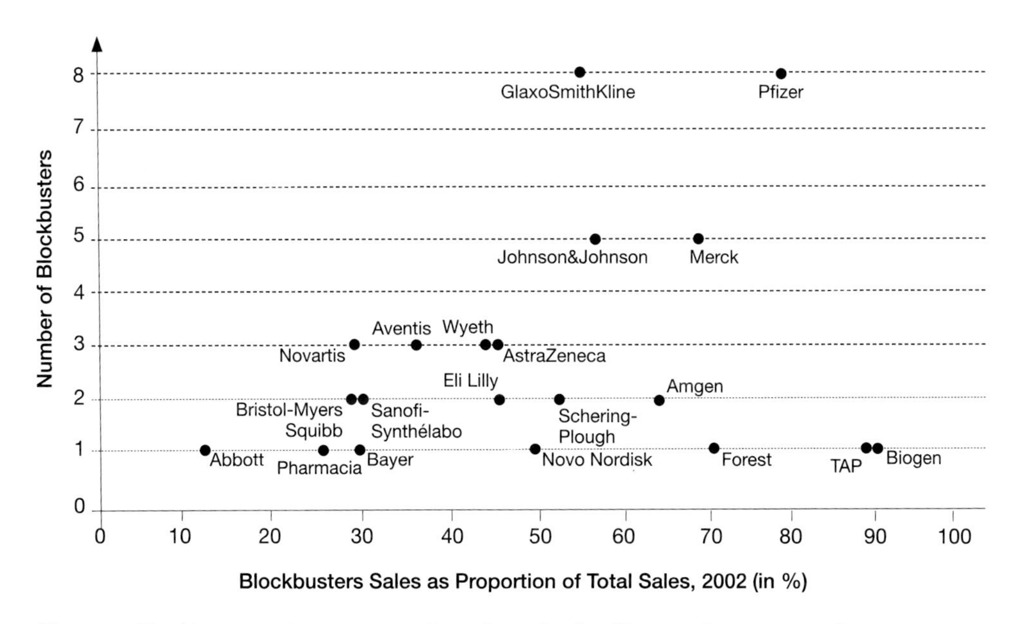

Figure 4: Blockbuster sales as proportion of total sales (Source: Reuters 2003).

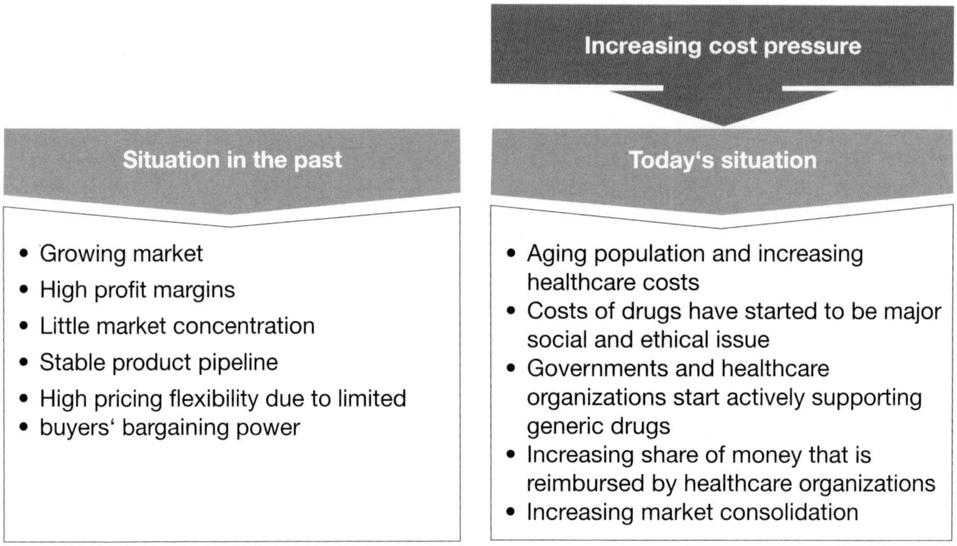

Increasing cost pressure

Situation in the past	Today's situation
• Growing market • High profit margins • Little market concentration • Stable product pipeline • High pricing flexibility due to limited • buyers' bargaining power	• Aging population and increasing healthcare costs • Costs of drugs have started to be major social and ethical issue • Governments and healthcare organizations start actively supporting generic drugs • Increasing share of money that is reimbursed by healthcare organizations • Increasing market consolidation

Figure 5: Increasing cost pressure.

bear higher risks as they might not allow the pharmaceutical company to recoup their R&D investments easily due to their limited market size. Additionally, broadening market-reach across several niche markets bears an additional risk of market failure due to a lack of focus and diversification disadvantages.

Besides the trend towards multi-buster drugs, the increasingly fierce financial pressure of restrictions in health care spending has led to an increasing cost consciousness of buyers in many countries. The current debate in Germany regarding the introduction of a "Positive List" for cheaper generic drugs, also underlines this development. Political and ethical discussions concerning the access to cheaper drugs for the low-income population have intensified the cost pressure and mitigated this issue to the pharmaceutical companies. At the same time – particularly in the US – the buyers' bargaining power has vastly increased. While just 5% of the US population was covered by health insurance in 1960, this ratio has increased to about 80% today. In the US, 'Managed Care' Organizations have significantly gained in market share. The 'Managed Care' Organizations buy healthcare coverage from healthcare providers (e.g. hospitals, health insurances) for a fixed price and negotiate cheaper rates for drugs. This leads to a higher price pressure and subsequently lower sales prices for pharmaceutical products as indicated in Figure 5.

I.3 Increasing Competition

The recent situation in the pharmaceutical industry can be characterized by its intensified market consolidation (Figure 6). Several mergers and acquisitions have transformed the former strongly fragmented industry to one with a significantly higher market concentration. At the same time, the former growth rates have slowed down. While the industry was traditionally characterized by double-digit growth rates, the growth expectations have been lowered to around 5-8% per year. Furthermore, Gary Pisano, Professor at Harvard Business School, has identified a growing technological parity in the field of R&D. Today, companies of any nationality can locate their R&D facilities in any particular region to tap its technological expertise. Companies can also gain access to state-of-the-art technology through collaborative relationships with other companies or universities. A highly mobile scientific and engineering labor force and relatively weak intellectual property protections are additional factors encouraging the rapid diffusion of technological know-how and competencies across countries and companies (Pisano and Wheelwright 1995).

In addition, the longer developmental times have resulted in a reduction of the effective time of patent protection for a new drug. This allows manufacturers of generic drugs to gain market share by offering cheaper substitutes only a few years after a new drug has been introduced on the market. Hence, the market share of generic products has increased from 33% in 1990 to 47% of units sold in 2000. The expected growth rates of 13% p.a. for generic drugs exceeded by far the expected growth rates for ethical drugs. The introduction of a "Positive List" for cheaper generic drugs in Germany will further intensify this situation.

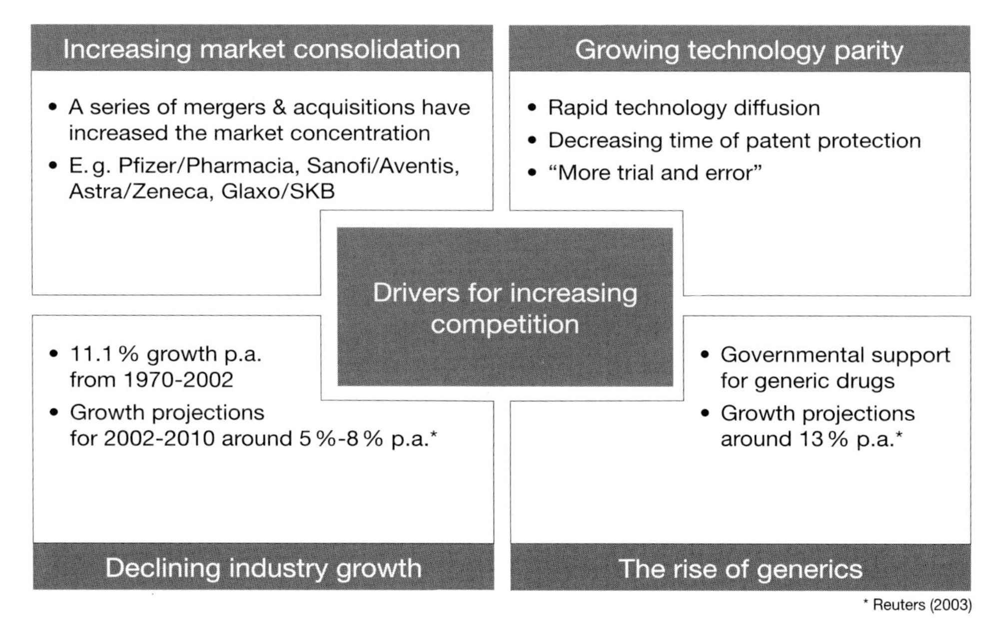

Figure 6: Drivers for increasing competition.

I.4 Increasing Costs and Low Operating Efficiency

"The problem is what we call the critical volume. There is a certain sales volume that you have to exceed if you want to survive. One factor is the market share, which is important to raise awareness among the physicians. And you need a certain sales volume per sales representative. A rule of thumb is that you need 800,000 DM sales revenue per sales rep. Taking into account that you need in minimum around 70 sales reps to penetrate the (West) German market, you have to generate at least 50-60 million DM sales revenues to stay in that market. However, this requires an adequate product portfolio with a rich product pipeline of innovative products. If a company does not meet those requirements it will not survive."

Spaethe 2001

The citation shows where much of the money goes in the pharmaceutical industry: high investments in R&D to capitalize on a broad product portfolio and a massive global sales force to penetrate the highly heterogeneous market for drugs. The more companies are investing in R&D, the more they have to recoup their investments by selling their drugs on a global scale and penetrating existing markets more intensively than in the past. Hence, rising costs of R&D lead to even bigger marketing budgets, which in the end turn out to be a vicious circle.

As a result, between 1990 and 2000 expenses for marketing and sales increased by 300% (Reuters 2003). Among the sixteen biggest pharmaceutical companies, marketing and sales today account for 41% of sales (Caspar 2003). Surprisingly, according to that study, the second highest cost driver of a pharmaceutical company with a share of 36% of sales is manufacturing and not R&D as one might expect (Caspar 2003). Based on our survey that was conducted among 95 pharmaceutical locations in Europe and which also included pharmaceutical small and medium-sized enterprises (SMEs), manufacturing with 31% of sales even accounted for the highest cost position of a pharmaceutical company. Among generic manufacturers, this ratio rises to about 50%.

Hence, besides R&D and marketing, manufacturing has become a major cost factor of a pharmaceutical company. Taking those figures, it is surprising that efficiency in manufacturing has not been a major focus in the past. However, the industry is waking up. Surprisingly, this time the FDA took the lead and started to promote innovation and continuous improvement in the pharmaceutical industry. The initiative "Pharmaceutical cGMP for the 21th century" which was launched in 2002 intended to enhance and modernize the regulation of pharmaceutical manufacturing. It is also the first time that the FDA focused on economics in manufacturing when claiming waste reduction and value added as a result of high quality performance. McClellan, chairman of the FDA, complains that in many other high-tech industries (e.g. semi-conductors) innovation in manufacturing has yielded significant productivity improvements while the pharmaceutical industry has not managed to do so (Caspar 2003).

Regarding the operational performance figures (e.g., inventory turn-over rates or utilization rates), the pharmaceutical industry is lagging far behind other industries. The survey "Operational Excellence in the Pharmaceutical Industry" which is described in detail in chapter III reveals that it is not uncommon to have stock turn-over rates of about 1-2 per year, while other industries, such as the consumer goods or high-tech industry, have turnover rates of 16-20 or even 50, respectively. The limited productivity of the capital employed stems from previous high safety stocks, as companies were eager not to lose a single sale because of the high gross margins attached to each product. Several mergers and acquisitions resulted in complex production networks that also limited the productivity of the fixed assets. This is because similar products are produced at several sites. However, as yet a restructuring of the complex production networks has not been done.

Pharmaceutical companies usually mention the huge number of regulations from national agencies and institutions as a main reason for their low efficiency. These agencies stipulated authorization and registration procedures and were responsible for causing high costs especially due to quality insurance and inspections. Discussions at FDA Science Board and Advisory Committee meetings identified the following major contributing factors (FDA 2004):

- Routine pharmaceutical production is conducted by running a plant at rigidly defined operating conditions described in Standard Operating Procedures (SOPs). Too often in the past regulatory submission contained limited information concerning the specific root causes of those conditions. As a result, these conditions became regulatory commitments and plant operators were expected to always reproduce exactly these same sets of conditions. This type of operation can be considered a "static manufacturing operation" because it creates a mind-set that "product is approved and validated - do not change".
- Process control is predominantly based on documented evidence of compliance with SOPs which generally included a "fixed process time" and laboratory based testing of in-process materials. "Real time" in-process information about the variability of certain process parameters (e.g. particle sizes) and how they affect product quality is usually not available.
- A quality system that is based on a "static manufacturing operation" and a limited understanding of the sources of variability cannot facilitate continuous improvement as in absence of good information; attempts to adjust a process can potentially create new problems.

As a result, in the past pharmaceutical manufacturing used to be static and mainly inefficient. It seems that the current state of manufacturing pharmaceutical products is no longer acceptable. If the pharmaceutical industry wants to catch up with other industries, then it has to undergo major changes.

I.5 Implications for Manufacturing

"Innovation will remain a crucial factor for pharmaceutical companies. At the same time pharmaceutical companies will have to search for new ways to improve efficiency. Hence, the future pharmaceutical firm will be characterized by a "Hollywood-like" culture of creativity, innovation and flexibility while striving to enhance the rate of productivity and efficiency similar to the automotive industry."

Pisano (Professor Harvard Business School)
and Günthardt (CEO Siegfried Ltd.)

According to Pisano and Günthardt, the pharmaceutical industry is facing two main challenges: firstly, companies have to increase the number of new products while, secondly, efficiently managing their existing resources. While the industry was traditionally highly concentrated on increasing the R&D output, today's situation requires a different strategy which also includes Operational Excellence issues. Hence, the industry is facing a situation in which it has to increase the effectiveness of its R&D activities while it has to simultaneously improve the efficiency of producing new drugs. However, these two approaches require entirely different organizational characteristics. While an effective R&D organization requires a structure that enables creativity and innovativeness, a manufacturing organization requires a structure that enables process optimization and cost reductions through continuous improvement programs. Hayes et al. raise the question why the US has managed to invent genetic engineering while it is seemingly incapable of producing a more defect-free car than Toyota. They state that the emphasis on breakthrough innovation and the emphasis on incremental improvements illustrate two highly contrasting approaches to improvement. The same skills and managerial psychology that enable an organization to conceive and carry out breakthrough projects may hamper it in a competitive environment where success is based on a series of small steps rather than on a few dramatic breakthroughs (Hayes et al. 2005).

To accommodate efficiency and innovativeness issues in the pharmaceutical industry, Pisano and Günthardt see three possible ways of how to achieve it: either developing complementary capabilities internally ("internal model"), gaining access to those capabilities through mergers and acquisitions ("acquisition model") or through alliances ("alliance model") (Pisano and Günthardt 2003). All models are based on the assumption that efficiency and productivity will become much more important in the pharmaceutical industry than it was in the past. However, this will not be an easy task for pharmaceutical firms that have configured themselves around the expectations of repeated breakthroughs, as it bears little resemblance to one that takes the incremental continuous improvement approach. Managers and workers have different skills, instincts, and psychological mind-sets; and furthermore the incremental approach requires a lot of "low-level expertise" – that is, expertise low at levels in the operations organization, yet not low-level expertise (Hayes et al. 2005). Developing this kind of expertise is a long process. Great effort must be spent on recruiting workers and managers who are both loyal and amenable to long periods of training. Once hired, these people's capabilities must continually be improved and expanded, through both formal education programs and job assignments that provide a broad understanding of the company's products, processes, and competitive environment (see chapters IV and V). Firms that adopt a focused, long-term incremental improvement approach must therefore develop the kind of managers who can stimulate and facilitate this kind of progress, maintain resource allocation systems that support it, give compensation and promotion systems that encourage it, and measurement systems that can track it. The great advantage of such systems is that since home-grown capabilities take a long time to develop, and are therefore difficult to imitate, they can provide a sustained competitive advantage (Hayes et al. 2005). The Pfizer case study in chapter IV gives an example of the challenges that a big pharmaceutical company is currently facing when it is adopting an incremental approach to continuous improvement.

However, there are several reasons that provide evidence that such an approach will pay off:

High cost saving potentials in the field of technical operations

The cost potential of pharmaceutical manufacturing is expected to be tremendous. Our study "Operational Excellence in the Pharmaceutical Industry" reveals that more efficient manufacturing could translate into EUR 500 million of cost savings over the lifetime of a USD 1 billion-a-year blockbuster drug. (see chapter III). Vocke und Jäger estimate that about 60% of all costs attached to a pharmaceutical product are determined by an optimized management of the supply chain (Vocke and Jäger 2004). Hence, optimizing the pharmaceutical supply chain can yield significant overall cost savings.

The role of pharmaceutical manufacturing in the past

According to a framework from Wheelwright und Hayes (1985), there are several generic roles that the manufacturing function can play in a company. At one extreme, manufacturing can offer little contribution to a company's market success. At the other, it provides a major source of competitive advantage.

The lowest stage represents an "internally" neutral orientation toward manufacturing: top managers regard the function as neutral and incapable of influencing competitive success. Consequently, they seek only to minimize any negative impact (e.g. compliances, stock-outs etc.) it may have. The fourth and most progressive stage of manufacturing development arises when competitive strategy rests to a significant degree on a company's manufacturing capability. As noted in Figure 7, the role of manufacturing in stage-4-companies is "externally supportive", in that it is expected to make an important contribution to the competitive success of the organization (Wheelwright and Hayes 1985).

According to Charles Cooney at MIT, most pharmaceutical companies today see manufacturing simply as a matter of compliance with regulatory requirements, rather than an opportunity to cut costs and production time. Hence, for most pharmaceutical companies, manufacturing can be regarded as "internally neutral". Manufacturing has to comply with certain regulatory requirements and thereby minimizing the downside risk of failing to meet regulatory standards. However, trying to cut costs and achieve parity with the best competitors would just enable a company to get from stage one to stage two (see Figure 7) to become "externally neutral".

Obviously, just by focusing on efficiency issues a pharmaceutical company cannot reap the full benefits of its manufacturing function. If pharmaceutical companies expect manufacturing to actively support and strengthen the company's competitive position, it has to climb stage 3 or even stage 4 and truly regard their manufacturing unit as a strategic asset. In the following section we present some benefits that cannot be reaped by pharmaceutical companies that view manufacturing as just an enabler to cut costs.

Accelerated time-to-market and rapid scale-up

In many more situations than is generally imagined, the development of manufacturing technology heavily influences new product introductions (Pisano and Wheelwright 1995).

Stage	Role	Characteristics
Stage 1	**Minimize manu-facturing's negative potential: "internally neutral"**	- Strategic manufacturing decisions by outside experts - Internal, detailed management control systems - Flexible and reactive manufacturing
Stage 2	**Achieve parity with competitors: "externally neutral"**	- "Industry practice" is followed - Planning horizon extended to incorporate a single business cycle - Capital investments = primary means for catching up with competition or achieving a competitive edge
Stage 3	**Provide credible support to the business strategy: "internally supportive"**	- Manufacturing investments consistent with the business strategy - Formulated and pursued manufacturing strategy - Systematically addressing of long-term manufacturing developments and trends
Stage 4	**Pursue a manufacturing-based competitive advantage: "externally supportive"**	- Anticipate the potential of new manufacturing practices and technologies - "Up front" involvement of manufacturing - Long-range programs in order to acquire capabilities in advance of needs ("competitive advantage")

Figure 7: Framework of generic roles of manufacturing.

Eager to shorten the time required in developing and winning regulatory approval for new products, senior executives often devote the vast majority of a company's R&D spending to product innovation. Since companies are in a rush to get their products to market, they tend to take their laboratory-scale methods and expand them to industrial proportions, rather than think of new ways to make pills on a much bigger scale (Economist 2002). Even if process development then manages to set up their processes in time, they often do not manage to supply all the necessary clinical trials in a timely fashion, which ultimately results in commercialization delays. After introducing the new product into the factory, it usually takes some time for manufacturing performance to reach normal long-term levels. A rapid scale-up is non-viable for several reasons (Pisano and Wheelwright 1995): The faster a company can ramp up production of a new product, the more quickly it can begin to earn significant revenues from the new product and recoup its development investments. Rapid ramp-up enables a company to penetrate the market quickly, gain broad market acceptance, and begin to accumulate experience with high-volume production.

Extended proprietary position and longer product life cycle

The declining effective period of exclusivity of pharmaceutical products restricts pharmaceutical companies in their efforts to protect the proprietary position of their products (Spaethe 2001). At the same time, especially Indian generics companies like Rambaxy or Dr. Reddy's, are rushing into western European markets and are challenging expiring patents of former blockbuster drugs (Pisano and Wheelwright 1995). Due to the weak intellectual-property protection in countries like China or India, it is getting even more important to develop innovative process technologies that are difficult to imitate. When a drug patent expires, proprietary process technology can be one of the best protections against intrusion by generic manufacturers (Pisano and Wheelwright 1995). Furthermore, innovative formulation forms can help to stretch the normal life cycle of drugs. One successful example is Bayer's Aspirin brand that has managed to still capture a significant market share in the very competitive pain reliever market by managing a variety of different process technologies and by being able to offer various products that provide customized features.

Hard to manufacture biotechnological products
Especially in the field of biotechnology, manufacturing can create significant challenges. As product characteristics such as consistency, purity, size, reliability etc. are directly determined by the specifics of the production process, the link between process technology and product characteristics is particularly tight in biotechnology. Slight changes in the genetics of cells used in the production process, reaction conditions, or purification processes can make the difference between having a product that is safe and therapeutically active and having one that is not (Pisano and Wheelwright 1995). Hence, for example being able to manufacture complex large molecules can still be a true source of competitive advantage for a pharmaceutical company today.

The examples provide evidence that Operational Excellence does not have to mean operational efficiency. They also provide evidence that in many companies the role of pharmaceutical manufacturing has to be redefined according to its business strategy. To become truly excellent means to develop unique capabilities which are hard to duplicate. For most pharmaceutical companies the objective will be not to achieve the lowest prices, and by that pursue a lost cost strategy. Due to the many challenges the industry is currently facing, increasing operating efficiency will be a "must-do" for most pharmaceutical companies. However, from a strategic perspective it will be important that pharmaceutical companies have configured their operations appropriately in support of their chosen strategy. A company that is entering new niche markets with innovative products will require different sets of organizational capabilities than that of a company trying to become market leader in a highly saturated market.

To align its operations with its business strategy, certain operations management practices (from which most of them are borrowed from the Toyota Production System) can help to transform the company according to its chosen strategy. The objective of the following book, that was written on the basis of a 2-year project run by the University of St. Gallen and the APV (Arbeitsgemeinschaft für Pharmazeutische Verfahrenstechnik/International Association for Pharmaceutical Technology), Mainz (Germany), was to analyze the current status of pharmaceutical manufacturing with regard to the level of Operational Excellence and to find out whether companies that have implemented those practices yield a better performance than those that have not. Interesting to know whether there are certain practices in the pharmaceutical industry that work better than others, it is important to understand that there is not *one way* of becoming excellent.

The book can only provide a framework of ideas, and not a solution. The solution has to be customized to the specific challenges that each company is currently facing.

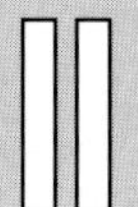 A Reference Model for Operational Excellence

II.1 Introduction

Michael Kickuth and Thomas Friedli

The focus of the project 'Operational Excellence in the Pharmaceutical Industry (OPEX)' was to find out the current "level of Operational Excellence" in this industry and, by that, being able to provide answers on how to improve the operational performance of pharmaceutical companies in Europe. Hence, the first question that we asked ourselves was: "What is Operational Excellence?"

Over the past century this question has generated various activities all over the world; in particular at the beginning of the1980s this question had attracted many American scholars. In the early 1980s, U.S. industry had just begun to realize that Japanese competitors had successfully captured significant market shares in many of the largest U.S. industries like: automotives, computer peripherals, office machines and machine tools. The reasons for this decline sounded a common refrain (Hayes et al. 2005): in the eyes of the customers, imported products provided higher quality, better value for money, and greater responsiveness to customers' demands for greater product variety. American companies realized that the reason why they had fallen behind their foreign competitors was not rooted in their inability to develop and market innovative new products or their lack of financial strength compared to their foreign competitors, rather that the major source of competitive advantage of most foreign competitors was their Operational Excellence. Based on the world class manufacturing project in 1984, Hayes and Wheelwright published their book "Restoring our Competitive Edge: Competing through Manufacturing", describing world class manufacturing as a set of practices, implying that the use of those "best practices" would lead to superior performance. Several scholars agreed with them and could find linkages between the implementation of certain practices and the performance of companies. Two of the most famous scholars that have carefully described leading practices in the automotive industry were James Womack and Dan Jones with their work on "lean thinking".

A different perspective on Operational Excellence was taken by Loch et al. (2003) in their book "Industrial Excellence," which summarized the experience from the Industrial Excellence Awards (IEAs) since 1995[2].

Arguing that certain "Best Practices" disappear over time, Loch et al. argued that the *tree* of Operational Excellence takes root at the top of a plant. Over the eight years of the Industrial Excellence Award their conviction has strengthened, and that – more than competitors, more than technology or government regulators – the key threat potentially facing any industrial unit is a change in its leadership. To their mind there is no question that the ability of a plant manager to articulate a clear direction, to communicate this vision, and impress upon all collaborators a collective responsibility for the unit's sustained performance is a key characteristic portrayed by the managers of the Excellence Award winning units.

This approach also fits with our experiences. When we were discussing the first draft of our reference model with a senior manager of a global pharmaceutical company who was responsible for the optimization of several plants in Europe, he told us to take care of the management quality of each plant that we were visiting: "When I compare the plants in Europe that I am responsible for, they often use the similar equipment, technology and run fairly the same processes; however, they perform quite differently. To my mind one of the key factors that differentiate the good plants from the bad ones is the quality of the management." In the following chapter, Christoph Loch provides us with an overview of the framework that is used in the Industrial Excellence Award survey and how he and his colleagues have operationalized the *fuzzy* world of Management Quality.

As complementary work we will then develop the OPEX reference model used for "measuring the level of Operational Excellence" in our study in the pharmaceutical industry.

2 The IEA aims to identify excellent factories in France and Germany. Since1995 the IEA has been offered in collaboration with the French industrial magazine L'Usine Nouvelle. Since 1997 the IEA has been offered to German plants and industrial units with the title of "Die beste Fabrik", in partnership with the German economic weekly Wirtschaftswoche.

II.2 Management Quality and Factory Performance

Christoph H. Loch and Stephen E. Chick

Manufacturing in the pharmaceutical industry has been different than that seen in other industries in two aspects: first, technologies and processes have been highly rigid because of the regulatory requirement that the formulation used in clinical trials be faithfully replicated in mass manufacturing. Second, manufacturing has been treated as less important than research & development (R&D) and sales because manufacturing incurs a smaller fraction of total costs. Manufacturing has not been seen as central in producing competitive advantage.

As the pharmaceutical industry enters an era in which developing and selling blockbuster drugs will no longer be sufficient to sustain the business, both of these differences when compared with other industries are beginning to disappear. In a more cost sensitive environment (in particular, generics), manufacturing efficiency, quality, and improvements will matter more. Excellent manufacturing will increase in value. But what is "excellent manufacturing management" that produces competitive advantage? The "good manufacturing principles" that have been traditionally used in the pharmaceutical industry will no longer suffice. Excellence in manufacturing is also relevant as new technologies arise with biotechnological innovation. The industry needs to learn from developments in other industries.

In this chapter, we explain a model of industrial excellence that has been validated across a number of different industries. It focuses on *management practices* (as opposed to specific technical procedures). In conversations, managers implicitly seem to agree that they can recognize a good factory when they see one; they believe that a successful management team is likely to succeed when placed in a different plant, even one with completely unrelated technologies. Based on the "Industrial Excellence Award" that we have carried out in Germany and France since 1995, we develop an *operational framework* of excellent plant management (Loch et al. 2003), which a manager can translate into actions and which leads to competitive advantage.

The fuzziness of manufacturing management quality

Much prior work has examined aspects of how manufacturing may lead to competitive advantage. But the results have not given an answer that can easily be translated into action. Manufacturing strategy refers to two sets of decisions that contribute to competitive advantage: (1) defining the *mission* of the manufacturing function (the "manufacturing task"(Skinner 1969), and (2) a pattern of *consistent choices* concerning "bricks and mortar" (facilities, technologies, and capacity) and "infrastructure" (organization, quality methods, and workforce policies) in order to accomplish this mission (Hayes et al. 1989; Miller and Roth 1994; Skinner 1969). A major question in strategy research is *how manufacturing strategy brings competitive advantage?*

Porter (1980) proposed that competitive advantage rests on *uniqueness;* and the so-called "resource-based view of the firm" holds that resources, or competencies, can provide a competitive advantage *if* they are difficult to imitate (Wernerfelt 1984). Indeed, empirical studies have shown that internal resources play an important role in determining a firm's success, more than industry membership or market share (Powell et al. 1996; Rumelt 1991). *Unique competencies that are hard to imitate* allow for competitive advantage or a situation where some competitors earn dramatically more than others.

However, it has not yet been shown operationally *what* these firm-specific resources are. A number of general factors have been proposed, such as culture (Fiol 1991), or know-how as a system of skills, technical and managerial systems, and values (Leonard-Barton 1992). The manufacturing strategy literature has offered a specific factor, namely the ability of identifying correct trade-offs in a given environment and proactively aligning organization and programs with these trade-offs (Schonberger 1982; Skinner 1969; Swamidass et al. 1987; Ward et al. 1995). However, the causal relationship between manufacturing strategy and performance remains ambiguous (Miller and Roth 1994).

During the decade of 1985 to 1995, Total Quality Management (TQM) was seen as a powerful set of programs to improve a firm's performance, but has since declined in popular attention (De Meyer 1993; Powell 1995). TQM is an integrated management philosophy emphasizing quality for the customer through the reduction of waste, training, leadership with consistency of purpose, stable processes that are in (statistical) control, and a continuous emphasis on improvement (Juran 1986; Walton 1986). However, the empirical evidence of the benefit of TQM programs is mixed (De Meyer 1990; Ittner and Larcker 1997; Schmenner 1991).

Powell (Powell 1995; Rössl 1990) found that individual TQM *programs* (such as SPC, benchmarking, or continuous improvement programs) represent imitable tools. Only three behavioral, tacit and intangible resources seem non-imitable: top management commitment, an open culture, and empowerment. Powell saw only these as true sources of sustainable advantage, independent of the implementation of formal TQM tools. But these results were not easily operational, and their applied evidence was weak. Powell et al. (1996) concluded that "the resource-based view remains essentially theoretical, and would benefit from a deeper empirical base to support its claims."

A complementary view of manufacturing strategy has been offered by the literature on business process reengineering (BPR), which has brought a *focus on processes* to the debate (Blackburn 1991; Davenport 1993; Hammer and James 1993; Loch 1998). This literature has proposed that superior performance can be achieved by changing the structure of a small number of key business processes, defined as an ordering of work activities in space and time, with a beginning and end, and clearly defined inputs and (customer-oriented) outputs (Davenport 1993). The differences between BPR and TQM are a more explicit focus on processes and an emphasis on "radical" rather than continuous changes, but the two views are compatible and complementary (Hammer 1996).

The BPR literature has produced a substantial amount of anecdotal evidence that processes offer a great potential of strategic performance improvement, which are difficult to imitate due to culture, incentives, knowledge, and existing systems (Blackburn 1991; Hammer 1996; Stalk Jr. 1988)[3]. However, the evidence remained anecdotal and inconsistent. According to the accounts of some authors, 80% of BPR efforts failed, and consequently, BPR had run its course by the end of the 1990s.

3 In practical applications, BPR has often been used as a pure cost cutting tool, a narrow view that has not been supported by its proponents.

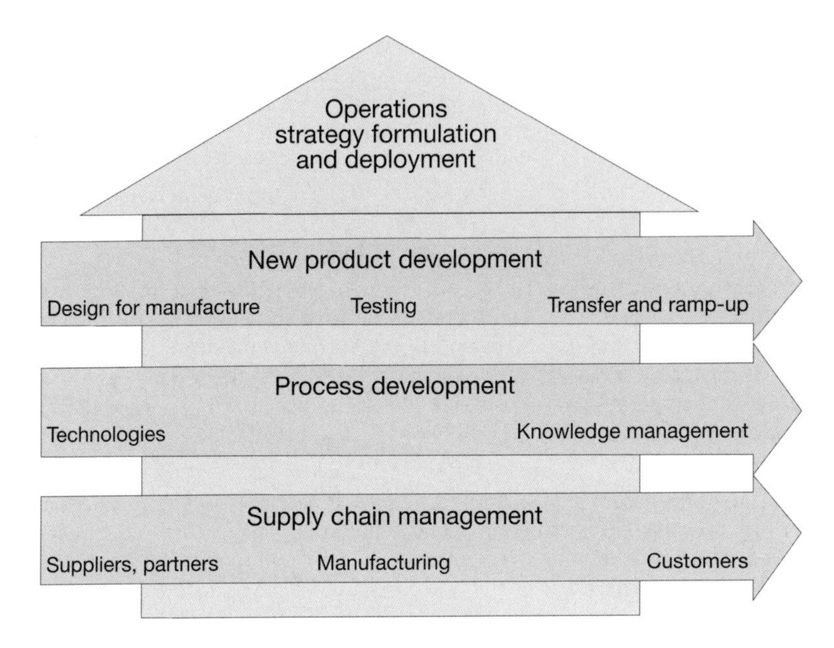

Figure 8: The plant at the intersection of four business processes.

A model of manufacturing management quality

In this section we develop a model of *manufacturing management quality.* We view the factory as situated at the intersection of four basic business processes: the supply chain, strategy deployment, product development, and process development (Figure 8). The management of these processes is characterized by six dimensions of management quality. Management quality drives performance and improvement and, finally, factory growth.

The plant at the intersection of four business processes

The Supply Chain Process

The supply chain process is concerned with the execution of current business, comprising the flow of goods and services from suppliers through the factory and its delivery channels to customers, as well as its associated information flows. For the supply chain to be managed as one process, performance information must be shared throughout the chain, and goals of the separate links in the chain must be consistent.

An integrated supply chain process manages physical production as an entire system, from procurement to customer integration. This includes "tearing down walls" between supply, procurement, internal operations, and downstream operations in order to engender cooperation in the pursuit of mutual long-term interest. Suppliers are enticed to participate in this never-ending search for quality and continuous improvement by the prospect of longer-term contracts and enduring business relationships. Furthermore, information on company and supplier performance must be shared throughout the industrial system. This includes feedback from customers *via* the distribution network and evaluation of suppliers in the procurement network, quality controls, benchmarking, and supplier and customer input on potential improvements of the industrial unit's processes. Such information sharing allows downstream clients to better manage the impact of problems arising upstream in the supply chain on their activities.

This shift to a more horizontal view of industrial activities is further fostered by the growing focus of many corporations on their core competencies. Focus is realized through the outsourcing to supply partners of a number of activities previously kept inside the firm. The imperative to incorporate the most technologically advanced components in their products has forced companies to increasingly scan the market for superior supply capabilities. The globalization of supplier networks has also added tremendous cost pressure and has resulted in further disintegration of traditionally integrated companies (Spears and Bowen 1999).

Customer integration has become the final link of the supply chain. The "Intel Inside" campaign reminds us that the supply chain reaches all the way to the customer's mind. A plant's performance does influence, certainly over time, the final customer's purchase decision and perceived satisfaction. Critical then is the correct definition of the customer, especially in the industrial context, where the immediate client typically differs from the final customer, and of what he or she seeks. Customer integration may indeed be a firm's differentiator and performance cause of an industrial unit. These issues too must be part of the supply chain debate inside an industrial unit.

The Strategy Process

The second basic process is concerned with the formulation and deployment of a consistent set of priorities, targets and strategy for the industrial unit, in a way that engages the entire unit. This means that it incorporates initiatives from the factory floor which leverages new capabilities developed there. Strategy deployment is necessary in order to create common goals, attain clarity with regard to the trade-offs and choices, to create fit across the different manufacturing activities (Porter 1996), to implement the manufacturing strategy at every level of the plant and, at the same time, to motivate initiatives from all employees to contribute to, or even change, the adopted strategy.

Possibly the most important leadership action is the design and execution of the process by which business strategy is formulated, information gathered and analyzed, and goals and progress measured, communicated, and evaluated. It is this "process view of strategic leadership" that we adopt; that is, the view that competitiveness is rooted in business processes more than in the innate qualities of any particular individual. If this were not the case, industrial units would have fortunes that go up and down with their leaders. This may be the case, but one should then talk about leadership excellence, and not industrial excellence. A leader is only as good as his/her support team; together, they formulate strategy and deploy it throughout an industrial unit.

A successful strategy has the various business processes "fit" together, eliminating options that would not make sense for the entire system. This aim for fit has to be clear to the actors of the various processes. This means that top management has to (1) communicate its strategy effectively, from middle managers to operators on the factory floor; (2) be open to input from these individuals regarding the problems that may arise in the pursuit of the chosen strategy. Excellent managers do not merely dictate what must be done; they clearly articulate company goals and the motivations behind them, while allowing for adequate flexibility in implementation (Porter 1996).

The New Product Development Process

The product development process consists of activities to improve the firm's current portfolio of products and services, as well as develop the industrial unit's next generation of products and services. This process is concerned with ensuring the company's future product and service portfolio.

In a competitive market, firms are required to regularly produce new products or upgrades of existing ones, whilst distinguishing their own products from those offered by competitors. Yet product parameters cannot be decided on in isolation from the industrial processes charged with manufacturing and delivering them. A new product does not always fit the factory's capabilities; the design or composition may require the plant to change its processes, or quite simply it may be inappropriate (Nevins and Daniel 1989). For example, product variety and product costs, design quality and costs all require trade-off between what is ideally desirable and what is economically justifiable. The speed and the effectiveness with which the product development process is managed are thus critical to the unit's performance; indeed, this is the place from which new responses to customer desires and challenges emerge. The product development process has come to the forefront of the industrial landscape.

The factory plays an important part in this business process in two ways: first, its capabilities may constrain the possible product and process designs and, second, design heavily influences the factory's cost structure through parts costs, ease and cost of manufacturing, and quality levels (Wheelwright and Clark 1992). The interface between the plant and new product development is the volume ramp-up of new products, the quality and ease of which is determined by the cooperation between plants and the R&D unit of the enterprise.

The New Process Development Process

This process refers to those activities aimed at the improvement of the industrial unit's processes and activities, whether they pertain to the supply chain, to product development, or to other tasks of the organization; including strategy formulation and deployment.

Here is one of the great contributions of Japanese manufacturers over the last decades: the insight that process improvement and development are the keys to industrial competitiveness. This was well described in the study of the automobile industry, *The Machine That Changed the World* (Womack et al. 1990).

Products and services are only the outputs of ongoing business processes. Competitiveness must thus be rooted in a superior ability of running these business processes. Furthermore, best practices diffuse over time, making process improvement an ongoing competitive requirement. Therefore, sustainable competitiveness must be rooted in a superior ability to improve one's processes. While regulations provide constraints, there is still ample room in pharmaceuticals to improve the four basic business processes.

This emphasis on learning has been fuelled by the IT revolution. The remarkable development of information technologies has promoted the view that information could now flow freely throughout the organization and become available to all. This associates process development closely with information and knowledge systems, which have both gained in prominence over the last decade. We recognize this important development by including process development as a separate process in our excellence framework.

Management Quality across the Processes

Performance and improvement across the four business processes, and ultimately factory performance, are driven by their *management quality*. We define management quality through seven dimensions described below (Figure 9).

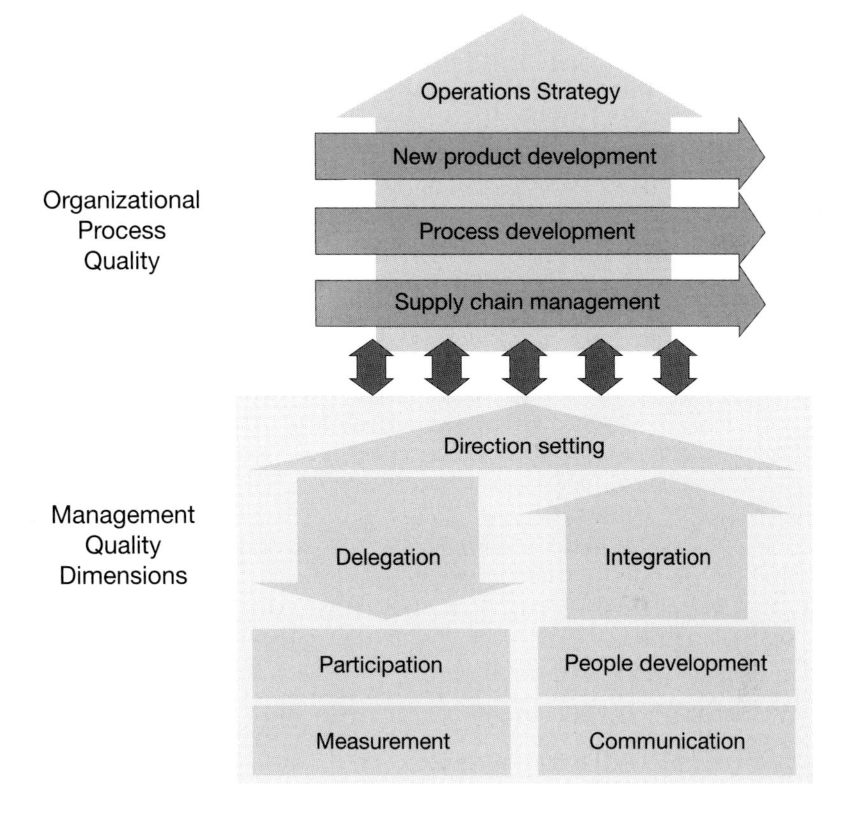

Figure 9: Management quality across the processes.

Dimensions of Manufacturing Management Quality

Fundamentals

Direction setting. Management starts with clear direction (or goal) setting. Short of a clear direction, actions can be partial at best, confusing at worst, with communication remaining incomplete and ambiguous. At the plant level, direction setting is facilitated by a clear focus (Skinner 1974). No one sets a better example of direction setting than President John F. Kennedy, when he challenged his fellow Americans to send a man to the moon; or than Winston Churchill when, as Prime Minister, he committed his British compatriots to resist the attacks on its territory during World War II. These examples underline the necessity for direction setting: to be clear, motivating, and operational. "Operational" means that upon hearing the direction set-out, each concerned individual will already be thinking of ways to contribute to the announced goal.

Delegation. Today, a factory is often characterized by complex and capital-intensive technology, and the need for faster response to changes in the competitive environment. It can no longer be run in a traditional command-and-control mode. Management must increasingly delegate decision making power to the various levels where the detailed knowledge of the manufacturing processes resides. Powell (1995) and Ittner and Larcker (1997) refer to delegation as "empowerment". For example, several winning plants had introduced fully autonomous lines (factories within a factory) with decision powers over quality, planning, and material flows. As one manager in consumer hygiene products plant put it: "We are going to the limit of the ability of our workers. I hold many one-on-one meetings with the technicians in charge of the project. They give a status report and I ask them if they need my help; the follow up is close. The combination of monitoring and helping not only reduces errors but also motivates the employees and makes them progress."

Integration. The complement of delegation is integration (Lawrence and Lorsch 1967). The more decision-making is decentralized, the more one must regularly re-align all to the common goal. This is the case both within the firm and in relations with suppliers.
Horizontal integration connects the plant with suppliers and customers along the supply chain or value chain. Many of the well-managed factories had full access to the customer's production planning system. Several were designated centers of technical expertise for the customer (with customer and competitor engineers on the team). One company had developed such a track record and mutual trust that the customer delegated important project management functions for product facelifts to the plant. "We do our best for the customer, so that everything runs 100%. That's our goal because we are part of the customer," commented the plant manager.

Similarly, on the supplier side, collaborative problem solving for mutual benefit has become wide spread. "We are not here to bleed our suppliers to death. We are here for all of us to do well. At the same time, we constantly re-evaluate them because they can be great today, but it does not mean that they will be great tomorrow. What is beneficial for us is to make the supplier progress with us. Moreover, we have internal programs in regards to quality among other items, and we deploy the same programs for our suppliers. It would not work for us if our suppliers did not advance as fast as us", explained the manager of a winning train-control systems plant.

Vertical integration applies to the strategy deployment process, including consistent sub-goals for all organizational sub-units. In the best plants, every worker knew the key performance priorities of the plant and could tell us what his or her contribution to these overarching goals was, in terms of quality, cost, volume, delivery times, or similar operational measures. Often, performance indicators and customer quality feedback were posted at the line, and the workers actually used the indicators to manage their daily work. Moreover, these cascaded goals were not simply announced from the top, but developed annually at every level by the manager with his/her direct-reports. The team would start with the deliverables to the next higher level, and every group leader or manager would offer what they were intending to do to reach the goals. If the aggregate result fell short, the team would collectively engage in problem solving until, together, they had a workable plan to achieve the targets. If it turned out that investments were needed to achieve the goal, this would be at least seriously considered. The process was not one-way, lots of modifications and ideas were fed back from the subsidiary levels of the organization to the top.

Temporal integration of the plant refers to collaboration with new product development. It has become standard in the best plants that production is represented in product development teams from the beginning. Manufacturing lines are regularly performing prototype runs, which cost capacity in the short run but help the plant to give input and to learn in the longer run. A superb example is the semiconductor facility of Thomson, which has become so proficient in testing new equipment and processes that this plant ramps them up and gives them away to other plants once they have been stabilized. Every single production worker is capable of running systematic experiments to find errors and improve yields. Over half of their time is spent on testing and process improvements, and yet the plant is highly productive.

Enablers

Direction setting, delegation and integration are supported by four enabling managerial practices if they are to function well.

Communication is necessary to both establish an open culture and to coordinate; that is, to equip empowered employees with the necessary understanding in order to make decisions that are consistent with the overall goals of the plant. This goes beyond posting indicators on boards. It includes an open-door policy, regular information about the overall strategy and situation of the plant, employee satisfaction surveys and open discussion of the working atmosphere. Note that this implies a trustful and constructive collaboration with unions and worker councils – "you have the worker council you deserve," observed one plant manager. Information for front line workers must be made concrete and operational rather than conceptual and abstract, but they are nevertheless interested in and capable of understanding the plant challenges and priorities.

Participation refers to motivating employees to contribute initiatives that go beyond their narrow job descriptions. As a demonstration, one plant manager lamented that "employees who responsibly manage a USD 60,000 budget in their sports club at home 'turn off their brains' when they enter the locker-room at work." We observed worker-led machine and process redesign where both the initiative and the project management came from machine operators, who were only supported by an engineer. In the best plants, suggestions do not get financially rewarded , but workers feel the masters of their own fate and change the face of their work place because they want to, not because they are paid for a suggestion. In several plants, management had put a group of technicians at the workers' disposal, and the workers decided what changes to make to the processes.

Employee development supports initiatives and processes by knowledge and skills. It refers to continuous training as well as the existence of career paths for employees to advance to broader tasks and responsibility. The Procter & Gamble plant in Crailsheim (Germany) has the strategy of doubling their output yet again (after having doubled already) without a headcount increase. This will happen through automation, with the twist that the workers are not de-skilled, but grow with the increasing technical sophistication of the process. Already when hiring workers, the plant looks for people with the potential to personally grow to a higher knowledge, gain responsibility and breadth of activities. In the best plants, we saw many examples of shift- or shop-managers who had started as machine operators and worked their way up, with training and support from the plant, to positions of significant managerial responsibility.

Finally, **measurement** is the systematic tracking of qualitative and quantitative measures of process performance and its drivers, providing feedback and the understanding of where to best target improvements. At Honeywell in Germany, for example, workers have on-line access to all process indicators, and plan work, maintenance and improvement efforts autonomously based on them. Mastery of statistical process control is by now quite widely spread, but Solvay in Laval (France) pushed the method further: when they perceived a small number of tendonitis cases on the line, they applied their problem solving skills to finding the root causes of the injuries, and to eliminate the problem (caused by the ergonomic character of some assembly operations). As a result, new tendonitis cases completely disappeared. This improved, above all, workplace quality, and as a non-anticipated side-effect, the effort paid for itself within under a year because of reduced absenteeism in the plant!

II.3 Developing the Operational Excellence Reference Model for the OPEX project

Michael Kickuth and Thomas Friedli

When we started the OPEX project the first challenge that we had to tackle was to develop a reference model for Operational Excellence that would help us to measure the operational performance of pharmaceutical plants in a structured and systematic way. For us the starting point for developing the OPEX model was the Manufacturing Management Quality Model by Christoph Loch (described earlier). Different from other Excellence models (e.g. EFQM model, Malcom Baldrige model, Excellence model by Peters and Waterman (1982), this model managed to truly operationalize the fuzzy term of Management Quality in the specific context of manufacturing.

However, due to several reasons that we will explain later, we also decided to integrate the more technically oriented practices (which are not included in the framework by Christoph Loch) like Just-in-Time production (JIT) or Total Productive Maintenance (TPM) into our framework. For that purpose, we used the Toyota Production System (TPS) as the reference model of choice. The Toyota Production System is, arguably, the paradigm for operations in a wide range of industries. With its principles that can be found in many companies, it provides a good framework for structuring the technically oriented practices in a system approach that also takes into account the interlocking effects between the different practices.

The system's distinctive practices – its *Kanban* cards and quality circles, for instance – have been widely introduced elsewhere. Indeed, following their own internal efforts to benchmark the world's best manufacturing companies, GM, Ford, DaimlerChrysler and Audi have independently created major initiatives to develop Toyota-like production systems. Companies that have tried to adopt the system can be found in fields as divers as aerospace, consumer products, metals processing, and industrial products (Spears and Bowen 1999). But few of them have been truly successful with their efforts to adopt the Toyota Production System to their specific requirements.

This was the point where we started to question whether it makes sense to adopt the TPS and transfer it to the pharmaceutical industry: too many companies (no matter whether they came from the automotive industry or elsewhere) have failed to introduce a Toyota-like Production system. The most cited reasons for that were the following ones:

Reason 1: "Best practices" do not work

Hayes and Pisano and also Christoph Loch argue that the problem is that simply improving manufacturing – by, for example, adopting "Best-practices" like Just-in-Time (JIT), TQM or some other three letter acronyms – is not a strategy for using manufacturing to achieve competitive advantage. If managers pin their competitive hopes on the implementation of a few best-practice approaches, they implicitly abandon the central concept of a strategy in favour of a generic approach to competitive success. Consequently Hayes and Pisano ask: "How can a company expect to achieve any sort of competitive advantage if it's only goal is to be "as good as" its toughest competitors?" (Hayes and Pisano 1994)

We totally agree with Hayes and Pisano; that for most companies (especially in the automotive industry) it is hard to achieve a competitive advantage by implementing certain principles of the Toyota Production System (TPS). However, the objective of our project was not to provide any participating company some sort of competitive advantage by implementing "Best-practices" from other companies. The main objective was to identify possible ways to improve the operational performance of pharmaceutical companies in general. Having a closer look to the companies that are often cited as companies having unsuccessfully adopted the TPS – notably Nissan or Honda[4] – those companies might not have managed to become as good as Toyota in the field of manufacturing – but they have succeeded in recent years by differentiating themselves in other areas of competition. However, despite not being as good as Toyota in manufacturing they have nevertheless significantly improved their operational performance by implementing certain principles of the TPS. While the TPS did not help them to achieve competitive advantage, it definitely helped them to improve their operational performance quicker than they would have done without having learned from a company like Toyota. This is exactly what we were aiming for when we started the project.

Reason 2: The success of the TPS lies in its cultural context

Several scholars have argued that the success of the TPS lies in its cultural roots and is therefore hard to apply to another cultural context (Delbridge and Turnbull 1993; Elger and Smith 1993). However, Toyota has successfully introduced its production system all around the world (e.g. US, UK etc.). At the same time many Japanese companies have fallen short of Toyota standards and did not manage to implement the TPS successfully. Obviously the cultural context is not the reason why the TPS is hard to adopt.

Reason 3: The TPS is not just a tool-set of practices – it is a scientific way of approaching problems

A very interesting analysis of the TPS comes from Spear and Bowen (1999). In their article *"Decoding the DNA of the Toyota Production System"* they also question why few manufacturers have managed to imitate Toyota successfully – even though the company has been extraordinarily open about its practices. Hundreds of thousands of executives from thousands of businesses have toured Toyota's plants in Japan and the United States (Spears and Bowen 1999). Only few of them have managed to find the secret roots of Toyota's success.

After having studied the Toyota Production System for four years and having examined the inner workings of forty plants in the United States, Europe, and Japan they came up with a totally different explanation of the success of the TPS.

To their mind, the key to the success of the TPS lies in its rigorous problem-solving process that requires a detailed assessment of the current state of affairs and a plan for improvement, that is, in effect, an experimental test of proposed changes. Consequently they conclude that the Toyota Production System can be regarded as a "community of scientists." With anything less than such scientific rigor, change at Toyota (and the TPS is continuously changing) would amount to little more than random trial and error – a blindfolded walk through life.

---

4 Which were examples from Hayes and Pisano for companies that did not manage to replicate the TPS successfully.

Reason 4: The TPS is a system of practices – All parts of the system are closely linked to each other

Several scholars conclude that the main reason why most companies fail to adopt the TPS is rooted in its interlocking character. Commonly cited problems in the implementation of certain elements of the TPS are those related to cultural resistance to change, lack of training and education (Crawford 1988), lack of coordination of the different departments, and confusion about the relationship between certain sub-systems (e.g. Just-in-Time and Continuous Improvement) (Safayeni 1991). Some scholars conclude that especially the joint optimization of practices that are socially (e.g. practices than can be related to the Management Quality framework such as delegation or participation) and technically oriented, should lead to a good performance; which is also strongly supported by the social-technical theory[5].

Many companies have realized that just implementing isolated elements (e.g. *Kanban*) will not yield any success. Hence, understanding the Toyota Production System as a "system of interlocking practices" (Loch et al. 2005) is crucial when a company aims to successfully adopt the Toyota Production System.

Lessons Learned

Taking into account the multitude of different perspectives on "Operational Excellence", we concluded that the OPEX model has to fit the following requirements:

- The OPEX model is based in part on the well known "technically oriented" practices made famous by Toyota in the manufacturing world (e.g. Just-in-Time)
- The OPEX model also has to include the more socially oriented aspects of the TPS that stem from a deeper business philosophy based on its understanding about problem solving and people management
- The OPEX model has to include the aspect of management quality as a vital facilitator of Operational Excellence
- The interlocking effects of several elements of Operational Excellence have to be taken into consideration

Analyzing Existing Reference Models of the Toyota Production System

Taiichi Ohno, one of the founders of the TPS, developed a simple representation of the TPS – a house (Figure 10). There are different versions of the house. We will shortly introduce the two most often published reference models of the TPS – the traditional one which we will call the "TPS-house" and the *"Genba Kanri"* model. Based on that we will consolidate the lessons learned and develop a model that fits with our requirements:

---

5 According to the social-technical theory, "management must recognize that the success of an enterprise depends upon how it works as a socio-technical system, not simply as a technical system with replicable individuals added to fit"; Emery, Thorsrud & Trist (1964).

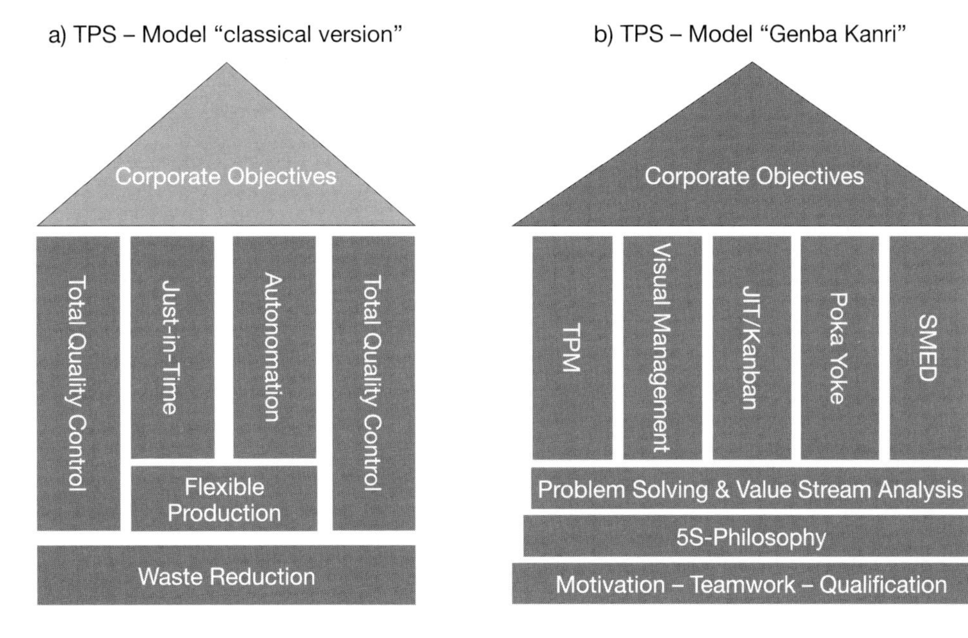

Figure 10: Models of the TPS.

The TPS House

Waste reduction

The heart of the Toyota Production System is the elimination of waste. Toyota has identified seven major types of non-value-adding waste *(Muda)* in business or manufacturing processes; which are described below (Liker and Choi 2004):

1. Over-production: Producing items for which there are no orders, which generates such wastes as overstaffing and storage and transportation costs because of excess inventory.
2. Waiting (time on hand): Workers merely serving to watch an automated machine or having to stand around waiting for the next processing step, tool, supply, part, etc., or just plain having no work because of stock-outs, lot processing delays, equipment downtime, and capacity bottlenecks.
3. Unnecessary transport or conveyance: Carrying Work-in-Progress (WIP) long distances, creating inefficient transport, or moving materials, parts, or finished goods into or out of storage or between processes.
4. Over-processing or incorrect processing: Taking un-needed steps to process the parts. Inefficiently processing due to poor tool and product design, causing unnecessary motion and producing defect. Waste is generated when providing higher-quality products than is necessary.

5. Excess inventory: Excess raw material, WIP, or finished goods causing longer lead times, obsolescence's, damaged goods, transportation and storage costs, and delay. Also, extra inventory hides problems such as production imbalances, late deliveries from suppliers, defects, equipment downtime, and long set-up times.
6. Unnecessary movement. Any wasted motion employees have to perform during the course of their work, such as looking for, reaching for, or stacking, parts, tools, etc. Also walking is regarded as waste.
7. Defects: Production of defective parts or correction. Repair or rework, scrap, replacement production, and inspection means wasteful handling, time, and lost effort.

Each of the following principles of the Toyota Production System aims to reduce the different sorts of waste:

Total Quality Control (TQC)

The two basic pillars of the TPS house are devoted to the goal of quality. TQC practices include all the modern quality assurance methods like Statistical Process Control, Design of Experiments, Failure Mode and Effect Analysis (FMEA), Quality Function Deployment (QFD) etc. Besides the technical aspects of quality management, it also includes certain principles that describe the deeper quality philosophy based on Toyota's understanding of quality and people. Those principles can be summarized as follows:

- "Define the value from your customer's perspective"[6]
- "Respect, develop, and challenge your people and suppliers"
- "Go see for yourself to thoroughly understand the situation" (Genchi Genbutsu)[7]
- "Use visual control so no problems are hidden"
- "Standardize tasks for continuous improvement"
- "Capitalize on the creativity of your people for continuous improvement" (Soikufu)
- "Use only reliable, thoroughly tested technology"

Just-in-Time (JIT)

The JIT principle is probably the most visible and highly publicized characteristic of the TPS. The basic idea behind the JIT principle is to reduce waste *(Muda)* within the value stream[8]. To be a JIT manufacturer requires a way of thinking that focuses on making the product flow through value-adding processes without interruption (one-piece flow) and a "pull" system that cascades back from customer demand by replenishing only what the next operation takes away at short intervals.

---

6 ... which also include all internal customer-supplier relationships.

7 *Genchi* means the actual location and *genbutso* means the actual materials or products. It means that the first step of any problem solving process, development of a new product etc. is grasping the actual situation. Toyota promotes and expects creative thinking, and innovation is a must; but it should be grounded in thoroughly understanding of all aspects of the actual situation. Toyota expects that its employees and managers must deeply understand the process of flow, standardized work, etc. as well as have the ability to critically evaluate and analyze what is going on.
(Liker and Choi 2004).

8 The value stream starts at the moment the customer gives an order to the point when the cash is collected.

To eliminate waste, the JIT concept provides a multitude of practices that either help to create flow e.g. techniques for reducing set-up time reductions such as Single Minute Exchange of Die (SMED)[9] or techniques to level the workload *(Heijunka)*[10] e.g. introducing Takt time[11] or techniques to optimize the shop floor layout; and pull production (e.g. techniques for replenishing based on actual usage such as *Kanban* replenishment systems).

Autonomation (Jidoka)

Autonomation, means equipment endowed with human intelligence to stop itself when it has a problem. Autonomation, or *Jidoka* – using the Japanese expression – is a further pillar of the TPS. *Jidoka* should facilitate 100% "build-in-quality" by directly resolving problems at the point where they occur. It subsumes a number of methods that allow detection of defects when they occur and automatically stop production so an employee can fix the problem before the defect continues downstream. There a several techniques that can be related to the *Jidoka* concept. One core element is *Andon, which* is a light system that allows signalling at each production step that signals help is needed to solve a quality problem (sometimes it also displays the actual Takt time and, by that, also facilitates flow- and pull-production). The following statement indicates the philosophy behind *Jidoka* and *Andon: "In the case of machines, we build devices into them, which detect abnormalities and automatically stop the machine upon such an occurrence. In the case of humans, we give them the power to push buttons or pull cords – called Andon Cords – which can bring our entire assembly line to halt. Every team member has the responsibility to stop the line every time they see something that is out of standard. That's how we put the responsibility for quality in the hands of our team members. They feel the responsibility – They feel the power – They know they count"* (Liker and Choi 2004). Hence, there are two major advantages of a *Jidoka* system: it allows to solve problems directly at the root cause and brings the problem to the surface and it makes employees accountable for high quality at each station or production step. Other techniques that are related to the concept of *Jidoka* are *Poka Yoke*[12] or automatic line stopping systems which are usually designed with built-in sensors to detect any deviation from standard; and in case of deviation lead to an automatic stop of the production line.

Flexible production

The TPS tries to be as flexible as necessary. Elements that facilitate its flexibility are its ability to pursue a mixed model production and its multi-skilled workforce that is able to perform different tasks. The objective of the mixed model production is not to build products according to the actual flow of customer orders, but to take the total volume of orders in a period and

---

9 SMED is a shortcut for Single Minute Exchange of Die and is a method of systematic seeking for setup time reduction, according to a quantified target. It discriminates operations that MUST be done while machine is stopped, called internal setup, from those possibly done while machine runs, called external setup, and useless operations.

10 *Heijunka* means levelling out the production schedule in both volume and variety. A levelled schedule or *hejunka* is necessary to keep the system stable to allow for minimum inventory.

11 Takt is a German word for rhythm or meter. Takt is the rate of the customer demand – the rate at which the customer is buying the product. Consider a worker that is working seven hours and 20 minutes per day (440 minutes) for 20 days a month and the customer is buying 17.600 units per month, the worker should make 880 units per day or one unit every 30 second (Liker and Choi 2004).

12 *Poka Yoke* refers to mistake-proofing (also error proofing or fool proofing). These are creative devices that make it nearly impossible for an operator to make an error.

level them out, so the same amount and mix is being made each day (this element can also be related to the JIT system, above). When the customer demand decreases, the multi-skilled workforce allows reduction of the actual Takt time. Consequently the number of workers that are required per shift decreases and the remaining workers now has to perform more tasks while still meeting the precisely defined operating time for each task.

However, this does not mean that Toyota is pursuing a "build-to-order" production system. Toyota has found out that it can create the leanest operation and give customers better service and better quality by levelling out the production schedule. The reason for that is that the reduction of too much waste due to non-value adding activities *(Muda)* causes other sorts of problems which are called *Muri* and *Mura*. *Muri* means over-burning people or equipment which is in some respect on the opposite end of the spectrum of *Muda*. *Muri* is pushing a machine or person beyond natural limits. *Mura* means unevenness. Unevenness results from an irregular production schedule or fluctuating production volumes due to internal problems, like downtime or missing parts or defects. Consequently Toyota tries to avoid under-utilization as well as over-utilization because it does not lend itself to quality, standardization of work, productivity, or continuous improvement. The example provides evidence that Toyota, while being highly flexible compared to most other automotive manufacturers, is very eager to balance high flexibility with a smoothly levelled workload.

Differences between the Toyota House and the Genba Kanri reference model

Even though both reference models have been developed from former Toyota employees, they put emphasis on different aspects of the Toyota Production System. This underlines the fact that shortly summarizing and visualizing the major principles of the TPS is not an easy task. Different from the Toyota House, the *Genba Kanri* model includes a multitude of more social oriented practices that refer to the work organization. Similar to the Management Quality Model from Loch et al. (2003), it stresses delegation (teamwork), empowerment/participation and qualification/people development as crucial elements for the success of the TPS.

What does this mean? While most people talk about teamwork when they give a lecture about the Toyota Production System, they sometime forget that Toyota also strongly supports individual excellence. Toyota has established an excellent balance between individual work and team effectiveness. Qualification and people development refers to the fact that Toyota puts tremendous efforts in finding and screening prospective employees that fit with the Toyota culture and afterwards it puts even more efforts in developing them (Liker and Choi 2004). Hence, true empowerment and participation (which are crucial for driving continuous improvement) is a result of a long-term development process; that can take up to 3 years.

While the social oriented practices of the *Genba Kanri* reference model fit well with most principles from the Management Quality model from Loch et al., there are several other differences to the TPS house concerning the more technical oriented practices. Different from the TPS house, one core element of the *Genba Kanri* model is the concept of Total Productive Maintenance (TPM). TPM is designed to maximize equipment effectiveness, improve overall efficiency by establishing a comprehensive productive-maintenance system during the life of the equipment, whilst spanning all equipment-related fields such as planning/buying, use, maintenance etc. Furthermore it also stresses visual management as an important principle. Visual Management is any communication device (manual or electronically) that is used in the work environment that shows the worker (and management) at a glance how work should be done and whether it is deviating from the standard. It provides the workforce with updated information of process and performance information; and by that assists the deployment of a decentralised workforce organization.

In addition to Visual Management, there are two further elements of the *Genba Kanri* model which are, on first sight, not included in the TPS House: *Poka Yoke* and SMED. However, we have seen that those elements have been characterized as sub-elements of *Jidoka* and JIT in the TPS house.

Conclusion

Both reference models give some interesting insights into the major principles of the TPS. However, due to several reasons we decided not to take one of those models as the Reference model for the OPEX project:

- The TPS house does not take into account the aspects of "Management Quality" in the context of Operational Excellence. It solely concentrates on the more "technical" aspects of the TPS (e.g. JIT).
- While definitely being an important principle of the TPS in a high-volume production environment (like automotives), it is questionable whether the *Jidoka* (Autonomation) principle can be regarded as one of the "core pillars" of a generic reference model that is supposed to be applicable to any sort of industry. Conversely, the TPS house does not take into consideration the principles of TPM even though TPM obtains relevance in most capital-intensive and highly mechanised industries such as the process industry (Spath et al. 2003).
- While the *Genba Kanri* reference model takes into account the more social oriented aspects of Operational Excellence, it also bears some shortcomings with regard to the consistency and logical order of its principles. The model mixes higher-level principles such as JIT or TPM with single methods or techniques (e.g. SMED or *Poka Yoke*) that could be subordinated to those principles.
- Furthermore, unlike the TPS house, the *Genba Kanri* model does not stress the scientific rigour and structured way of problem solving which is typical for the concept of Total Quality Control (a core element of the TPS house) and according to Spear and Bowen the "DNA" of the TPS.

The OPEX reference model

Our following characterization of Operational Excellence tries to integrate the notions of both TPS reference models as well the notions of Loch et al. (2003) on management quality. It further tries to integrate the ideas of Spears and Bowen (1999) with regard to the scientific rigour of problem solving at Toyota which they regard as the true success factor of the TPS.

We define the OPEX reference model as a system that comprises several sub-systems (see Figure 11). Each sub-system by itself is critical; but more important is the way the elements reinforce each other. First, there is a technical sub-system of the OPEX reference model that can be regarded as a tool-kit, comprising the well known practices like Just-in-Time or TPM; and structuring them in a logical and consistent manner. Second, there is a social sub-system that takes up the quest for an operational characterization of management quality and work organization that focuses on supporting and encouraging people to continually improve processes (and by that, applying the "technical" practices in ways to contribute to the overall goal of the company).

Technical System		
TQM-System	**TPM-System**	**JIT-System**
• Process management • Customer integration • Cross functional product development • Supplier quality management	• Preventive Maintenance • Housekeeping • Usage of new technology	• Set-up time reduction • Pull production • Layout-optimization • Stabilized planning
Basic elements		
Standardisation Visual management		
Management System		
Direction setting Management commitment Employee involvement & continuous improvement Functional integration & people development		

Figure 11: The OPEX reference model.

The technical sub-system

The objective of the technical sub-system of the OPEX reference model was to analyze the level of implementation of the technical oriented practices. When structuring the different practices in the field of Operations Management, we decided to distinguish between (core-) principles and techniques/tools. Principles usually span a multitude of techniques/tools that can all be characterized by a certain underlying goal or a notion. For example, we regard JIT as a core principle of Operational Excellence as it is rooted in the notion of eliminating waste, and provides a multitude of techniques/tools (e.g. SMED) to achieve that goal. Based on our first plant visits that we performed in the pharmaceutical industry, we realized that most of the tools (e.g. *Poka Yoke, Andon* etc.) are not well-known. Consequently, we decided to structure the OPEX model on the high-level principles of Operations Management without trying to mix it with single tools.

Thinking about most of the major Operations Management principles [e.g. JIT, TQM or 'three letter acronyms' as Hayes and Pisano (1994) call them] they usually aim at a certain area of concern that many companies are facing (e.g. low quality, high inventories); and most companies implement them in order to solve their problems. Whilst we do not want to give a further lecture on the problems that a company will face if it just implements those principles in order to fix problems and tries to catch up with its competitors, we think that there are three, "three letter acronyms" that should structure the most important principles of Operational Excellence in a logical and consistent manner, namely: JIT, TQM and TPM.

Each of those major principles should reinforce each other. With its focus on achieving the goal of "one-piece flow" and minimal buffer inventory, the JIT concept requires stable and robust processes. With its strong focus on variance minimization, the TQM concept can be regarded as a complimentary concept as it should lead to a less variable (better controlled) manufacturing process that, in turn, reduces the need for safety stock buffers. In mass production, when a machine goes down, there is usually no sense of urgency; the maintenance department is scheduled to fix it while inventory keeps the operations running. However, in a JIT environment, equipment break downs will soon stop producing and by that create a crisis. Hence, the concept of Total Productive Maintenance (TPM), where everyone learns how to clean, inspect and maintain equipment becomes a crucial element of an excellent operation.

For each of the core principles we will now introduce the sub-elements that we have measured:

Just-in-Time (JIT)

Due to the fact that in most industries the heterogeneity of customer requirements and dynamism has significantly increased in recent years, JIT manufacturing has become a crucial element for most companies to increase flexibility without building up huge inventories. Comparing the *Genba Kanri* model and the TPS house that we previously introduced, JIT was also the only principle that was included in both reference models. We define pull-production, set-up time reduction, lay-out optimization and stabilized planning *(Hejunka)* to be the core elements of JIT production.

Whilst **pull-production** helps in reducing overproduction, it is inventory and **set-up time reductions** that can help to reduce the average lot size and enable an improved material flow throughout the manufacturing processes. With the need for standardized, stable, reliable processes we regarded the element **stabilized planning** *(Hejunka)* as a further element of JIT. Stabilized planning, which means smoothly levelling out the production schedule in both volume and variety, should keep the JIT-system stable and allow for minimum inventory. Apart from waste caused by overproduction and excess inventory, an integrated JIT program also endeavours to reduce all kind of excessive movement caused by excess material and handling movement. Hence, **lay-out optimization** based on close arrangements of people, machines, workstations in a processing sequence is a further basic principle of a JIT implementation.

Total Quality Management (TQM)

According to Spear and Bowen (1999), the key to the success of the TPS lays in its rigorous problem-solving process that requires a detailed assessment of the current state of affairs and a plan for improvement; that is, in effect, an experimental test of proposed changes. According to Spear this approach makes the TPS unique. Having a closer look at the concept of TQM, one will find that TQM is, at its heart, a very rigorous problem solving process that is based on facts rather than *gut feel*. Today, the concept of 6-Sigma has become much more popular than the term TQM. The difference between both concepts lay in the even stronger orientation of the 6-Sigma concept on the statistical measure sigma; standing for standard deviation[13]. The Case Study "6-Sigma at a Pharmaceutical plant" in chapter IV provides evidence that the scientific rigour to approach problems is not just ingrained in Toyota. Companies that have truly internalized the principles of TQM or 6-Sigma also try to set-up operations as experiments to continuously isolate variables that cause deviation and, by that, are continuously able to improve their processes. Consequently we decided to incorporate the principles of TQM[14] as one major pillar of the OPEX model.

---

13 See Annex: About the 6-Sigma concept on page 122 for a short comparison between the TQM and the 6-Sigma concept.

14 We intentionally decided not to use the expression 6-Sigma, because we wanted to raise awareness that most principles of Operational Excellence have a long history and should not be regarded as a "fashion".

However, TQM (as well as 6-Sigma) goes beyond the statistics. TQM is a total management commitment and philosophy of excellence, customer focus, continuous process improvement and people and supplier development. We define process management, customer integration, supplier quality management and cross functional product development to be the core elements of a TQM-System.

Process management is defined as documenting, measuring, analyzing and improving processes; and thus reducing process variances to a minimum level. Process management includes all the common tools of quality management that aim to find and control root causes of deviation (e.g. Cause and Effect Diagrams, Pareto Analysis, Design of Experiments, Statistical Process Control etc.). A high level of documentation and standardization usually goes in hand with human and organizational dysfunction (e.g. unmotivated workforce, high absenteeism etc.); hence a few decades ago job-enrichment was developed as an antidote. However, successful process management is more likely to manifest from peers working in **cross-functional teams** than from industrial engineers. TQM specialists suggest that companies should choose vendors primarily on the basis of quality rather than solely on product price. Moreover, **supplier quality management** aims to integrate suppliers into the internal quality system (e.g. by jointly developing processes) to ensure high quality levels. To achieve excellent quality, it is essential to know what customers want and to provide products to meet their needs **(customer integration)**. Furthermore, TQM specialists suggest that **cross functional product development** should help to translate customer requirements into high quality products.

Total Productive Maintenance (TPM)

Both principles, TQM and JIT, refer to certain ideas of how to manage processes to achieve high quality products while eliminating waste. However, we have not tackled the role of technology in our reference model. Within the TPS, the main role of technology is to be reliable and serve people and processes. At Toyota, new technology is introduced only after it is proven through direct experimentation with the involvement of a broad cross-section of people. First, it will go and see first-hand the nature of the value-added work being performed by the workers for the particular process. It will look for new opportunities to eliminate waste and even- out the flow. Toyota will then use a pilot to improve the process with the existing equipment, technology, and people. When it has accomplished as much improvement as possible with the present process, Toyota will ask again if it can make any additional improvements by adding new technology. If it determines that the new technology can add value to the process, the technology is then carefully analyzed to see if it conflicts with Toyota's operating principles (Liker and Choi 2004). All those issues refer to the strongly supporting role of technology within the TPS that aims to serve and support processes and people. Besides the supportive role of technology, a further issue is the reliability of the technology. An existing and integrated concept that embraces both issues, the reliability of the existing equipment and the effective usage of new technology, is the concept of Total Productive Maintenance (TPM). Consequently, we decided to incorporate the concept of TPM as a further major pillar of the OPEX model. We define the following elements to be the major principles of TPM: preventive maintenance, autonomous maintenance, housekeeping, cross-functional training and the usage of new technology according to the principles of TPM.

TPM is designed to maximize equipment effectiveness, improve overall efficiency by establishing a comprehensive productive-maintenance system during the life of the equipment, whilst spanning all equipment-related fields such as planning/buying, use, maintenance etc. Moreover, it engages the participation of all employees, from plant management to shop-floor workers and thus promotes productive maintenance through motivational management techniques and voluntary small group activities. TPM is usually divided into short-term and long-term elements. In the short-term attention is focused on an autonomous maintenance program for the production department, a planned and **preventive maintenance** program for the maintenance department, and skill development for operations and maintenance personnel. In contrast, the long-term elements of TPM focus on the already mentioned principles concerning the **usage of new technology** which should be designed to support people and processes.

Autonomous maintenance can be described by considering the four main goals of the TPM program. First, the program brings production and maintenance people together in teams to stabilize conditions and halt deterioration of equipment. Second, by effectively developing and sharing responsibility for the critical daily maintenance tasks, production and maintenance people are able to improve the overall "health" of the equipment. Through autonomous maintenance operators learn to carry out important daily tasks that maintenance people rarely have time to perform. These **"housekeeping"** tasks include cleaning and inspecting, lubricating, precision checking, and other light maintenance tasks. Third, TPM is designed to help operators learn more about how their equipment functions, what common problems can occur and why they occur, and how those problems can be prevented through early detection and treatment of abnormal conditions. This **cross-functional training** allows operators to maintain equipment and to identify and resolve many basic equipment problems. In a TPM program, maintenance technicians are held accountable for completing maintenance tasks within a scheduled time-frame while still meeting production requirements. Using standardized operating procedures helps to increase schedule compliance which is an important indicator for the health of a TPM system.

The basic elements

After structuring the OPEX model according to the three "sub-systems" JIT-, TQM- and TPM, we realized that there are some common practices that are shared by all three sub-systems, and are not unique to each of the programs: for example Cross-functional training, employee empowerment and teamwork, standardization and visual management. We decided to differentiate between the technical practises like standardization and the more social oriented aspects like employee empowerment or cross-functional training (that we will discuss later).

The following two technical oriented practices can not be solely related to JIT, TQM or TPM: **standardization** and **visual management**. We call them basic elements because they can be regarded as a basic pre-requisite for successfully implementing TQM, TPM as well as JIT-principles. As Imai (1986) explained so well in *Kaizen*, his book on continuous improvement, it is impossible to improve any process until it is standardized. One must standardize, and thus stabilize the process before continuous improvement can be made. But standardization does not just refer to the processes; it also includes the standardization of technology and equipment. If new technology has been thoroughly evaluated and regarded as supportive, Toyota will broadly implement it and integrate the new technology into its standard operating procedures. Hence, standardization can be regarded as a common supportive element for JIT, TQM as well as TPM. A further basic element is visual management. It provides the workforce with updated information of process and performance information and that assists the deployment of JIT-, TQM- and TPM-principles (e.g. visual management can provide timely information regarding JIT-related information like the actual takt time to enhance flow as well as TQM- or TPM-related information like process variability or equipment reliability to improve problem solving).

The "social" sub-system – the Management System

We closely base our model of management quality on the model of Loch et al. (2003) and on some of the classic motivation theories (Maslow's Need Hierachy, Herzberg's Enrichment Theory, Taylor's Scientific Management). We merged some elements from Loch et al.'s model due to statistical and conceptual reasons (e.g. some variables strongly inter-correlated with each other, so that we decided to merge them) and also added an element which is management commitment.

Based on those sources, we developed a management quality model where management quality can be summarized as follows: "Motivating and aligning people to work for a common goal." To achieve that people need autonomy to feel that they have control over their job and belong to a team **(people involvement)**. Targets have to be clear and consistent as well as challenging **(direction setting)** and supported by the senior management **(management commitment)**. People have to get feedback on their progress frequently and timely and have to be multi-skilled developed according to their potentials **(functional integration and people development)**.

Direction setting: We totally agree with Skinner (1974), Hayes et al. (2005) and Loch et al. (2004), that the implementation of certain practices only makes sense if it the management has formulated a strategy that is based on clear and consistent objectives. However, we decided to merge the variable integration from Loch *et* al.'s model (see page 32 ff.) and the variable direction setting due to the fact that they were highly inter-correlated and conceptually close related.

Management commitment: Several studies provide evidence that management commitment is a crucial element for facilitating change processes which is a prerequisite for process improvement. Especially the TQM literature stresses management commitment as one of the key success factor. Because senior management create the organizational systems that determine how products are designed and produced, the quality-improvement process must begin with management's own commitment to quality. However, management commitment is not just crucial for rolling out a TQM program. The same is true for rolling out a JIT- and TPM-program. Management has to promote a culture that supports the people doing their work.

Employee involvement and continuous improvement: Similar to Loch et al., we also include employee involvement into our management quality model. We see that one major managerial challenge is to get all employees involved to think about continuously improving the current situation. Toyota for example managed to get some 80,000 improvement suggestions per year at their Georgetown plant in the US. This is just possible if process improvement is a common task for everybody and not just for few smart industrial engineers.

Functional integration and people development: A workforce that is eager to contribute to the goals set by the management, but lack proper know-how to do so, can not support those goals. As there is delegation of complex decisions e.g. like autonomous problems solving, then this can only be successful if employees are given the chance to acquire new knowledge. Furthermore, the flexibility of the technical system that we have introduced (especially the concept of mixed model production) requires a multi-skilled workforce that can perform different tasks. Consequently, functional integration and employee development is a basic pillar for goals set by the plant management. We also agree with Loch et al. (2004), that people development is an essential tool to foster employee participation. However, we also want to incorporate the aspect of feedback and reward as an enabler for motivation. Organizational scientists stress that rewards go beyond money. It could be praise from a supervisor or peer or it could be winning an award. The important point is that the positive or negative reinforcement comes as quickly as possible after the action.

The Status of the Pharmaceutical Industry

Michael Kickuth and Thomas Friedli

The objective of the following chapter is to provide answers to the following questions:

- Based on the current challenges of the pharmaceutical industry described in chapter I: "How do companies *actually* respond to current industry changes?" "What drives pharmaceutical companies to become 'operationally excellent'?"
- Due to the pharmaceutical industry's specific characteristics: "What are the main levers to increase operational performance in the pharmaceutical industry?"
- "To what extent are practices of Operational Excellence (especially Lean Manufacturing Practices) implemented today?"
- "Is there any empirical evidence to support the notion that implementation of Operational Excellence practices, drives performance up?"
- "Does Operational Excellence matter in an industry that can be characterized as R&D and marketing driven?"

This chapter has been developed on the basis of a European wide study that was conducted between August 2004 and June 2005 involved personally addressing some 400 managing directors, site-leaders and Vice-presidents of Operations of pharmaceutical companies across Europe (Figure 12).

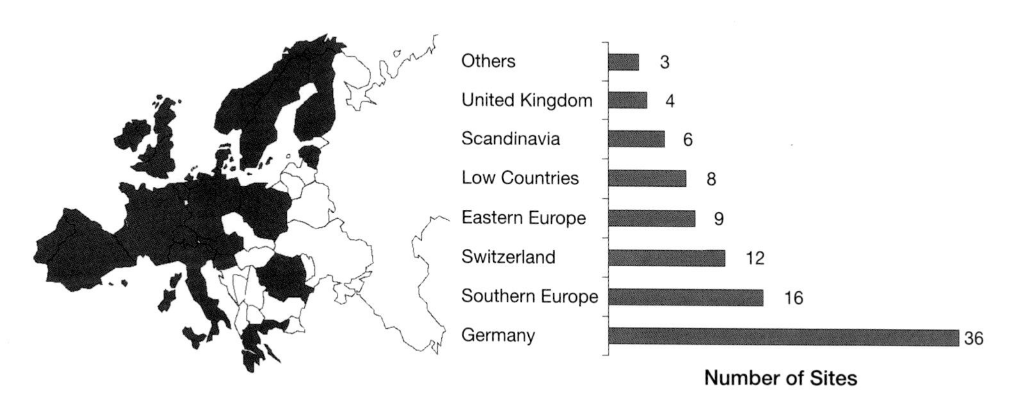

Figure 12: Geographical overview.

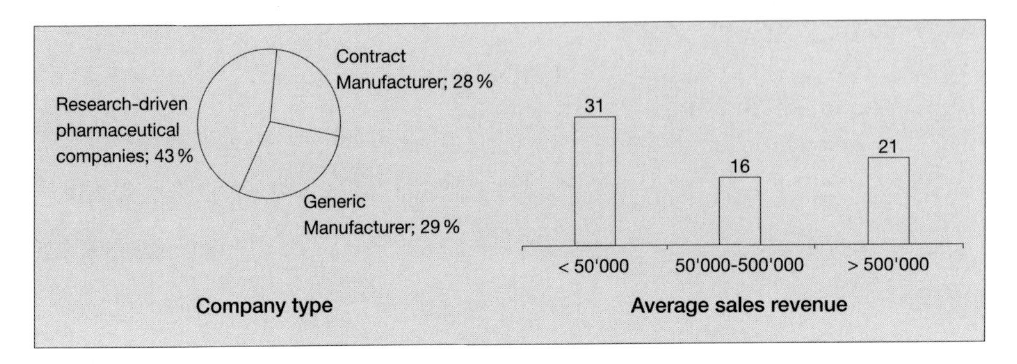

Figure 13: Structure of the participating companies.

Ninety-four organizations and production plants from twenty different European countries participated in the broad study (some 20 others in the additional site visits); to explore in great detail whether the hypothesis of James Womack is valid, namely: that the pharmaceutical industry is truly an industry which is lagging behind other industries with regard to lean thinking.

Consequently, we tackled three classes of pharmaceutical organization: first, the research-driven pharmaceutical companies, then generics companies and finally the contract manufacturers.

Our empirical-qualitative study, based on questionnaires, was combined with some twenty on-site plant audits in chosen companies. We refer to these findings when it helps to explain some of the statistical analyses; and will summarize some points at the end of this chapter.

The following figures provide some more information about the sample that has been analyzed. Figure 13 shows that most of the companies that have participated are R&D-driven companies that manufacture ethical drugs. However, there are also a fairly high number of generics and contract manufacturers that have participated in the study. Furthermore, there is a wide range concerning the average sales revenue. While most of the participating companies can be regarded as "Pharma-SMEs" with revenues of less than EUR 50 million, there are also some of the globally operating pharmaceutical companies that have contributed to the study. Twenty-one companies in the sample generate sales revenues with more than EUR 500 million and six of the ten biggest pharmaceutical companies in the world are represented in the sample. This provides strong evidence that Operational Excellence seems to be an issue for all kind of pharmaceutical companies, no matter their type or size.

III.1 How Do Pharmaceutical Companies Respond to the Changing Environment?

Michael Kickuth and Thomas Friedli

In responding to the forces of change in the business environment, pharmaceutical companies are increasingly following competitive strategies that are based on reducing costs.

Among a set of twelve alternative strategic initiatives, the option of improving operating efficiency was rated with the highest priority when asked "How important is it in meeting business strategy." Some 90% of companies are planning to give a greater attention to improving operational issues. The three most important initiatives in meeting business strategy were identified as:

- Increase operating efficiency
- Address niche markets
- Achieve competitive pricing

An increasing share of companies seems to pursue a strategy that is based on cost issues. Obviously efficiency improvements in the operational processes of procurement, production and logistics are becoming more crucial.

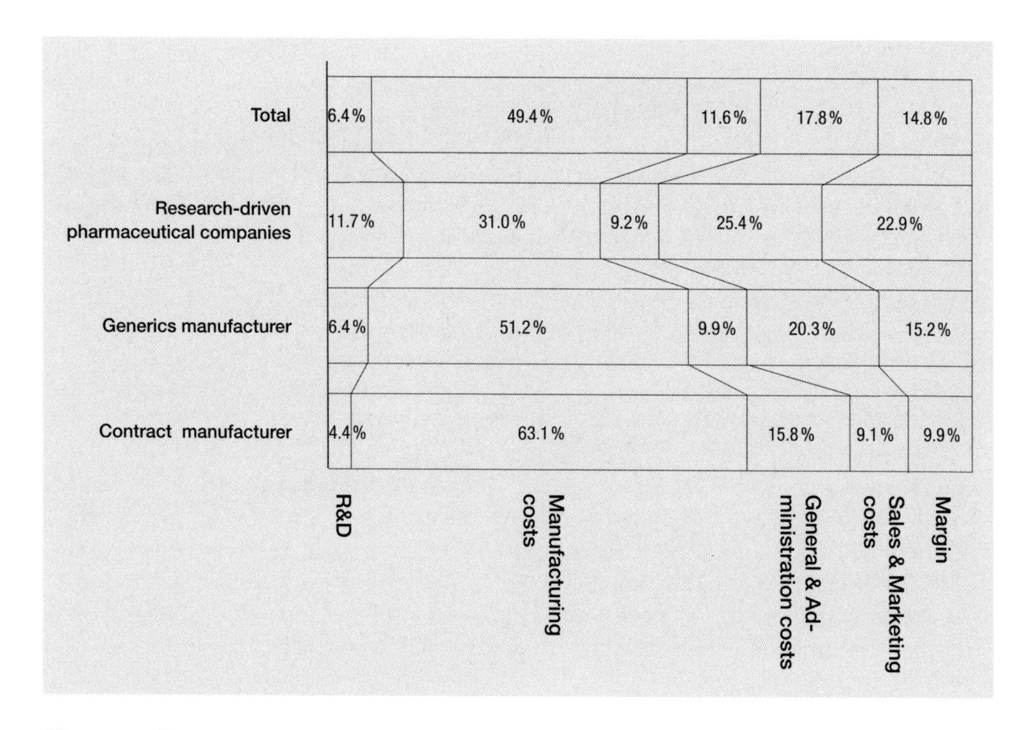

Figure 14: Cost structure – Company level.

However, a business strategy based purely on cost issues appears not to pay off; as a high R&D ratio seems to boost profitability. Whilst companies with an R&D ratio lower than 5% have an average Return on Sales of around 10%, companies with an R&D ratio of more than 10% have an average Return on Sales of some 20% (see Figure 14). Conversely, pharmaceutical companies increasingly question whether solely focusing on R&D will be a sustainable strategy in future. With cost of sales of around 30%, manufacturing accounts for the second highest cost factor among the research driven pharmaceutical companies in our sample. Among generic manufacturers, this ratio rises to about 50%; and to more than 60% among the contract manufacturers (see Figure 14).

III.2 Cost Savings Potential – What is the Main Leverage for Streamlining Operations?

Michael Kickuth and Thomas Friedli

Taking a closer look at manufacturing costs in the pharmaceutical industry at the level of the production unit, it is an interesting exercise to discover what the main leverage for streamlining manufacturing operations is. The combined costs of purchased materials, direct and indirect labor and equipment account for the highest portion of the overall manufacturing costs (Figure 15).

Comparing the 10% best performing plants in the sample with the average plant identifies potential cost savings that could add up to around 16% of the total costs of a typical manufacturing plant (see Figure 16). With average total costs of around EUR 40 million for a typical manufacturing plant, this can be translated into around EUR 6.5 million annual cost savings. Some of the biggest differences between an average plant and the best performing plants are described below:

- A difference of around EUR 1.5 million in comparison to the average costs for QC/QA per direct labor between the top 10% and the peer group.
- A difference of EUR 1.4 million in comparison to the costs for maintenance per direct labor between the top 10% and the peer group.
- A difference of EUR 840,000 lower annual depreciation (if assuming a 5 year depreciation time for excess capacity investments) when comparing the asset utilization of the top 10% with the peer group.
- A difference of EUR 710,000 by taking the internal quality performance (e.g. scrap rates, number of rejected batches etc.) between the top 10% and the peer group.

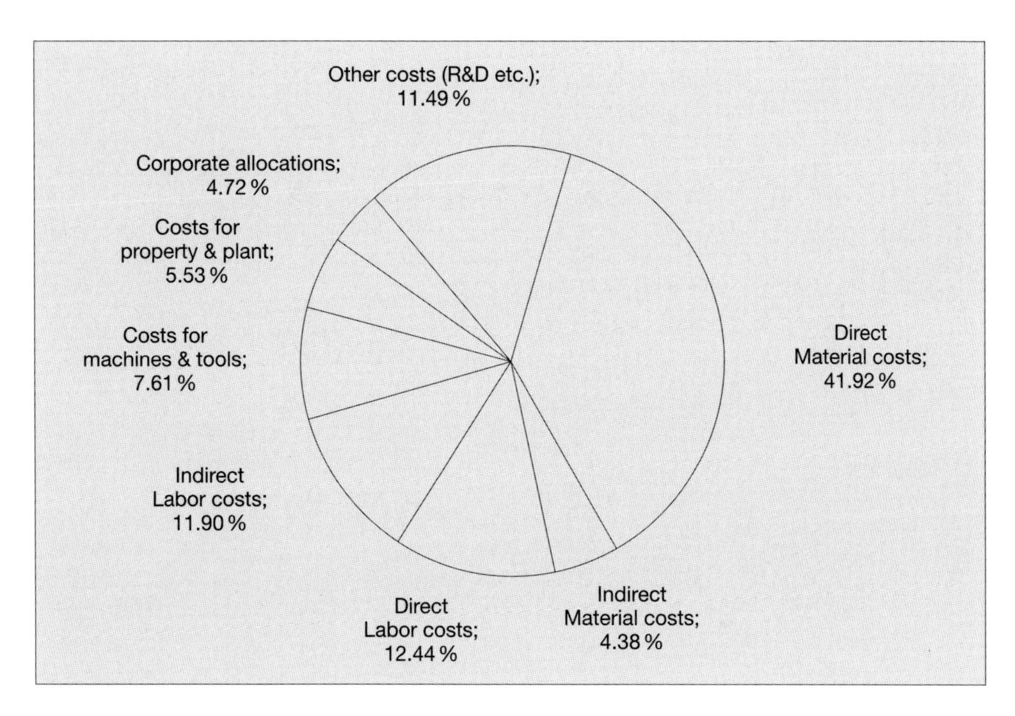

Figure 15: Cost structure – Plant level.

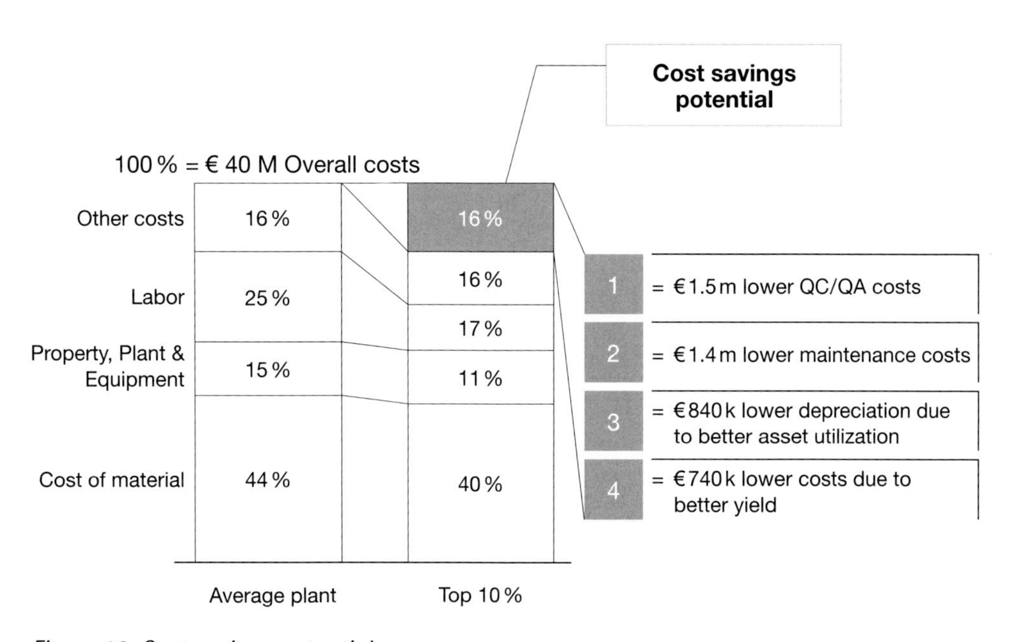

Figure 16: Cost savings potential.

Analyzing the capital employed, the story does look quite similar. The 10% low performing plants have in average finished goods stock turns of approximately two. Applying an average gross margin of around 60% for pharmaceutical products, the typical plant in our sample employs around EUR 45 million working capital in its inventories. Taking the very low debt/equity ratio of most pharmaceutical companies, the cost of capital for keeping those stock levels can easily add up to more than EUR 5 million a year.

Extrapolating those figures to the potential cost savings over the lifetime of a USD 1 billion-a-year blockbuster drug, efficient manufacturing could translate into around EUR 500 million overall cost savings.

However, to realise those cost reductions, it is important to find out more about the 'mechanisms' for deployment of Operational Excellence in the pharmaceutical industry.

III.3 Linking Practice to Performance: Testing the Operational Excellence Model

Michael Kickuth and Thomas Friedli

The overall hypotheses of the project "Operational Excellence" is that the right implementation of modern principles of Operational Excellence will lead to a significantly higher performance among pharmaceutical manufacturing plants and thus lead to a higher overall business performance of the company.

The basic model for testing that hypothesis has already been presented in chapter II.

Outcomes of the TQM Model

The pharmaceutical industry is World Class with regard to (external) customer-oriented quality performance measures. With an average complaint level that is far lower than 1%, the industry seems to be not far from excellent (see Figure 17).

Hence, the next question: "Is high quality 'built into the system', or is it a result of high inspection activity/cost?" Taking into account the high regulatory requirements from the FDA and other registration agencies, the answer is not surprising: "It is a result of high inspection costs". Companies that are performing well in terms of external quality performance are having much higher inspection costs than their low performing peers (in terms of external quality performance metrics).

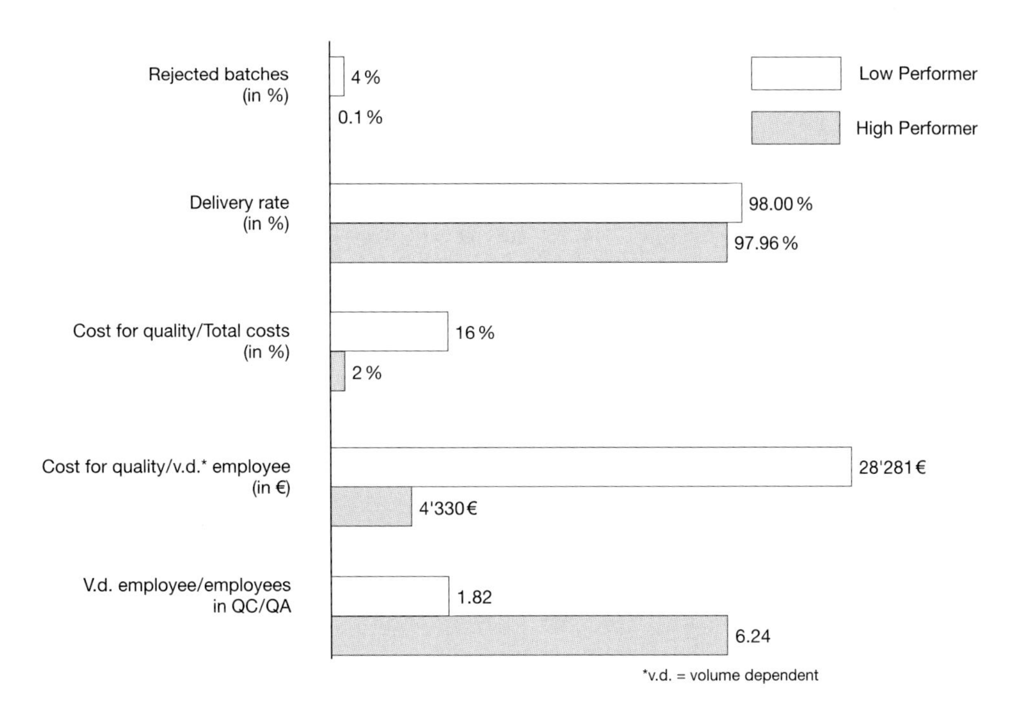

Figure 17: TQM performance measures.

As there seems to be a trade-off between high quality and low quality costs, the challenge is how to stop this vicious circle. The figures provide an indication. Whilst teamwork and cross-functional training, as well as cross-functional product development, do not seem to have an impact on any of the quality performance indices, it appears that the integration of external partners into the quality system seems to pay off (e.g. suppliers, customers).

Strongly supported by our data is the basic assumption of TQM that, quality can only be achieved when companies know what customers want. Plants that are frequently getting feedback from their customers on quality and delivery performance and are frequently surveying their customers' requirements are performing much better than those that have not integrated their customers into their quality system.

Companies that integrate their suppliers into their quality systems, likewise, seem to perform better. Companies that jointly develop their processes with their suppliers, and put high emphasis on quality aspects among their suppliers, have a higher supplier-quality performance, as well as lower internal rejection rates.

A further underlying assumption of TQM is that a quality improvement process must begin with top management commitment. This must emanate from senior managers as they create the organizational system that determines how products and processes are designed and supported. Strong management commitment to quality and its improvement leads to a higher performance, in terms of lower complaint rates and high service levels. Even though some of those practices do not have an impact on external quality performance, they can affect internal quality performance indices (e.g. number of rejected batches). However, none of them help to lower quality costs. Interestingly, the only practice that helps break-up the vicious circle of quality performance and quality costs is process management.

The high impact of process management as a means for increasing the overall TQM performance sounds surprising, as the pharmaceutical industry is an industry in which a wide range of operating procedures have to be documented to gain approval for operating a plant. However, this exemplifies the point that solely documenting a process does not help to improve it. Those companies that have understood that the main objective of process management is to reduce uncontrolled variances in processes or outcomes are those that have managed to have high quality performance whilst not incurring higher costs of quality control. It is noticeable that besides documenting processes they also measure the quality of their processes. Moreover, these companies make use of statistical process control data to reduce variances. Furthermore, they are trying to identify root causes of variability and are continuously taking appropriate steps to improve processes.

The latest initiatives launched by the FDA to foster a modern industry of quality and process management offer a great opportunity for pharmaceutical companies to reduce operating costs. Undoubtedly such initiatives are leading the pharmaceutical industry along the right direction. Regulatory guidance on Process Analytical Technologies (PAT) will allow pharmaceutical companies to continuously monitor process variability, and thus help improve manufacturing processes. Furthermore, the risk-based current Good Manufacturing Processes (cGMP) will free up the industry from prescriptive rules and hopefully help by substituting "non-value-adding documentation" with a state-of-the art process management system. Figure 18 summarizes all causal relationships between certain practices and quality related performance indicators that proved to be statistically significant.

Outcomes of the TPM Model

The pharmaceutical industry is a truly capital intensive industry. As much of its fixed assets are tied up in plant and equipment, an efficient usage of these resources should help to reduce the capital employed. Furthermore, stable-running machines and equipment helps in designing stable processes; and thus increase planning adherence. Such measures are a crucial element for implementing a JIT system. Therefore in the next phase of our work we analysed the impact of Total Productive Maintenance (TPM) on operational performance measures that are closely linked to equipment utilisation and maintenance.

There appears to be a fairly high level of implementation of TPM practices in the pharmaceutical industry. With an average level of implementation of 67%, it is the most widely used Operational Excellence practice. However, on the performance side, the pharmaceutical industry is far from excellent. With an average Overall Equipment Effectiveness (OEE) rate of about 50%; and with the lower percentile having an average rate of 20%, there is clearly room for improvement (see Figure 19).

Many of the companies that we talked with during our plant visits supplied data that was based primarily on "soft measures". These data gave allowances for interruptions, such as planned maintenance and material shortages; but did not count line stops of less than five minutes. Finding a consistent, reliable measure based on an OEE philosophy looks to be a first step that is needed for improving equipment utilisation. Reducing the level of unplanned maintenance should be a second action. With an average level of unplanned maintenance of approximately 30%, many companies seem to have problems with running stable manufacturing processes. As stable-running equipment directly influences JIT-performance

Practice \ Measure	Complaint Rate	Rejected Batches (internal)	Supplier Quality Performance	Cost of QC/QA	Overall TQM Performance
Management Commitment	●				
Process Management					●
Cross-Functional Product Development					
Customer Integration	●				
Teamwork/Cross-Functional Training					
Supplier Quality Management		○	○		

● much higher performance ○ higher performance

Figure 18: Linkages between TQM practices and TQM performance.

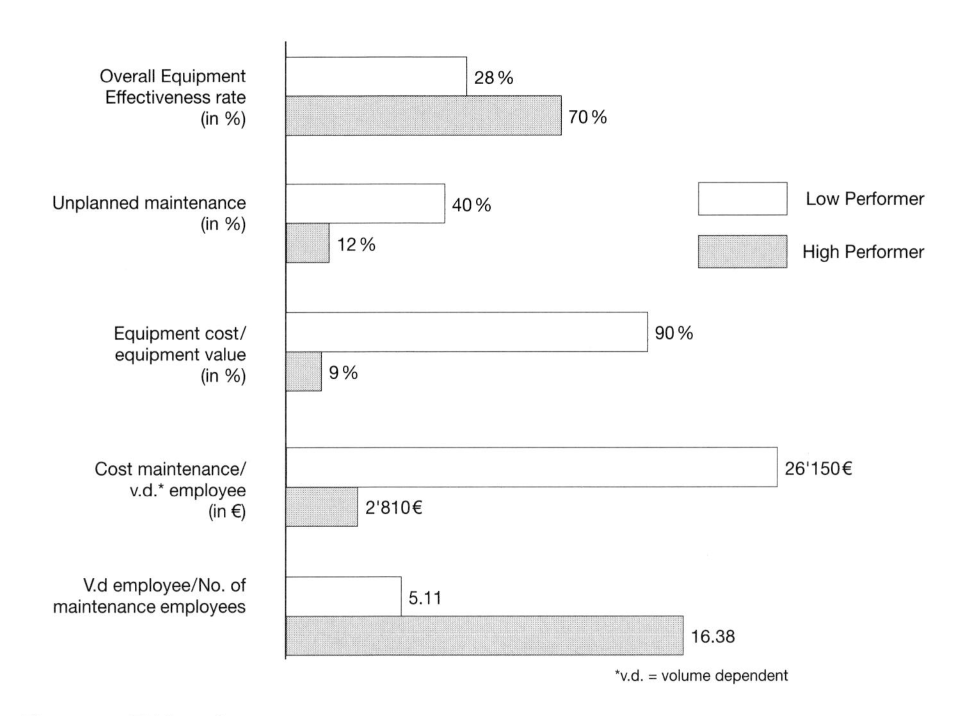

Figure 19: TPM performance measures.

(e.g. work-in-process due to buffer stocks) or TQM (e.g. scrap rates), unplanned maintenance is a crucial indicator for assessing TPM-performance. However, the data provides evidence that a high level of unplanned maintenance correlates with high equipment utilisation rates. This indicates that plants operating at peak capacity may potentially encounter more equipment and process problems and thereby affect product quality.

The challenge is how to cope with this situation. Analysis of the data suggests that the preferred option would be to bring down unplanned maintenance. The data provides evidence that unplanned maintenance levels are correlated with the number of rejected batches and associated with higher Work-in-Progress stocks; which support the notion that each single element of an integrated production system is highly correlated with others. There is strong empirical evidence that shows that autonomous and planned maintenance helps bring down unplanned maintenance levels. Companies with a formal preventive maintenance program with maintenance plans, checklists, standardized functional descriptions and a high level of employee participation (e.g. involvement of the operator into the decision making process when purchasing new machines) have a significantly better performance (see Figure 20). Furthermore, a high level of functional integration simultaneously helps to increase equipment utilisation.

Whilst preventive maintenance helps to support stable processes, the greatest leverage for reducing overall maintenance costs is linked to using appropriate equipment. Companies that are actively developing proprietary equipment have significantly higher maintenance costs

Practice \ Measure	Unplanned Maintenance	Overall Equip. Effectiveness	Maintenance Costs/ mach. value	Volume dep./ maintenance employees
Preventive Maintenance	●			
Standardization	●			○
Team work/Cross-functional training		●		
Housekeeping				
Standardized supplier technology			●	●
Proprietary process development			higher costs	

● much higher performance ○ higher performance

Figure 20: Linkage between TPM practices and TPM performance.

than companies that (mostly) rely on their equipment vendors. The ratio, in terms of volume dependent employees *versus* maintenance employees, is also far higher among companies that are placing high emphasis on developing proprietary equipment. This indicates that maintenance of proprietary developed equipment leads to significantly higher maintenance efforts. Obviously, most of the companies that are actively developing proprietary equipment pursue a strategy to gain competitive advantage from a pharmaceutical-technology perspective and not from a TPM-perspective; being one of the main objectives is to design easy-to-use, stable equipment that helps to reduce set-ups and maintenance time.

Outcomes of the JIT Model

While undertaking plant visits in the pharmaceutical industry, we observed that companies tended to be over-stocked when compared to other industries that we have experience of. In the past, the limited productivity of the working capital employed came from high safety stocks, as companies were eager not to lose a single sale due to the high gross margins attached to each product. However, whilst gross margins, especially in the generics industry, tend to be much lower, and the cost-to-volume ratio of drugs is much higher than in most other industries, it is interesting to explore whether Just-in-Time practices could help to eliminate waste (especially working capital employed) and thus lower manufacturing costs. Furthermore, a comprehensive JIT-program can help to cope with increasing complexity brought about from heterogeneous customer requirements and smaller average lot sizes that will expose pharmaceutical plants in the future.

In terms of JIT implementation the pharmaceutical industry seems to be lagging behind other industries. The average level of implementation of JIT practices (57 %) is the lowest score among all four major categories. Especially in terms of pull production, there seems to be a low level of implementation. However, on the performance side, there are companies in the sample that are having high stock turnovers even when compared to other industries. While the top 10 %, in terms of stock turnovers, has in average raw-material turns of 35 and finished goods one's inventories of about 13, these measures do not give the total picture (see Figure 21).

However, there are several interesting outcomes if viewed from a less aggregated level. Companies that performed well, in terms of high stock turn-over, had also worked intensively on reducing their set-up times (Figure 22). They had previously implemented a philosophy of flow production; and in particular their work-in-progress stocks were much lower than those of their peer group.

The main leverage for reducing stocks, while simultaneously sustaining high service levels, are similar to those of other industries.

They understood that flexibility for most of the pharmaceutical plants is determined by adaptability at their packaging line; and thus have extensively worked at reducing set-up times in this area. They typically have average set-up times in their packaging centre of some 40 minutes.

Based on their high flexibility they have very short freezing periods (between 2-3 days) and thus a very high planning adherence of around 98-99 %.

By managing to reduce their set-up times, and having optimized their machine layout, they could reduce their cycle times to between 15 days (liquids) and 25 days (solids) while moving their stocks quickly through the manufacturing process with reduced Work-in-Progress (WIP) and stock-turns of about 35.

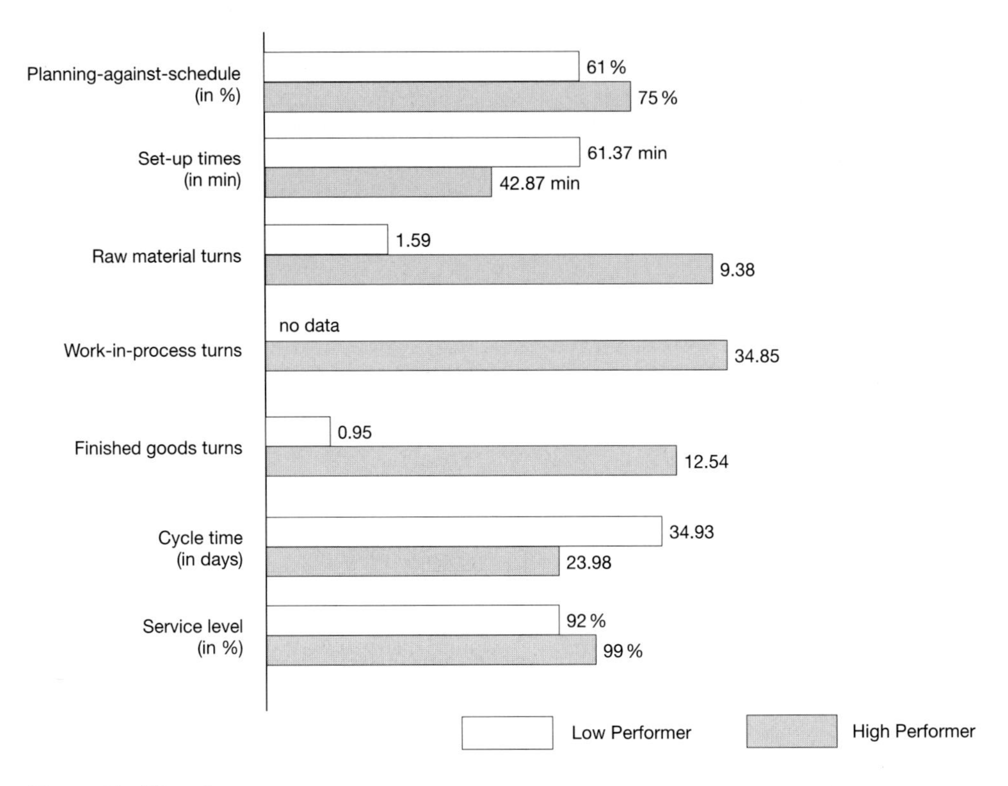

Figure 21: JIT performance measures.

Practice \ Measure	Stock turns (Raw material)	Stock turns (WIP)	Stock turns (Finished goods)	Service level	Cycle time
Layout optimization				●	○
Pull-production					●
Set-up time reductions	○	●		●	●
Stabilized Planning				●	

● much higher performance ○ higher performance

Figure 22: Linkage between JIT practices and JIT performance.

The statistical data indicates that there is a very high correlation between the average set-up time at the packaging line and the average WIP and raw material turns in the manufacturing process. As the packing line seems to be a bottleneck for most pharmaceutical plants, a reduction in set-up times would have the highest impact on WIP and raw material turns; and would also improve the average cycle times of the pharmaceutical plant.

Interestingly, even among the top 10%, companies did not make extensive use of common pull-practices such as *Kanban* or other standardized demand-triggered replenishment signals. Successful companies appeared to have put greater emphasis on set-up time reduction and layout optimization. The question arises, whether a pull system is an approach that can be transferred to the pharmaceutical industry with its specific demands and sourcing patterns. Obviously, within the inventory management field, there is no "one size fits all" approach that can be applied for every pharmaceutical company. Today, pharmaceutical products are not as customized as automobiles. Furthermore, many drugs do have very stable demand patterns and there are certain "best-selling pack sizes" where it can be useful to build up inventory in "campaigns" to free-up productive capacities during times of peak demand.

However, things are changing. Some 83% of all respondents expect an increase in heterogeneity of customer preferences. The more that drugs are manufactured with different packaging sizes and forms or "flavors" the more traditional push approaches will not be suitable for sustaining current service levels without having huge inventories.

Outcomes of the Model: Management System

"Do the management systems of pharmaceutical manufacturing plants support world class manufacturing?" The answer is: "It depends". Whilst in terms of fluctuation and absenteeism or employee development, the companies that have participated in this research are not far away from 'excellent organizations in other industries'. The pharmaceutical industry seems to lag behind other industries when it comes to continuous improvement. In pharmaceutical plants the number of suggestions is on average only one suggestion per employee per year (see Figure 23). This picture is more daunting when cost savings due to improvement suggestions are considered. There are a few companies generating between EUR 200 and 1000 cost reductions per employee per year.

The larger section of the companies only generates savings of less than 10 EUR per employee per year or does not even measure this index (Figure 23). Some 64% of all plants did not measure the number of suggestions per employee, and 68% of all plants could not provide data concerning cost reductions brought about from suggestion schemes. By analyzing the management system of pharmaceutical plants we tried to find out the main leverages for improving management performance, and in particular continuous improvement. By linking the implementation of the management practices with the management performance measures we found that the overall implementation of the practice is a strong predictor for management performance. The regression is highly significant and explains almost 30% of variance, which is fairly high for a regression with one independent variable (which is the practice variable) and one dependent variable (the performance measure).

When considering solely the implementation of self directed work teams, the results indicate that it does not have an impact on the average number of suggestions per employees (Figure 24). But when combining teamwork with cross-functional integration, teamwork does boost the average number of suggestions per employee; and leads to a lower level of absenteeism.

However, a high level of teamwork goes in hand with a higher level of overhead, which contradicts our hypothesis that: "Group work should help to reduce the level of hierarchy

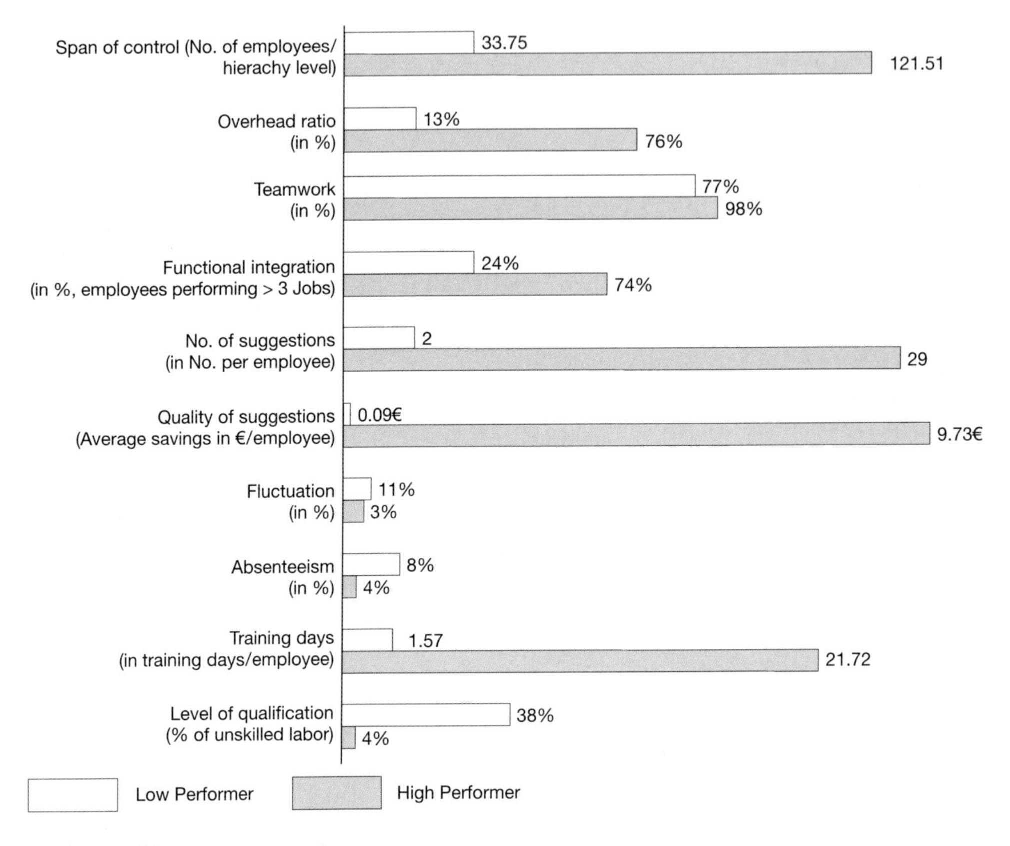

Figure 23: Management performance measures.

and the overhead ratio, as more indirect work is supposed to be performed by the production teams". It appears that the implementation of teamwork still needs a particular level of staff to support production teams; and has not managed to play the same role in decreasing the level of hierarchies and overhead like it has done in the automotive industry. Furthermore, cutting overhead seems to be a fairly simplistic way to reduce costs. Companies that have very low overhead ratios tend to have a higher number of absenteeism and have interestingly a significantly lower number of suggestions per employee. Hence, just cutting overhead can also lead to lower performance in certain other performance indicators.

So, apart from teamwork and a certain level of support staff: "Which other leverages do plant managers have to enhance a continuous improvement process?" While companies with a formal continuous improvement program based on quality circles, suggestions schemes etc. did not have a better performance in terms of quality and quantity of suggestions, it was seen that *direction setting* combined with strong *management commitment* tended to have a significant impact on the quantity of improvement suggestions. This shows that management has to have clear objectives and has to show personal commitment to the

Practice \ Measure	Fluctuation Absenteeism	No. of sugg./ employee	Average savings/ employee	Employee flexibility	Lean hierarchy
Direction setting		○			
Teamwork					higher overhead
Cross-functional training	○	●		●	higher overhead
Continuous improvement programs					○
People development				●	○

● much higher performance ○ higher performance

Figure 24: Linkage between management principles and management performance.

improvement process. However, the quality of the improvement process is heavily dependent on the number of training days. Plants with a higher number of training days per employee could realise higher cost savings per employee.

"What about the qualification of the workforce?" The major impact of qualification is in terms of overhead. Companies that have a low level of unskilled employees tend to have a significant better performance in terms of overhead. Arguably, a higher skill level helps plants to transfer indirect work to direct labor and, thereby, reduce the number of staff that is responsible for supporting the direct labor. Furthermore, a high level of qualification strongly correlates with quality performance (e.g. level of rejected batches). Those outcomes go in hand with our experiences when undertaking plant visits. When measuring employee development, the average number of training days per production worker was used. The results indicate that the pharmaceutical industry is performing quite well compared to other industries. However, most of the training is completed to cope with changing regulatory requirements (e.g. FDA). There is very little training with regard to continuous improvement (e.g. problem-solving skills, *Kaizen* workshops etc.). This also helps to understand why the pharmaceutical industry is characterized by a good performance in employee development (measured as number of training days) but very low performance in terms of continuous improvement.

These results provide evidence that most of the pharmaceutical industry have not yet successfully implemented current practices of work organization. Companies that have implemented teamwork, cross-functional integration, quality circles, suggestions schemes etc. often do not perform better than their peers who still rely on a more Tayloristic work ethos. It seems that some of the companies are currently 'stuck in the middle'. While most of them have started to implement modern work practices, only a few have realised significant improvements.

III.4 Linking Operational Excellence to Overall Plant Performance

Michael Kickuth and Thomas Friedli

While applying the Operational Excellence model we concentrated on internal operational performance measures and attempted to discover how certain practices affect stock turns, scrap rates or other performance indicators that measure the efficiency of pharmaceutical plants. Though it is interesting to know whether a plant is doing things right, it is at least as important to find out whether a pharmaceutical company is effectively using its operations to gain competitive advantage.

We measured effectiveness of plants on two levels. First we took an overall operational performance measure that comprised internal productivity measures, the dependability, the flexibility and the quality of a plant. While we mainly focused on the TQM section for internal quality measures, the external quality measure was based upon the complaint rate (as this measure provides insightful information of the quality of the final product as perceived by the customer).

Furthermore, service level is addressed as this provides an answer to issues of dependability of a pharmaceutical plant. Besides cost, quality and delivery, the flexibility of a plant plays a major role when assessing its capability to react to changes in the market. Increasingly demanding and fragmented markets require manufacturing processes that can respond to the need for a variety of customized features. As flexibility is hard to measure by using quantitative data, we recoded plant managers' 'perception' of volumes, product mix- and product flexibility. These perceptions were aggregated to give an 'overall flexibility measure'.

JIT and TPM practices have the biggest impact on overall operational performance measures. Companies that have implemented JIT-principles and are consequently reducing their set-up times, have optimized their plant layout to enhance short cycle times; and are now attempting to level capacity with current demand. These companies have significant higher service levels and higher flexibility. Interestingly TPM practices seem to have an even higher impact on quality performance measures than TQM practices. While TQM has a significant impact on quality performance, a much higher variance of quality performance is explained by the implementation of TPM-practices. Obviously, stable running machines and equipment ensure better and more predictable quality; and simultaneously help to increase service levels due to the lower levels of unplanned maintenance. Beside the implementation of JIT-practices, TQM does have an effect on flexibility. While JIT-practices mainly affect volume and product mix flexibility, the highest impact on new product flexibility comes from implementing TQM practices such as cross-functional product development and customer integration.

Analyzing the linkages between the level of Operational Excellence of a plant and its overall plant performance, we could present strong empirical evidence to support the argument that certain leverages of Operational Excellence directly influence overall plant performance.

III.5 Does Operational Excellence Matter from a Corporate Perspective?

Michael Kickuth and Thomas Friedli

Linking Operational Excellence to Business performance

While our unit of analysis throughout the project was the pharmaceutical plant, one of the most interesting challenges was to find out whether Operational Excellence has any impact on overall business performance. The reason for that is, that few managers in the pharmaceutical industry view manufacturing as a primary source of competitive advantage. Most pharmaceutical companies do not want to lose sight of what they see as their true source of advantage: namely, product research and development. While our main purpose of the project was not to shift attention from R&D to manufacturing, we were curious to know whether Operational Excellence has any impact on business performance.

Within the survey, we mainly relied on objective measures based on financial or operational data. However, we chose to use qualitative perceptual measures to explore how the company performed from a corporate perspective. The reason for that was that most managers do know sufficiently well how their overall business is performing in their specific market compared to their direct competitors (e.g. sales, return on sales or market share) while there is a usually a lack of understanding with regard to operational performance figures (e.g. stock turns).

We did not expect Operational Excellence at one plant to have a major impact on business performance, as some of the bigger companies in the sample are managing complex production networks that often comprise more than 50 production plants around the world.

However, when linking Operational Excellence to business performance, the results provided evidence that Operational Excellence does significantly improve business performance. Plants that perform well in terms of Operational Excellence usually belong to a company that also significantly performs better in return on sales and market share when compared to its competitors. Furthermore, this correlation does not change significantly when analyzing the linkage between Operational Excellence and business performance for smaller companies that have a single production site. Arguably, the degree of excellence of one single plant – or a few plants – in a global pharmaceutical company is a strong predictor for the operational performance of its world-wide operations network; and thus for its overall business performance.

Analyzing the main Operational Excellence leverages, the statistical data provides evidence that Operational Excellence can explain around 20% of variance in return on sales improvement rates of pharmaceutical companies; and around 13% of variance in overall business performance (which is an aggregated super scale measuring increase in sales, increase in ROS and increase in market share of the company; see Figure 25).

Companies that have a high level of implementation of JIT, TPM, TQM principles, also have an effective management system, and performed much better in terms of return on sales growth than their industry peers. Furthermore, those companies could also significantly gain market share in their industry. Obviously, excellent operations do directly affect business performance of pharmaceutical companies.

So, returning to the main question of the project: "Does Operational Excellence matter?" The data provides us with a clear answer: "Yes, it does". However, the data also provides strong evidence that today most of the industry is far from excellent.

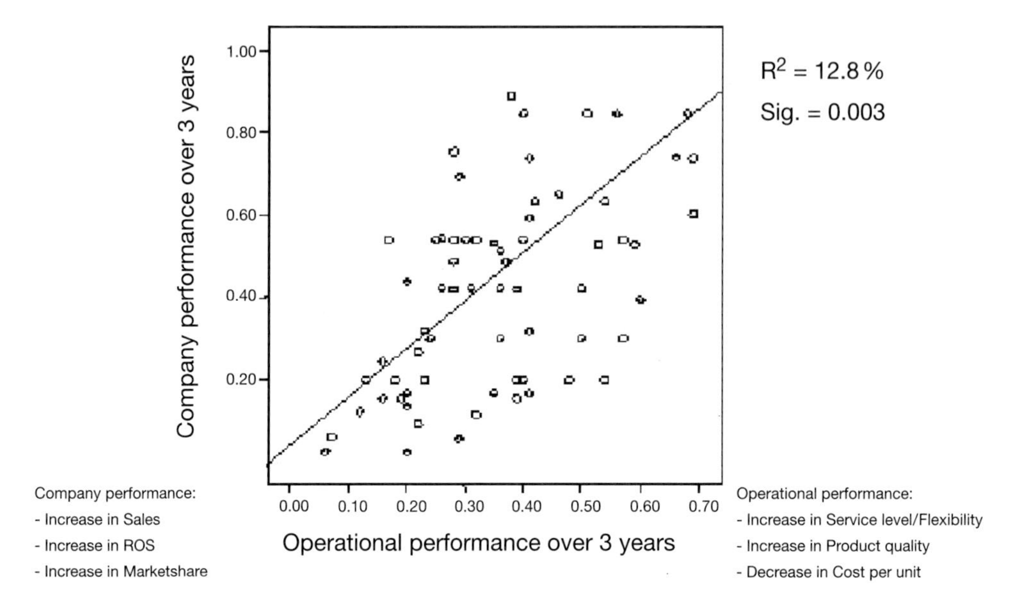

Figure 25: Relation between operational performance and company performance.

III.6 Insights from the Plant Audits

Peter Thaler and Thomas Friedli

Between January and July 2005 we visited and analyzed some twenty plants in Europe on site to get an in depth qualitative understanding of the facts behind the figures of our survey.

The results of these analyses strongly support the findings and interpretations previously described.

We will deepen some of them along our model of Operational Excellence outlined in chapter 2. We will first describe some general impressions which cannot be attributed so clearly to one of the four dimensions of the model.

General Impressions

A successful implementation of any Operational Excellence program starts at the top of the organization. We have seen companies starting a program with a big event inviting all operational and functional leaders, and we have experienced companies with less support from the top management where the operational management had to struggle selling the strategy. A clear mission statement is a minimum requirement to support any process striving for Operational Excellence. It is not so important that the company's mission statement includes the achievement of Operational Excellence into its mission statement itself if any of these Operational Excellence activities are seen as an enabler to achieve the mission of the company. We found that those companies claiming their Operational Excellence program as an enabler for their mission are even stronger in making progress. When visiting some plants we got different pictures of the commitment of the top management. We learned that frequent visits typically accelerate the speed of implementation of the program and strongly contribute to the change of mindset and ways of working such initiatives typically request. Frequent visits of the CEO, General Manager or the site leader can make a change and if frequently repeated will keep the momentum. The time commitment is marginal with respect to the leverage effect such a behavior can have. When we had the opportunity to talk to managers at different levels of the organizations we found that:

- Manufacturing is often not seen as a complex system with many interdependencies. Due to this lack of a holistic view,
  - initiatives to improve performance are mostly focused on single tools and techniques;
  - employees understand their single activities but not the importance for the whole process and the impact on the business; and
  - the strategy is not well communicated down to the operational level and employees are therefore not able to see the big picture.
- Some specifics of the pharmaceutical Industry obviously impede improvements:
  - A lot of formal regulations impact the scope of action. This is also why self directed working teams do not operate in the way they would do in other industries.
  - Concerns of having to go through re-registration procedures have a negative impact on the motivation to improve processes.
  - A hierarchical organization supports routine processes but is not flexible enough in an ever changing environment.
  - Based on the past performance of pharmaceutical companies with rather high profit margins, the average worker in the plant does not feel the pressure to improve processes. There is a far stronger tendency to preserve the status quo than to think about improvements. In one of the plants we visited it became clear that their will be no further communication of the study results in the company as the manager was afraid of being asked critical questions from higher level management and the work council.
  - There seems to be a higher reluctance in management of pharmaceutical plants to consider shop floor realities than in other industries. We also found that walking the talk is not a strong routine within manufacturing.
- There is a lot of non-value added in indirect overhead positions:
  - Instead of enabling processes to perform better and making them leaner, new positions are created for indirect, non-volume related personnel to better control performance of the volume related personnel.

- Support processes are not harmonized with the main processes. The importance of excellence in supporting processes such as material transport is not seen as essential for the overall performance. When we tried to discuss topics such as transport quality there was blank astonishment in the faces of our counterparts. Especially QA/QC do not understand their role as service provider for the main processes but see their role only as the custodian to maintaining regulatory compliance, they are not really partnering with those actually concerned with quality standards. In many of the plants we observed a kind of silo mentality with a few exceptions.
- The main matter of concern is to supply the market and the customer with the product. Cost awareness plays a very subordinate role in ensuring "total customer compliance", nor are there any considerations of how one could achieve the same standard with lesser cost.

We realized that most companies commit to a program to achieve Operational Excellence in these times of difficult environmental conditions. We found two drivers for it: the pressure of the need and the need to strategically prepare the company for the future where manufacturing becomes a strategic asset to the company. Companies starting on the pressure of the need typically have a burning business case and decide on hiring a consultant company to head for quick wins. In most cases, these companies hit the target of quick wins but lose on sustainability of their strategic initiatives in the long run. Other companies anticipate the change in their environment and launch a program for a long lasting paradigm shift. Although these companies also hire consultants to get started, they try hard to transfer the knowledge into their own operation from the very beginning. A few companies took this approach, and it was obvious that harvesting the fruits of success took longer but the achievements were more sustainable and longer lasting because a paradigm shift had taken place. These were the companies where we saw that their program started from the top management with a clear vision and was communicated throughout the entire organization to make sure that every employee knew about it and understood it.

We also experienced that coaching during the execution of such programs plays an important role in all these processes. Companies providing coaching capabilities from within their own organization typically achieve better results than companies where coaching is provided by external resources. However, internal coaching resources need to be developed first in particular to support principles of Operational Excellence. So, at the very beginning, a combination of both might be the right approach. Our observation is that companies taking the lead for coaching as quickly as possible did a better job than companies giving the lead to external consultants. Another aspect of coaching we experienced is the hierarchical level where to focus the coaching. Coaching of executives is important, coaching of the middle management to change their mindset is better but most important is to coach those who are concerned. The formula we found is the internal qualification process. We saw excellent examples of this, in particular in those companies which maintain a department for organizational development for that purpose. Another important point of consideration is how a company values the individual contributions which support an Operational Excellence program. The best results we have seen were obtained when achievements of Operational Excellence were part of the Annual Performance Review. Such an approach definitely increased the speed of execution combined with the mission of the company where goals have been defined as enabler to achieve the mission. During one of our plant visits we experienced an example of best practice. Those concerned in the execution of the project built a high performance team reporting to the high level executives. Such an approach can be achieved twofold. The company either establishes an execution task force leadership team or operational performance teams for the duration of their assignment. Such assignments were in some cases also part of a personal development plan of a person in charge of leading the team.

Impressions along our reference model

1. Management System

Half of the companies we visited told us they had teamwork implemented. A closer look revealed that this kind of teamwork is rather informal and not structured enough to gain the maximum benefit out of it. The teams are, by the standards of other industries, not self directed working teams. We would say that the actual level of teamwork implementation is only around 20 %. When we discussed this point with several managers we found one logical explanation: the role of middle management is not really defined in such a system, and the introduction of self directed working teams would inevitably lead to a loss of influence and control on the part of the middle management. In many companies this was one of the reasons for eliminating middle management positions to achieve less hierarchical layers and for transferring more responsibility to the shop floor supervisors. Apart from that, this is also a matter of qualification. While we experienced high standards of technical qualification we missed distinctive leadership skills at the shop floor personnel and supervisor level.

There were only a few companies where we experienced the existence of a flexible workforce and noticed the visualization of training schedules in common areas to achieve this objective. We found that, compared to other industries, absenteeism and fluctuation rates were low in most of these plants. When we asked shop floor people about job satisfaction, they unanimously stated that they liked to work in the pharmaceutical industry but felt that the workload was too high. When we discussed this topic with the line managers, we suggested that, to increase the level of job satisfaction, shop floor personnel should not work "harder but smarter. This could be achieved by eliminating the numerous non-value adding activities we saw when we walked through the plants.

In the sites we visited, there is generally no communication strategy in place. This is not a matter of information being available, but of directing this information to the addressee. Typically information is spread at a general level, but not focused on target groups and therefore not very effective. It is unstructured, less pertinent, sometimes even filtered when cascaded down the organization. Our experience is that communication was also blocked or filtered as a result of the functional organization. However we found a few examples of a process oriented organization where self directed working teams were implemented more successfully. We also found that visualization concepts are implemented everywhere but with different success rates. We have seen glossy high performance slides provided by departments outside the area of responsibility of those concerned. On the other hand we have also seen good examples of simple run charts maintained by those concerned. Maybe those are handwritten, less glossy, less nice to look at, but they definitely serve the purpose in a better way. They basically aim to improve the performance of the teams and are not designed to control the performance of the team top down. We found a few places where process performance was visualized in real time mode, by means of dash boards. Interestingly enough monitoring systems have been set up almost everywhere because of state-of-the-art technology but are not widely used.

Quite a good example we saw in one plant was a visualization system based on a Balanced Scorecard and brought down to the shop floor level. However the targets of the Key Performance Indicators (KPIs) were not very ambitious and reflected only easy to achieve targets. If we found unfavorable results they would have been related to the adverse circumstances and not to the system or to poor performance. We particularly missed a good visualization of performance in almost all of the visited plants. In one plant we found an excellent monitoring system installed. However when having a closer look at it we realized that performance metrics were not based on common standards, for instance in the calculation of OEE. This way the plant could show an average OEE of 70%. If calculated according to standard rules, the OEE value was down to about 40%. This finding strongly supported our impression that there is a big potential for OEE improvements in pharmaceutical plants which is not recognized due to insufficient reporting systems. One plant manager told us that nobody wants to make his or her life more uncomfortable by setting ambitious targets. In our view, this is one of the reasons why there are problems in establishing a culture of continuous improvement in the plants. The KPIs are often highly aggregated so that it is not possible to draw any conclusions. Moreover, the cycles of monitoring actual performance against targets are very long, typically we found cycles of between three months and a year.

We found that working teams only had short-term objectives or mainly dealt with trouble shooting which probably results from the lack of robustness of the underlying processes. The lack of long-term performance objectives is obviously related to the fact that, in many cases, there are no long-term business plans which anticipate milestones of performance goals defined by financial and non-financial KPIs. We noticed that companies with a clear manufacturing vision have a distinct competitive advantage over others as they have laid the foundation for long-term business planning.

We also observed a certain lack of a continuous improvement culture for TQM relevant aspects. There is either no effective employee suggestion system in place, or if there is one, it is not very successful. With a factor of one to a hundred, the average number of suggestions per operator is very low compared, for instance, with the assembling industry.

2. Total Productive Maintenance

TPM is only realized in parts, but not as a strategic initiative. A lot of isolated activities are carried out but no overall systematic approach could be identified.

Concerning the equipment in use we got the impression that the pharmaceutical plants are not accustomed to defining their requirements and communicating them to the machine suppliers. We found for example a feeding device for tablets which could only be removed by loosening seven hexagonal bolts. There is no or only little influence taken on the suppliers to improve such standard practices. We also found some very simple aluminum molding parts which were bought for a price per piece of 30,000 Euro without any discussion, a price which is far higher than what a car manufacturer would pay for this kind of molding part.

We discovered that overall equipment effectiveness was rather low. During our visits, we noticed in almost all plants that two thirds of the equipment was idle and one third was running, on the basis of a three shift operation. This is on the one hand a consequence of over-capacities but on the other hand also a problem of unplanned machine downs, short stoppers and lack of timely material support. Given the low level of TPM activities we are not surprised about the big variation of some KPIs such as set-up time, cleaning time or machine downtimes and unpredicted maintenance.

What was rather astonishing for us is that standard methodologies to support housekeeping like 5S and Visual Workplace which could also help to fulfill the GMP requirements were often not implemented or not even known. One example we have seen indicated a space for material supplies of about 50 square meters but there were no markers to indicate a minimal and maximum inventory level. This shows that 5S and Visual Workplace are not connected with Kanban or replenishment systems supporting JIT production.

In a few plants we found that line operators were trained to perform simple maintenance tasks, something which worked well and enriched the daily activities of the workers. Good visualized working instructions supported this approach.

Product complexity, particularly in the area of packaging, is getting higher and higher and one line manager told us they did not have the technology to cope with the increasing number of smaller orders, and that their equipment was designed for big orders and campaign production.

To conclude our observations with respect to TPM, there are some good examples of good practice, some elements of TPM in implementation, but in none of the sites we visited we found that TPM was exhaustively implemented.

3. Total Quality Management

The understanding of quality management is mostly focused on FDA and GMP requirements since the pharmaceutical industry is highly regulated. The necessary steps and procedures for out-of-specification documentation are described in detail but almost nothing is in place that goes beyond this. Even this documentation lacks clarity. When we talked to different process owners of the same company about the time available to react to OOS there was no common understanding of how to solve the problem immediately except the GMP requirements which request problem solving within a certain period. The missing point is to address the actual problem right after its occurrence at the place where it became evident. One plant was an exception as it had a routine in place to address a problem with simple to use problem solving tools. The argument for not dealing with the problem right after its occurrence was that they had to get on with manufacturing the product and could therefore not stop the machine.

There were generally no problem-solving routines in place. Problems in performance were not tracked back to the roots, and instead of this, performance indicators were often adapted to the situation and the causes attributed to operator failure. This would logically require re-training of the operator but without any investigation of the real root cause.

We realized that in some companies the subject matter of root cause analysis was addressed by introducing 6 Sigma or other adequate root cause analysis tools. When we discussed this with the site and quality operations leaders they explained that such an approach was requested by the FDA's 21st century GMP initiative. From the examples of improvement projects we have been provided with we expect that this will have a positive effect on Operational Excellence. We also saw some good examples of Process Analytical Technology (PAT) which have been realized in some plants. When we talked to the line managers, they see the introduction of such means as a way not only to automate their processes but also to learn more about their processes and enhance process robustness. In one plant we found a good example where the packaging process was monitored with high-speed cameras to gain better insight in the motion of packaging material during the packaging operation.

Widely used tools from other industries such as FMEA, QFD or Poka Yoke are unknown. All companies have a certain amount of formalized procedures when dealing with their external suppliers but have great deficits in understanding the importance of their internal customers. We realized that there are many self inspections and audit programs in place. These programs are usually highly standardized if they address subject matters of GMP or EHS compliance. The tools of Value Stream Mapping to improve performance were widely unknown.

Besides the self inspections all companies often have to go through inspections by regulatory authorities or customers. Normally these audits are prepared with a lot of internal effort. If there was a system in place to ensure inspection readiness all the time no special preparation would be needed for these audits.

Standard operating procedures (working instructions which describe how to run the process) are often not user friendly as they do not take advantage of visualization and we found them very detailed and difficult to read.

In some of the plants we saw efforts to standardize the size of blisters. We found that blister formats vary by millimeters although they contain tablets of the same size and number of tablets per blister. This is just one example which shows that the full potential of standardization is far from being realized.

Continuous improvement with respect to product and process optimization is often inhibited by the highly regulated environment of the pharmaceutical industry. If products or processes are changed, re-registration procedures may be required which are associated with high cost and lengthy approval processes. These processes are not standardized and may therefore vary considerably in the global markets. In some countries, it may take years to get approval while in others, approval is granted much faster, a factor, which strongly contributes to the high product complexity.

4. Just-in-Time

As outlined in the previous chapter there is almost no approach of a Just-in-Time (JIT) strategy in pharmaceutical plants.

The underlying problem with implementing a JIT strategy is the lack of process robustness which can be found in almost all plants. Compared with other industries where a Sigma level of 4 to 5 is common standard, the average Sigma level in pharmaceutical processes is between 2 and 3. The Sigma level of the end product is, however, above 5 and higher, due to strict regulations and quality controls. This means that there is much rework and rejects along the manufacturing process. Long cycle times are the consequence. Again we found a few plants addressing the issue of cycle time. There was one company working on the improvement of their process robustness with a low variability first to make their processes more predictable and then launched their cycle time reduction program as a logical second step.

However there are a few examples for a JIT strategy, one of them is the Faller AG, a supplier of cardboard packaging systems which tries to integrate itself in the processes of its customers delivering only when the material is needed. To make this happen on a broader scale some additional efforts are needed, in particular by increasing the planning accuracy. In the plants we visited we found examples where for a single step in the production process a time buffer of about 5 days was built in, adding to higher inventories throughout the process and leading to big fluctuations in overall throughput time. There are almost no activities in the plants for reducing inventories. When we asked a plant manager why he had no ongoing activities for inventory reductions he told us that as long as the responsibility for final product inventories was with the marketing department he saw no need for reducing inventories, an attitude which clearly reflects the functional silo mentality.

A good example of demand driven material supply was Capsugel. This capsule supplier is an integrated part of the plant's material management system, and delivery of material is triggered by demand. There are almost no inventories of empty capsules in the plant as inventory management became the supplier's responsibility.

We generally observed long changeover times and only a few sites actively worked on a changeover time reduction program. When we asked about the motivation for such an initiative we were told it served the purpose of OEE. Nobody thought about the reduction of campaign production to reduce the work in process (WIP). Typically all plants are sitting on huge inventories of finished goods as well as on raw materials. During our plant audits we also saw a lot of work in process, sometimes blocking the corridors with pallets of goods. And this although the ratio of storage place and manufacturing area is already 1 to 2.

Cycle times per order are extremely high. One reason for this is that tests of intermediate goods or in-process controls have to be performed. While some of them are necessary for quality assurance, others are non-value-adding activities.

Pharmaceutical plants typically operate with MRP systems. Demand driven manufacturing following the principles of a PULL production with Kanban is widely unknown, and we have seen this in only one plant. This is another consequence of the low Sigma level of the underlying process robustness.

To summarize our findings and observations with respect to the implementation of the JIT strategy, we would say this is the least advanced area in the pharmaceutical industry with a lot of good opportunities.

III.7 Special Insights from a Contract Manufacturer – The Case of NextPharma

Daniel Tykal and Hermann Osterwald

NextPharma was one of the contract manufacturers of our on site visit sample. What we found there was an outstanding example of a company continuously striving for improvements in its operations. It was established with the aim of providing best in class pharmaceutical contract development, manufacturing and logistics with a focus on solving customer needs in both innovative technologies and in conventional technologies. As we will describe in our last chapter there is a high probability that the importance of contract manufacturing for the industry as a whole will sharply increase in the coming years. So we took the opportunity to provide here an insight view into NextPharma's efforts to increase its Operational Excellence for the benefit of its customers.

Situation at the outset

Created in the year 2000 based on the anticipation of the increased outsourcing in the pharmaceutical market, the European group is today one of the most important independent actors in its sector, with expertise in third party development of pharmaceutical medicines, clinical testing, manufacturing and logistics. It has grown through acquisitions of existing outsourcing businesses and plants from Big Pharma and will continue to grow by internal and external growth.

The importance of outstanding operations for a contract manufacturer in today's business landscape

Investigations show that the market of pharmaceutical services undergoes the following trends:

- Development and manufacturing are becoming less important activities of Big Pharma and are already outsourced by the growing number of biotech companies

- Large pharma companies are focusing on Research and Marketing because:
  - Years exclusivity are reducing forcing increasing focus on life-cycle management
  - Fewer new drugs coming to market because authorities are demanding higher safety and efficacy
  - Production capacity utilisation is low (typically 20/30 %), inflexible and an inefficient use of capital

To follow these trends, a contract manufacturer organization (CMO) has to fit to the demands of its customers which means to offer as a minimum the quality and service the customers are used to from their internal suppliers. This will cost a lot of effort and many will therefore also push the ongoing consolidation process in the CMO market.

The ambition of NextPharma

Being uniquely positioned, the contract manufacturer provides a "one stop shop", offering drug companies, ranging from Big Pharma through generic, biotech and virtual companies a seamless process from inquiry through to product supply and distribution, supported by the strong focus on key accounts and expertise in project management. It will also develop further a global range of technologies in order to fulfill customers' unmet needs for seamless transfer of existing products or development work. To further strengthen its proposition value, it envisages moving towards FDA approval status, making it a global partner for hormones, cytostatics, steriles, liquids, semi-solids, pellets and specialised dry forms.

To support these visions, a number of strategic initiatives were also put in place, one of them is Operational Excellence.

As NextPharma participated in the drawing up and evaluation of the benchmark study described in this book, the company came to the conclusion that within the pharmaceutical industry there are similar deficits as shown in the well known MIT study for the automobile industry at the beginning of the 1990s. This study then lead to an unequalled innovation competition which more than doubled productivity and at the same time increased quality but reduced rework.

However, this lead also to a consolidation of the automobile component suppliers. Therefore, NextPharma decided to transform this challenge into a chance to be the first company in the pharmaceutical industry to implement an "Integral Production System" and through this to reach the leader position for the benefit of its customers and to keep it.

NextPharma's commitment to Operational Excellence

As the strategy focuses on providing technical solutions and working in partnership with customers, priority is to offer timely, competitive healthcare solutions of the highest quality as the pharma and biotech markets further develop. NextPharma`s solution offers large and innovative laboratories the benefit of cutting edge technology to reduce costs and launch their products quickly and efficiently. Whether it is solids, liquids, semi solids or niche technologies such as oncology or hormonal contraceptives, NextPharma provides technological expertise and key success factors including flexibility, rapid adaptation to the market and reach customer satisfaction by being excellent in their operations.

How to increase Operational Excellence – The NextPharma Improvement Program

For the NextPharma Production System (NPS), 5 main topics were defined with strong commitment of management (Figure 26).

Afterwards, the respective fundamentals were permanently trained such as the capture of key figures to control the processes, the preparation of binding rules for implementation, communication and information and the total integration of management in the whole process. This process was supported by management tools such as

- Manuals with concrete acting support
- Newsletters which describe single measures and leadership strategies based on the status of implementation
- Management workshops on the NPS contents
- Hiring a full-time NPS Coordinator who permanently monitors the process.

Already during the first year of implementation, a considerable increase in productivity and quality was achieved. This showed in an increase of the production output of up to 25% in one of the plants without hiring additional staff as well as in very positive feedback at customer audits and visits.

Systems	Production Principles
Continuous Improvement Process	• Eliminate any kind of waste
Just-in-Time	• Smoothing production process • Pull Production
Quality and robust processes/products	• Quick identification of problems and elimination of errors • Stable processes/products and preventive • Quality Management • Customer Orientation
Standardization	• Standardized methods and processes • Visual management/5S
Work structure and teamwork	• Leadership • Clear tasks and roles • Participation and development of employees • Teamwork structures • Work safety and environmental consciousness

Figure 26: Five main topics of the NextPharma Production System.

NextPharma has created well trained sales and customer service departments as well as separate centres of excellence targeting different areas such as beta-lactams, cytostatics, pellets, logistic services. Market approach is based on flexibility as the organization is well equipped and experienced to handle the uncertainties inherent to the nature of the outsourcing business. The strategic direction is to increase the percentage of manufactured products that come from in-house formulation development, as well as increase the coverage of supporting services including formulation development, clinical trial supplies and analytical services. For all four technologies, NextPharma focuses on offering the complete range of development services thanks to the implementation of a formulation development "centre of excellence" in accordance with market needs and meeting state-of-the-art technical standards.

The future of contract manufacturing

Today it is estimated that the turnover associated with contract research and manufacturing is around USD 30 billion[15], growing at close to 10% per year, main segments including: Discovery research, ADMET (Analytical, Distribution, Metabolism, Excretion and Toxicology), Clinical research, pharmaceutical and chemical development, full scale drug substance custom manufacturing, full scale dosage form manufacturing and final assembly or packaging.

The supply structure of the CMO market includes a wide spectrum of companies:

- Industry majors primarily active in contract manufacturing and clinical development segments, most often focusing on selected discrete segments of the industry, very few being active over a wide range of segments, capacity to offer integrated services, growing international presence
- Local champions, independent stand-alone companies with a more limited proposition value geographically and technically
- Spin-offs, created after an MBO/LBO, these companies still heavily dependent on contracts signed with the former mother-company
- Start-ups focusing primarily on drug discovery and development and to a lesser extent on formulation or drug substance development, small size, single activity type

This sector is highly fragmented as a majority of formulated product manufacturers have revenues of less than USD 50 million and many players limit themselves to a single product. There are over 300 contract product manufacturers in Europe alone (more than 1000 actors worldwide), focusing primarily on three types of activity: formulation development, dosage form production and packing. A number of companies are positioning themselves to take on significant manufacturing volumes from big pharmaceutical companies which are ready to strategically outsource formulation. Important to note that big pharmaceutical companies tend to establish long-term relations with a selected number of CMOs with whom they have sound contract manufacturing business processes in place for selection and management. Increasingly, they tend to exert price leverage, trying to extract price concessions in exchange of a large share of their business or guaranteed volumes, concentrating their sourcing on fewer suppliers. Facing this situation, CMOs are increasingly responding by consolidating their operations and broadening their service platforms in order to achieve better competitiveness and provide higher added value services.

15 Ernst & Young 2002 and Arthur D. Little 2003.

It is estimated that about 25 to 30% of R&D and 30 to 40% of manufacturing activities within the pharmaceutical industry are outsourced to third parties. With a penetration rate of only about 20%, secondary development and production offer significant growth opportunities.

The main factor fueling outsourcing growth is related to the increasing pressure facing big pharmaceutical companies to lower their manufacturing costs and assets base while securing access to the best resources when and if needed. It is worth mentioning that 27 brands that generated USD 37 billion worldwide sales in 2001 have faced patent expiration in 2005. In addition, average capacity utilization of many plants ranks lower than 50%. This situation increases pressure for the pharmaceutical industry in terms of time to market and financial returns. It highlights the need to secure state-of-the art development and manufacturing resources without inflating fixed cost.

In addition, pharmaceutical companies accumulated difficulties such as:

- FDA's very demanding positions for registration and manufacturing standards
- Delays in product launches
- Setbacks on molecules predicted to become blockbusters
- Climate of uncertainty following mergers having occurred within several companies

Therefore, there is an increasing need for pharma companies to focus the high capital expenditures on key competences such as

- Research
- Time to market
- Marketing/Sales
- Defence of intellectual property

In summary: patent expiry, R&D productivity and growing price pressure coupled with R&D budgets escalation, shorter drug lifecycle and low capacity utilization re-position outsourcing from a tactical to a strategic tool available for pharmaceutical companies to help them achieve long-term growth and success.

Due to today's market evolution and customers' expectations, contract manufacturers need to: reach a critical mass and adapt to market requirements, expand service range and tend towards a "one-stop-shop" concept, improve their profitability in order to finance new capacities in R&D, and finally, internationalize themselves to provide a global presence to their key accounts.

NextPharma's vision of this market for the next years therefore integrates a reduction of the number of small players, the transfer of more "quality" big pharma sites to third party market, and large outsourcing organizations growth, both big pharma and biotech companies and their outsourcing partners benefiting from this evolution.

The big steps forward NextPharma achieved in growth over the last 4 years to be today the number 3 secondary manufacturing CMO in term of sales were awarded in 2005 with the Frost and Sullivan Growth Strategy Leadership Award and will be continued over the next years.

IV Operational Excellence in the Pharmaceutical Industry: Case Studies from the Field

In this chapter we want to give some guidance for people responsible for implementing Operational Excellence programs. Based on selected case studies we go deeper into some of the topics discussed so far. We start with a case about launching an Operational Excellence program in a global pharmaceutical company: the case of Pfizer. It gives a good overview about several elements of Operational Excellence and how those pieces fit together. Case study two shows how Caspugel, the leading capsule manufacturer, set the floor for its improvement process with regard to Operational Excellence. The third case study highlights the point of maximizing equipment effectiveness by optimizing the whole supply chain: the case of Reckit Benquiser. Case study four is about successfully working with 6-Sigma in a pharmaceutical company. Case study five details the topic of JIT in a pharmaceutical environment. In case study six we leave the pharmaceutical industry and show the importance of management quality in a case study delivered by Christoph H. Loch, who already contributed to the management aspect to our model described in chapter II. We finish with a stage model for achieving Operational Excellence.

IV.1 Case Study: Launching an Operational Excellence Initiative in a Global Pharmaceutical Company – The Case of Pfizer Inc.

Michael Kickuth and Thomas Friedli

Pfizer: A leading pharmaceutical company

Pfizer is the leading research-based pharmaceutical company of the world. It discovers, develops, manufactures and markets innovative medicines for humans and animals. Founded in 1849 it has grown from a small business into a USD 52.5 billion global enterprise (2004), employing over 120,000 people worldwide. In 2004 it had an annualized net income of USD 11.9 billion.

Pfizer`s major business in 2004 included (Warren McFarlan and DeLacey 2004):

1. Prescription Medicines

   - Pfizer's pharmaceutical sales were No. 1 in the world, up from 14th in 1990. Pfizer reported that 11 drugs generated more than a quarter of a billion dollars in the first quarter of 2004 – all aiming to become billion dollar blockbusters. It has a market share in the blockbuster market of 18 %.
2. Animal Health Products
   - Full year Animal Health sales increase 10 % in 2002 to USD 1.1 billion and another 43 % in 2003 to nearly USD 1.6 billion.
3. Consumer Healthcare Products
   - With a long list of name brand products – Listerine, Benadryl, Actifed, Sudafed, etc. full year sales 2003 increased 20 % to more than USD 3.0 billion.

Pfizer is headquartered in New York. It has major research labs in Connecticut, California, Massachusetts, Michigan, England, Japan, and France.

Pfizer: Committed to Manufacturing

"Throughout its history, Pfizer has been unequivocally committed to research and innovation" (Rodengen 1999). Pfizer attributes much of its success to its values-driven culture and behavior, key aspects of which are innovation and strong customer focus. However, Pfizer also has a long history of manufacturing. Responding to an appeal from the US Government to manufacture penicillin to treat soldiers in World War II, Pfizer began production of penicillin and became the world's largest producer of penicillin in 1944. Until the late 1940s Pfizer was a bulk chemical producer and sold its products to other companies that branded them (Pfizer 1999).

As manufacturing has always been seen as a strategic asset, Pfizer is vertically integrated and performs most of its primary and secondary manufacturing in-house. Its manufacturing division is organized as a global function called Pfizer Global Manufacturing (PGM) that provides the three major businesses (Global Pharmaceuticals, Consumer Healthcare, Animal Health) with high quality products. This helps Pfizer to capitalize on its scale and to drive down costs. Costs of goods sold at Pfizer accounts for just 14.4 % of its revenue compared to around 30 % industry average (Pfizer 2004).

Operational Excellence at Pfizer – Starting with Right First Time

In 2003 PGM rolled out its Right-First-Time (RFT) strategy. RFT aimed to systematically reveal true root causes of unwanted variations in manufacturing processes. By doing so, Pfizer responded to changes caused by a paradigm shift from the Federal Drug Administration (FDA). This shift became evident in three FDA initiatives.

The first one aims to shift manufacturing from an empirical basis to a manufacturing science. The major objective of this initiative was articulated in the second progress report of the cGMP Initiative: *"Pharmaceutical manufacturing is evolving from an art to one that is now science and engineering based. Effectively using this knowledge in regulatory decisions in establishing specifications and evaluating manufacturing processes can substantially improve the efficiency of both manufacturing and regulatory processes. This initiative is designed to do just through an integrated systems approach to product quality regulation founded on sound sciences and engineering principles for assessing and mitigating risks of poor product and process quality in the context of the intended use of pharmaceutical products."* (FDA 2003b).

The evolution of pharmaceutical manufacturing to a manufacturing science is presented in Figure 27.

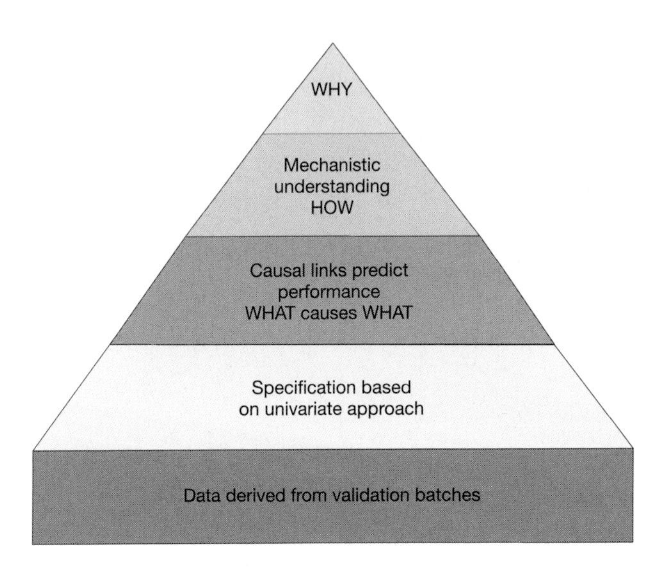

Figure 27: Evolution of pharmaceutical manufacturing (Source: Pfizer Right First Time Team).

The second regulatory guidance is on Process Analytical Technology (PAT), which is supposed to allow and encourage the use of equipment and protocols for continuous monitoring of manufacturing processes. By providing real time information about critical quality attributes or key process parameters as well as physical, chemical and biological characteristics of the raw material, PAT is crucial for developing a better process understanding in pharmaceutical manufacturing. Hence, it will be a main enabler for moving from a former empirical approach to the "desired state" of manufacturing science (see initiative 1).

The third initiative is a more general approach to manufacturing regulations titled risk-based current Good Manufacturing Processes (cGMP). Risk-based cGMP seeks to free the industry from prescriptive rules that are not necessary to ensure quality, and to concentrate the regulatory effort where the largest risk and the best opportunities for quality improvement are. Together, Manufacturing Science, PAT and risk-based cGMP are intended to promote innovation in manufacturing and logistics practices that ensure better, more predictable quality while increasing efficiency (Lockwood 2003). The initiatives aim to shift manufacturing from empirical to science based standards for manufacturing process quality.

The RFT strategy is driven by a global RFT leadership team (RFT LT). The RFT LT was responsible for rolling out the RFT strategy throughout the whole PGM division. This team includes senior PGM leaders each responsible for key geographical areas.

While PGM found themselves as competitive to Pharmaceutical industry standards, the RFT team realized that some other industries were significantly ahead of the pharmaceutical industry with regard to their robustness of their processes and efficiency. Across other industries it was not uncommon to achieve Sigma levels above 5-Sigma; and some "Best-Practice" companies like GE or Motorola had already managed to achieve Sigma levels that were close to 6-Sigma. Before GE started its 6-Sigma initiative, studies revealed that GE's operations were carried out between 3- and 4-Sigma, i.e., about 35,000 defects per million opportunities. According to company estimates, avoidable expenditure of USD 7-10 billion was being incurred in the form of scrap, reworking parts, correction of transactional errors, inefficiencies, and lost productivity. Within five years of its implementation of 6-Sigma, GE produced annual benefits of more than USD 2.5 billion for GE worldwide (Sirisha and Mukund 2002). Comparing the initial situation of GE with the current situation of the pharmaceutical industry, the situation in the pharmaceutical industry looks even more challenging. According to G. K. Raju (2003) most pharmaceutical companies today still operate in a range between 2- and 3-Sigma. But, what is the root cause for this? Some explanations offered include:

- Pharmaceutical manufacturing typically focuses on the end product to guarantee the highest quality standards for safety and efficacy with a sigma level exceeding 6-Sigma, but have a limited focus on the process itself.
- Therefore pharmaceutical companies usually have low process capabilities as there was little or no incentive in the past to develop a scientific understanding of their processes. This leads to a high rate of rework and rejects.
- Manufacturing sites usually operate in a fairly isolated way, without integrating process and information flow between suppliers, active pharmaceutical ingredient (API) plants and drug product sites as well as other ingredient sites.
- Pharmaceutical manufacturing processes are often complex and include many non-value adding activities.

The RFT team realized that an increase in overall manufacturing performance can only be achieved by increasing process capability first. While the elimination of waste is crucial for achieving sustainable performance improvements, the RFT strategy was not launched as a "cost-cutting exercise". The major objective of the strategy was to improve quality first by getting a thorough understanding of the sources of variation in the process and then to reduce variation to a minimum level. G. K. Raju's model of Operational Excellence in the pharmaceutical industry describes this as four levels of Excellence in plant capabilities, with each level requiring mastery of the levels below it (Figure 28).

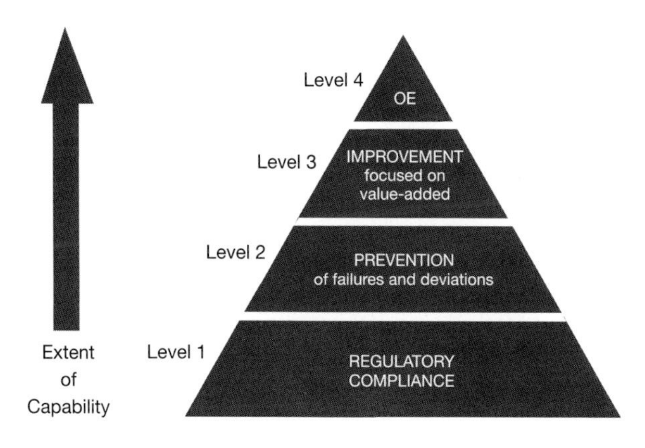

Figure 28: Levels of Operational Excellence (adapted from Raju 2003).

Level 1

– The main objective is to meet regulatory requirements by performing excessive quality control. Most pharmaceutical companies in 2003 tended to be a "Level 1" company. This was the situation that was also characteristic for most of PGM's operations in 2003. However, Pfizer was already on the move to climb level 2.

Level 2

– A company develops capabilities that help to get a scientific understanding about the process and root causes of deviations to move to a predictive performance rather than a reactive compliance. PGM has started at the end of 2004 to systematically perform capability assessments on their major products which will continue over the next years.

Level 3

– A company develops capabilities to understand value from the viewpoint of the customer and to eliminate waste – especially inventory, which reduces responsiveness and masks process problems. Once the capability assessments have been successfully completed and improvement projects initiated it will be the time for a company to combine 6-Sigma with projects focusing on value added, taking advantage of robust and highly reliable processes.

Level 4

– A company has eliminated all significant root causes for deviations (the company has reduced variability to a 6-Sigma level) and has simultaneously managed to eliminate all sources of waste throughout its operations (the company has become "agile"). At this stage a company has managed to tackle the two goals "Effectiveness" and "Efficiency" simultaneously becoming a leader in Operational Excellence.

Based on the four levels of Operational Excellence (Figure 28), the RFT strategy aimed to reduce variation to enhance process capability. It was mainly based on the 6-Sigma methodology.

While the 6-Sigma concept is strong in reducing variability of individual processes by providing a structure for addressing problems, it does not provide a means to analyze and optimise the operation in its entirety. For this reason a company also has to look to the concept of Agile Manufacturing. With its focus on the entire value stream, and on value-added activities, Agile Manufacturing helps to prevent the sub-optimizing and improvement of non-value-added steps that can happen when 6-Sigma is done alone. There is an obvious case for a harmonious marriage between 6-Sigma, which fixes individual processes, and Agility, which fixes the connections between processes (Liker and Choi 2004) (see Figures 29 and 30).

The deployment of the RFT strategy

For the deployment of the RFT strategy, Pfizer decided to adopt the 6-Sigma DMAIC (Define, Measure, Analyze, Improve, Control) mechanism throughout all levels of the organization. Each of the phases was designed in a way to ensure that the program is implemented in a methodical and disciplined way.

While the Define phase was already quite advanced as there was a clear objective what to achieve (see Levels of Operational Excellence), the question was *how* to Measure and Analyze the main areas of improvement. On a business level Pfizer defined the main issues of concern and linked those to several key performance indicators that should allow tracking the improvement process (see Figure 31).

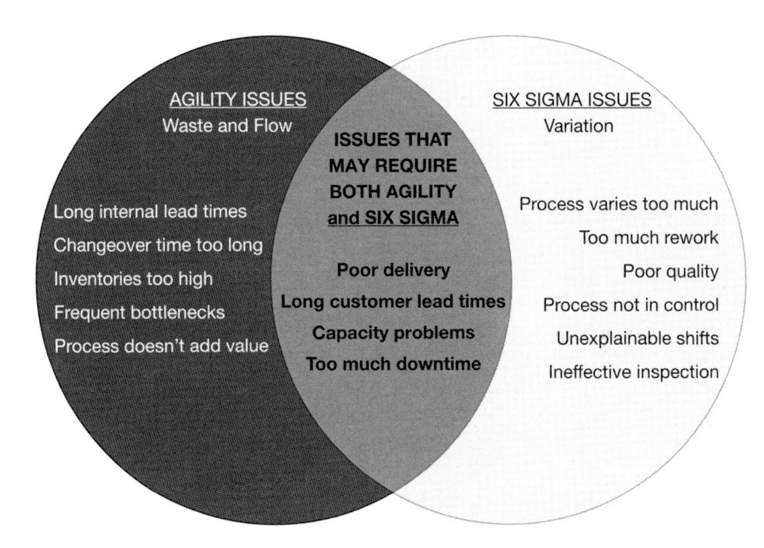

Figure 29: Issue of doing 6-Sigma or Agility projects (Source: Rath & Strong).

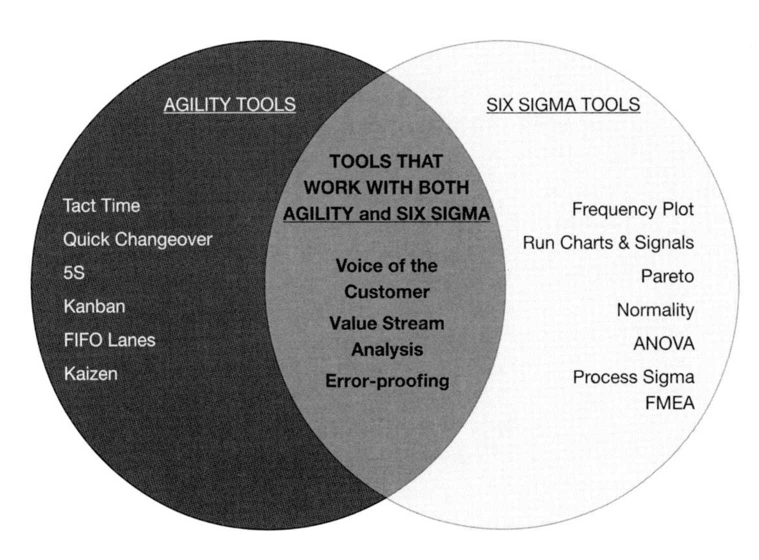

Figure 30: Combining 6-Sigma with Agility projects (Source: Rath & Strong).

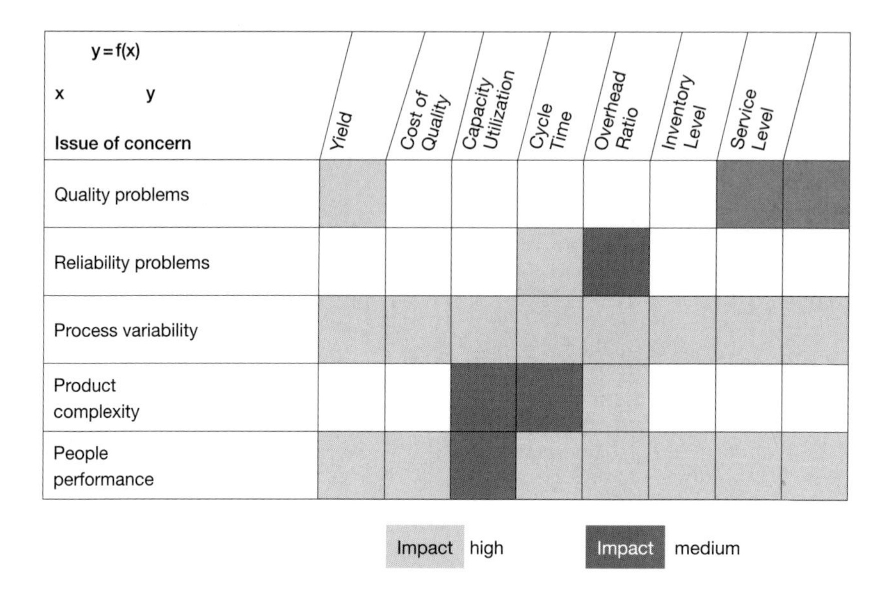

Figure 31: Key performance figures indicating the issues of concern (Source: Right First Time Leadership Team).

This analysis revealed that there were two issues of concern that affected all key performance indicators that were tracked by the RFT team. The number one issue of concern was process variability. Hence, the RFT team realized that its approach to first concentrate on a reduction in process variability had proved to be the right strategy. However, the analysis revealed that PGM had to pay attention to a further question that was expected to have a high impact on the success of the overall RFT strategy: How should PGM develop its employees and managers in a way that supports the RFT strategy to address the second main concern of how to enhance people performance?

For most industries the expectation is that process variability will be reduced through process improvement programs. However due to the high risks of doing things that do not comply with regulatory requirements there was little motivation to take the initiative to improve pharmaceutical processes. The new regulatory polices described in the 21st century cGMPs promises to change this situation. As a consequence, one of the major pillars of the RFT strategy was to create a culture of entrepreneurial action and leader behavior among all employees in the Pfizer group. Figure 32 clarifies the linkage between the PGM mission and the ambitious goal to increase effectiveness and efficiency of its processes, which was dependent on a cultural change within the PGM group.

After analyzing the main areas of improvement, the RFT team started to deploy the strategy throughout the organization. When Pfizer officially launched the initiative in 2003, two hundred top executives of PGM were invited to Florida, USA to understand the objectives as well as the importance of the RFT strategy. In the following months the global objectives of the RFT strategy were linked with the objectives of each plant by developing a "RFT site master plan". The RFT site master plan included "hard facts" that provided improvement potential based on RFT-related KPIs addressing manufacturing, laboratory and documentation deficiencies for the next five years, as well as a guideline concerning the number of RFT projects

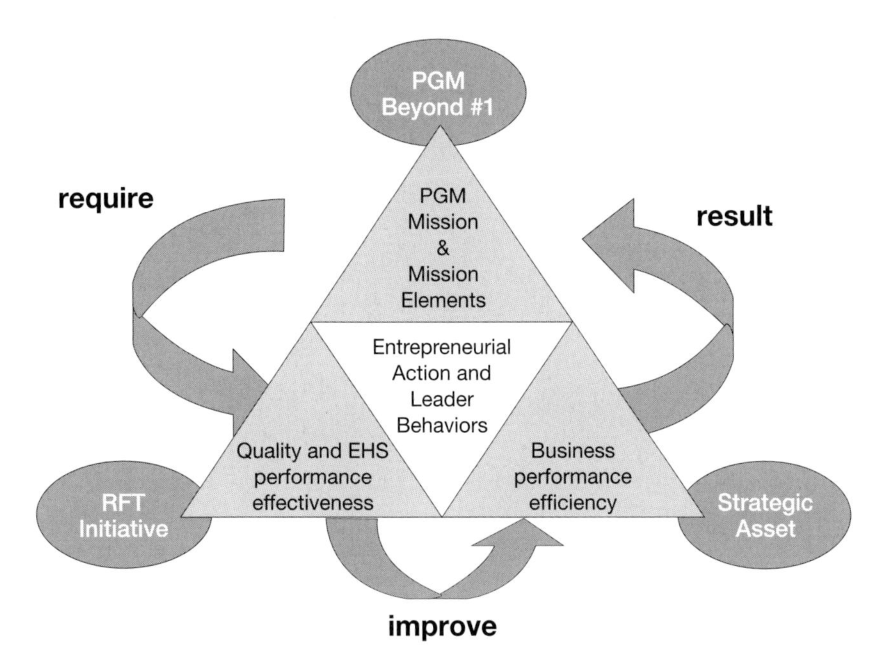

Figure 32: Sequence of the RFT strategy (Source: Right First Time Leadership Team).

and training programs that were to be performed by each plant. Beside the guidelines that addressed the more structural changes (e.g. the deployment of Process Analytical Technology or the integration of key suppliers), there were guidelines that addressed how to tackle the cultural change process (e.g. a communication and promotion strategy for the RFT strategy) at each site. While some projects were mandatory, most of the projects could be initiated by the plants themselves to ensure that bottom up initiatives would be encouraged by the RFT strategy. Initially RFT projects focussed on a specific problem that caused a deviation in a single process. Those projects were typically launched locally by the operator or the supervisor on plant level. In those cases where the problem directly affected other processes, a capability assessment of the whole process was performed by a cross-functional team that was responsible for eliminating all kinds of process deviations in the designated value stream of the particular product. Capability Assessment usually yielded several projects that had to be tackled by local persons in charge.

While there was a lot of freedom concerning the launch of RFT related projects, the RFT project was highly standardized concerning the RFT training program. Each plant received the same training modules to ensure equal initial conditions. Furthermore, this helped to develop a common language and understanding about the tools and their specific purpose.

The implementation progress was tracked by the steering committee (called RFT sponsors) that was comprised of representatives of PGM operational leadership and key functional leaders such as Quality and Technology and lead by the president of PGM.

While each site had at least one person that was responsible for the implementation of the RFT strategy, the RFT colleagues reported to their site leaders and not directly to the RFT LT. Each RFT area leader also reported to the area leader of his/her respective area of responsibility and was a core member of the area operational leadership team that was responsible for the respective geographic area. The rationale behind that decision was that the operational leadership team are in the position to take decisions and had budgeting responsibilities. An "external project member" located at each plant which had directly reported to the RFT LT would have faced much bigger problems to align the local people at each site to the program. Furthermore, the RFT team was designed as a limited duration function that will be terminated as soon as the principles of the program are deeply rooted into the organization. Hence, the role of the RFT team was more to act like a facilitator working like a consultant or coach and offering advice for each site.

When starting the project, the RFT LT was facing several serious questions how to roll out the strategy throughout the whole PGM organization, specifically:

- How would it be possible to establish a culture within the manufacturing unit that is process oriented and is based on a proactive rather than a reactive compliance culture?
- How to structure and deploy the RFT strategy including state of the art methodologies and deploy it globally throughout the plant network with more than 20,000 employees working in 100 plants in the world?[16]
- How to harmonize the program with the various local Operational Excellence efforts on plant level without sacrificing the momentum of local initiatives?
- How to organize a training program that fits the specific needs at the various levels and functions of the organization?

The training program

Training was one of the most important parts of the RFT strategy. At the beginning of the project, most of the training was performed by Rath & Strong, an external global operating consulting company, specialized on 6-Sigma training program. However, the objective was to internalise the training as soon as possible, so that it could be performed by PGM colleagues. Hence, at first the training curriculum designed by Rath & Strong aimed to train internal high profile employees that were intended to become RFT Master Black Belts and eligible to train other employees.

Employees who became proficient in RFT trainings were certified under different categories according to the level and core area of the proficiency. The various certifications included RFT Yellow Belt, RFT Green Belt and RFT Black Belt certifications (see Figure 33 for the different RFT certifications).

There were three major training modules each focusing on the specific needs of the target group. Method I training aims to develop a basic understanding of how to systematically approach problems. Furthermore, it aims to initiate a cultural change process as it was used to empower employees to continuously proactively think about how to improve a process. Quick fixes without adequate investigation should no longer be accepted. It became the major enabler for driving the cultural change throughout the organization. Method II and method III trainings are more analytical and are used to tackle problems that are more complex. Method III training is reserved for Black Belts only and demand strong analytical skills with regard to problem solving and statistical knowledge.

16 Figures based on 2003 data.

RFT Yellow Belt	A person that has completed a method I training program and has common understanding of the purpose of the RFT strategy and basic techniques.
RFT Green Belt	A person with working knowledge of RFT tools and methodology and who has completed a method II training program.
RFT Black Belt	A highly-skilled RFT expert who had completed method II and method III training and demonstrated mastery of 6-Sigma tools through the completion of a major process improvement project during a course of six months.
RFT Master Black Belt	A highly-skilled RFT expert that has, besides his technical expertise, strong coaching and leadership capabilities. A RFT Master Black Belt has to be influential and cross-functionally skilled. RFT Master Black Belts are eligible to train and mentor people.

Figure 33: Job descriptions of the different RFT certifications.

Figure 34 visualizes the different training modules with the emphasis on the deployment of the 6-Sigma principles.

The objective for the RFT strategy was, that at the end, 100% of all employees at PGM have received a Method I training, around 5% have been trained in Method II and around 1.5 % on Method III. By mid-2005 approximately 25% have been trained in Method I, 2.5% in Method II and around 1.2 % in Method III. Pfizer invested a substantial amount of money in RFT related training programs in 2004 which has continued in 2005. Since internal training resources have been developed this cash-out cost are starting significantly decline.

Lessons learned, Results and Challenges

By 2004, Pfizer began to reap the first benefits of the RFT strategy as the process capability started to significantly increase with processes becoming more robust and process variability decreasing. The Europe Area is representative of the results to date as shown in Figure 35, which demonstrates the major areas of improvements within Europe in 2004. While the highest portion of cost savings could be generated in the field of yield improvement, most projects that were conducted aimed to increase quality performance (measured by process variability) and did not directly tackle efficiency issues. The results also revealed the overall mutual reinforcement among the different dimensions of process improvement. To build cumulative and lasting manufacturing capability, management attention and resources should go first toward enhancing quality, then – while the efforts to enhance quality continue – attention can be paid to improving efficiency. In that case, not only can traditional trade-offs between either high quality or low cost be avoided, but in fact high quality can also enhance efficient processes. As a result, efficiency and effectiveness become supplementary goals. This is why PGM is considering the application of Agile Manufacturing principles, as they call it.

Topic	Method I	Method II Green Belt	Method III Black Belt
Business Case	Resolve basic deviations	Eliminate deviations	Eliminate variations
People	Individual initiative or team	Teamwork Green Belt	Interdisciplinary teams Black Belt
Skill Set	Basic knowledge in problem solving tools	Specialized in methodology	Standardized and certified trainers
Special Cause	Yes	Yes	No
Common Cause	No	No	Yes
Complexity of Problem	Low	Medium-High	Highly complex
Typical Tools	Problem definition: • Process Mapping • Cause & Effect • Brainstorming • Time Series Plot • Pareto Diagram	All from Method I and: • Capability Indices • Frequency Plot • Scatter Diagrams • Gauge R&R • Hypothesis Testing	All from Method II and: • Additional Hypothesis Testing Techniques • Additional Regression Techniques • Advanced DOE

Figure 34: Structure of the RFT training program (Source: Right First Time Leadership Team).

According to the leader of the RFT team, the most significant benefit of the RFT strategy was that it enabled the plants to understand the true root causes of problems and to create a common culture of how to tackle problems properly: *"In my opinion the most crucial aspect of the strategy was to initiate a cultural change that was essential to modify the way we approach the resolution of problems. Hence, I would say that 6-Sigma and in particular Method I training was a crucial element, as it raised awareness and helped align the people with the RFT strategy".*

While the cultural change process was the biggest benefit of the project, it also proved to be the biggest challenge. However, there were several factors that facilitated the success of the change process. First, there was a strong commitment from senior management at Pfizer towards RFT. Unlike many other research driven pharmaceutical companies, manufacturing has always been seen as a strategic asset that is an important element for the overall success of Pfizer. A further factor was the strong value-driven culture and behavior that was a crucial enabler for setting up the project and initiate the change process. It was also important

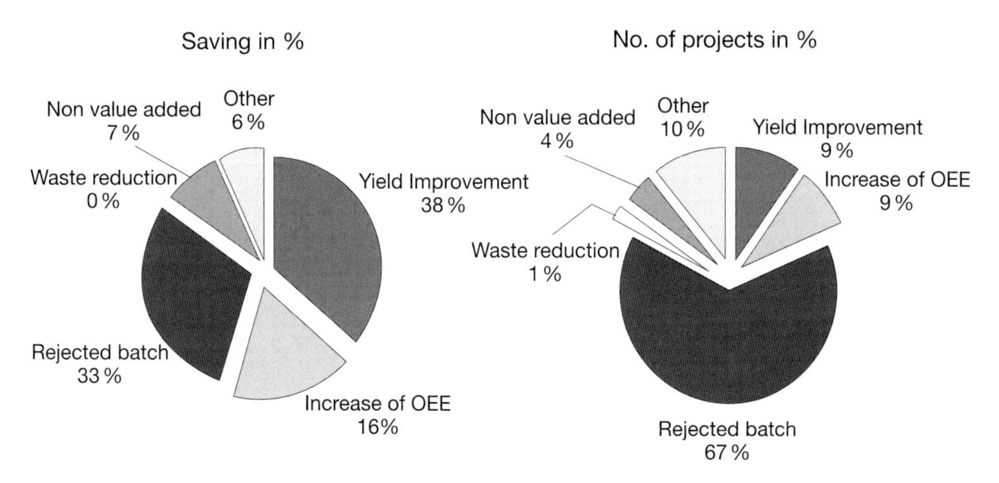

Figure 35: Project and cost savings overview at Pfizer.

that the project has not been launched as a "cost-cutting exercise". Efficiency improvements were always seen more like a "fall-out" as a result of stable and robust processes. The more the RFT strategy started to tackle efficiency issues; it became a specific challenge not to lose focus on the quality issues. However, as the RFT team never stopped stressing the importance of robust and high quality processes at first, they managed to achieve sustainable process improvements which also helped to align the people with the project.

Until 2005, PGM realized remarkable improvements on the variability of their processes. Inspection costs were reduced, as the RFT strategy ensured that quality was built into the process following the approach of continuous quality verification.

An outlook

To avoid losing momentum, and to capitalize on the reinforcing effects of an increased process quality, the RFT team is exploring further possibilities to expand the strategy by addressing the value added and continuous flow, both major principles of an Agile Manufacturing philosophy. By applying Agile Manufacturing principles the organization expects to increase their operational performance, reduce their cycle times and inventories, while, at the same time, even improve the customer service level. This consequently would allow Pfizer to achieve the next level of Operational. In the 4th quarter of 2005, Pfizer has started a pilot Excellence project to prove the concept of applying tools of a Value Stream Analysis. They refer to this as Method IV as it complementarily expands the established Method I, II and III training modules. This Method IV module, following also the principles of the DMAIC cycle, would include tools like Standard Work, Mistake Proofing, 5S and Visual Workplace, Set-up Reduction, Total Productive Maintenance and Demand Driven manufacturing. By doing so, it hopes to capitalize on the widely established project organization and the sense of "get-up-and-go" that was created by the RFT strategy throughout the organization.

The major challenge that the RFT team will be facing is to link the 6-Sigma part of the RFT project with the principles of Value Stream Mapping while not overstressing the people's willingness and capabilities to learn even more product and process optimization tools.

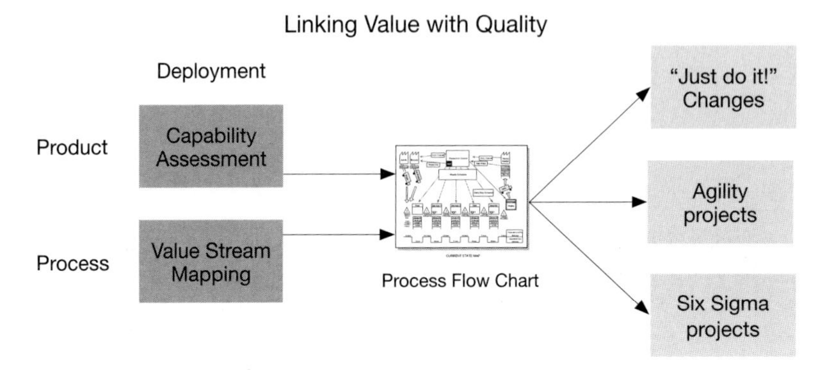

Integration of Method I, II and III with Method IV through:

- Capability Assessments (Product)
- Value Stream Analysis (Process)
- Orchestration of projects

Figure 36: Linking Agility and 6-Sigma (Source: Rath & Strong).

From the experiences that the RFT team have gained so far, when deploying 6-Sigma tools, the specific challenges of implementing Method IV tools would be different. While many 6-Sigma tools have proved to be quite demanding from a technical perspective as they sometimes require a thorough statistical knowledge, the implementation of Method IV tools will imply an even bigger cultural change due to their sometimes counter-intuitive nature. For many people that have been working on the shop-floor for a couple of years, it is hard to understand why in the future smaller production runs should be preferred, and quicker set-up times should primarily be used to further drive down lot sizes rather than to optimize the OEE of the equipment. Hence, the implementation of Method IV principles require a paradigm shift that is even more demanding than the cultural change process that is required for implementing 6-Sigma.

However, from a "theoretical" perspective, the integration of the 6-Sigma initiative with Agility should be feasible because of their complementary goals. People that were formerly trained on how to perform a capability assessment should now becoming proficient in performing a value stream analysis to see the big picture and identify priority areas to reduce non-value-added and discontinuous flow across the plants. As both, capability assessments and value stream analysis start with a mapping of the process flow, a process map proves to be a good starting point for integrating Agility projects with 6-Sigma projects. The difference between a capability assessment and a value stream map is simply the unit of analysis. While the capability assessment is focusing purely on the process capability of the processing steps with focus on the pharmaceutical manufacturing process, the value stream map expands this view to take in all relevant business process details – inventory levels, batch sizes, equipment efficiency, staffing and so on. Figure 36 shows how "Agility and 6-Sigma fit together".

By taking into account the different requirements and specific challenges, the RFT LT will evaluate the further deployment of the Method IV tools as a complementary initiative under the umbrella of the RFT strategy to further capitalize on the increased process quality of their processes, but have not taken any decision yet.

Despite those challenges the RFT LT is convinced that the RFT strategy was launched at the right time and the focus on process variability rather than operational efficiency proved to be the rigth strategy.

IV.2 Case Study: The Capsugel Way to Operational Excellence

Daniel Tykal and Thomas Friedli

Capsugel: The leading capsule manufacturer

Capsugel is a manufacturer of capsules. Initially part of the Warner Lambert/Parke-Davis Company, it is now a division of Pfizer Inc., a Fortune 100 global pharmaceutical company. Still focusing on the manufacturing of hard capsules – by far the largest part of Capsugel's business – the company is just beginning to increase its soft gel capsule business. Beside the traditional gelatin capsules it also produces two non-gelatin capsules. Capsugel customers include leading pharmaceutical companies as well as dietary supplement manufacturers. These two major markets account for the bulk of capsule usage. However, new industrial applications that use gelatin capsules are being developed.

Capsules are the dosage form of choice for dietary supplements. Many supplements utilize natural herbal ingredients that are difficult to compress into a tablet. Capsules provide a proven, safe and cost-effective dosage form.

Capsules provide "precision packaging" for small, delicate, and/or light sensitive products. Being safe and environmentally-friendly, the capsule shell provides a versatile and inexpensive way to package precise quantities of solids, semi-solids, or liquids.

With an annual capacity of more than 100 billion capsules, sales exceeding USD 500 million and about 2400 employees, Capsugel is the global market leader in the capsule manufacturing business – selling more than three times the amount of its next competitor. Capsugel has not always been the market leader in its business. But due to an impressive way of improvement with regard to Operational Excellence, Capsugel got ahead of its main competitors. In this case study the reader is provided with the "Capsugel way" of setting the floor for change in order to make Operational Excellence succeed.

The Capsule Manufacturing Process

The manufacturing process of hard gelatin capsules has remained essentially the same as in its original patent from the late 1800s but has been refined and automated by successive generations of pharmacists and engineers. The working principle of a modern high speed capsule manufacturing machine and the necessary subsequent operations (see Figure 37) can be summarized as follows (Jones 1987):

The gelatin solution is prepared containing the gelatin itself together with colorants and various process additives. The capsules are made by dipping and subsequent drying. The dried capsules are removed from the moulds and the caps and bodies are assembled. The assembled capsules are sorted, printed and packed. The correct viscosity of the gelatin solution is a key quality attribute for the subsequent processing steps.

The gelatin solution is placed in the machine in a jacketed, stirred container which is called a dip pan and its level is kept constant by a reserve of fresh, hot gelatin solution which is held in a jacketed container and is continuously fed into the main container controlled by a level sensing devise. The moulds on which capsules are formed are called pins and groups of these are set in line on metal bars. The whole assembly is called a pin bar. The moulds for both, cap and body have the same general form, the body being the longer of the two. Their form

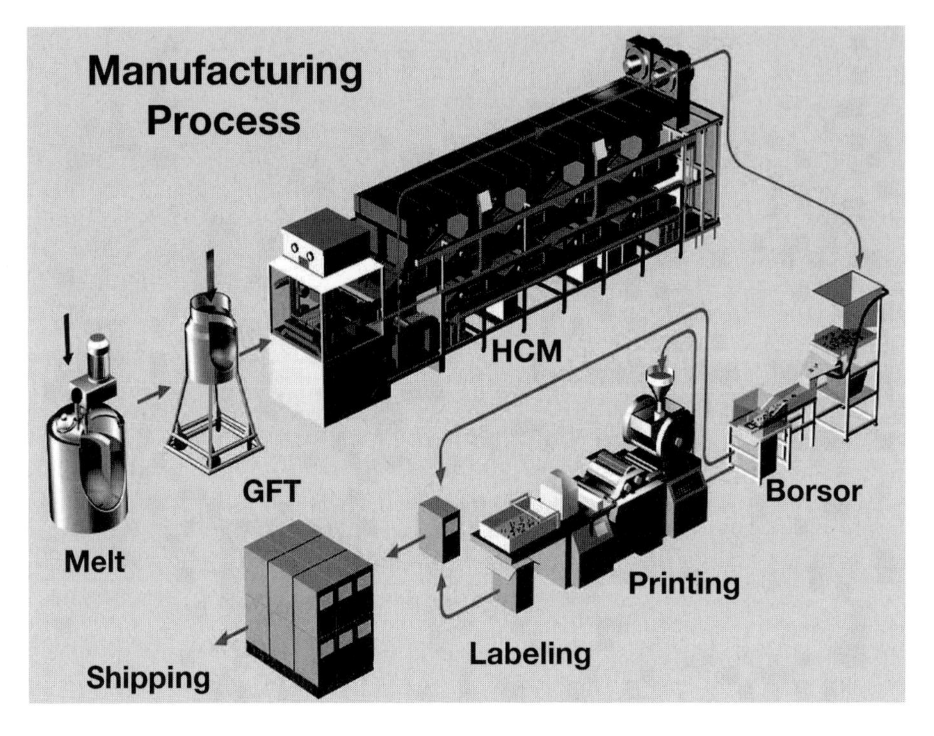

Figure 37: Capsule manufacturing process (capsugel archives).

is such that the capsules shell consists of two parts which are slightly but regularly tapered towards their closed ends. The pin bars are gently lowered into the gelatin solution then slowly withdrawn. Gelatin is picked up on the mould pins, the quantity being governed by the viscosity of the solution. To spread the gelatin evenly over the surfaces of the mould pins the pin bars are rotated about a horizontal axis as they are transferred from the lower level to a higher level of the machine, dipping the mould again and again in the gelatin solution. The pin bars are then passed through a series of drying chambers. In these, large volumes of controlled humidity air are blown directly over the pins to dry the film. The gelatin films formed on the pin moulds are longer than required for the finished capsule. This is because the lower edges of the films are of variable thickness so they need to be trimmed to a good clean edge at the length required. Capsules are made on moulds which are tapered and as a result are slightly bell shaped. The diameters are important quality attributes in two places:

The body diameter at the open end influences how the capsule halves fit together particularly when they are being rejoined on the capsule filling machine. The cap diameter at the closed end influences how the capsule halves stay together after closing. The hard gelatin capsule is manufactured to tight engineering tolerances despite the fact that it is made out of natural material by a dipping process. The nature of the method causes a small percentage of defective capsules to be produced. Immediately after manufacture the empty capsules are further dried to the final moisture and then either sorted mechanically or by electronic equipment. Hard gelatin capsules are usually printed with a variety of information, such as product name, code, product strength, logos or symbols.

Situation at the outset

In 1982, Capsugel was the number 2 in the market place – with regard to quality as well as to market share. Capsugel was also 2nd choice regarding new product introduction which is the lifeblood for pharmaceutical manufacturing. There was little global coordination. The one thing that was in common all over Capsugel was a heavy use of inspection as a means of quality – at least 100 % and if they wanted exceptional quality 200 %. The inspection department was the largest in the plant. It totaled up to 50 % of the whole workforce. At that time margins were shrinking and the management realized that it could not afford to stay the same. Looking at this picture in 1982, it is interesting to analyze which key success factors brought Capsugel up to its leading market position of today.

Setting the floor for change – beyond an artificial master plan

First of all, it has to be mentioned that there was no specific master plan that led Capsugel to its improvements. In the 1980s, every company in the industry had similar processes and inspection procedures and used similar – most often even the same – machines. There was no best practice that could provide an example for improvements. Therefore Capsugel looked for consultants that provided insights into other industries, especially the automotive industry, because it was outstanding with regard to Operational Excellence.

In 1982, Capsugel's process improvement started with Jim Harbour, a consultant who introduced the Toyota Lean Manufacturing concept to the US automotive industry. In the very first meeting he pointed his finger at Capsugel's president and said: "You are the problem. And if you don't change, this company will not survive." He then went on to tell why generally management is the problem in change processes and what one could do about it. The management has to set up the floor for change and support all change initiatives. That was a different way of thinking in contrast to the culture that existed in the company until that day.

Furthermore the participants of the meeting were confronted with the idea that the way Capsugel was ensuring product quality was not going to be successful in the long run. The quality problem was being masked by inspection. No one even challenged the inspection. That time it was just the way to make capsules. Capsules were manufactured and then inspected, trying to separate the good ones from the bad ones. The inspection rate was between 100 % and 200 %, meaning that every single capsule was inspected at least once and more often twice. Inspection processes are very lengthy; and are also very labor-intensive since colleagues visually inspect every single capsule. Hence, two issues appear: The issue of cycle time, but also the issue of non-value-added cost. Though the company had some engineers working on some problems, suggesting certain changes, no one systematically worked on root cause analysis.

Jim Harbour introduced the concept of having productivity and quality improvement teams. The first quality improvement teams were organized to focus on the upstream process and identifying the root cause of the quality problems at each manufacturing step along the whole manufacturing process – the first teams were on gelatin melting process, the second on mixing process and so forth. The first few teams were very successful in ruling out the cause of problems that existed in improving the process capabilities. It was so successful that people started to make a religion about it. The importance of the management and the company's culture for the successful introduction of an Operational Excellence program was also underlined by Edwards Deming. Teaching Capsugel's management on quality improvement and variation he continuously stressed the role of the management.

Figure 38 shows the number of major defects per 100,000 capsules from 1982 to 2003. It is obvious that Jim Harbour's appeal to the management positively influenced quality. This early success simultaneously motivated the employees to further improve the company's quality and processes.

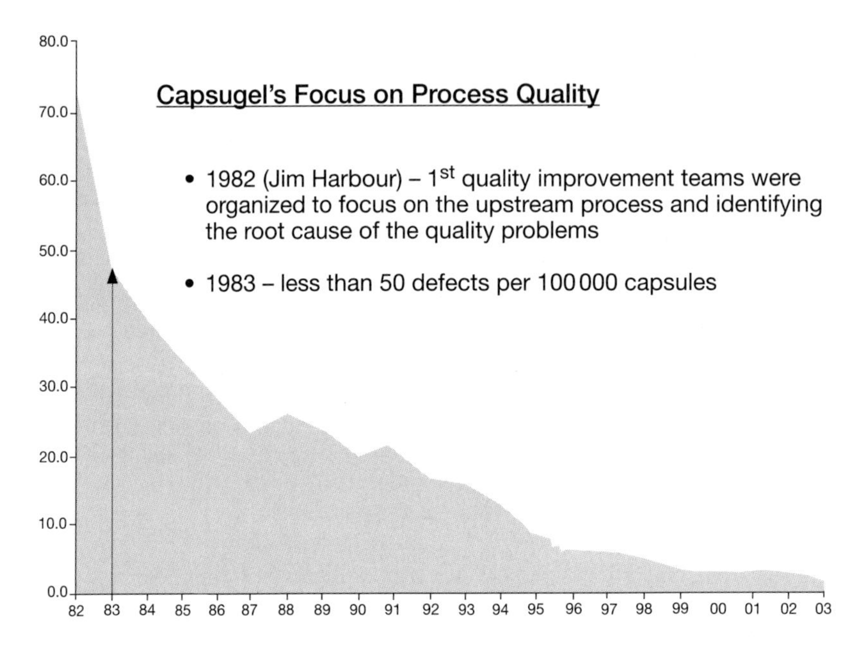

Figure 38: Capsugel's quality improvements 1982-1983.

Using Simple Statistical Techniques

Joseph Juran's Management of Quality introduced Capsugel to simple statistical techniques for teams to use. By studying the cost of quality concept selected employees could deepen their understanding where a company spends its money. The most important point that was taught was the necessity to improve the journey from symptom to cause to remedy. The journey from symptom to cause is difficult, but if done properly, then the journey to remedy is easy. This is the difference between trying to fix a problem and gaining process knowledge.

To ensure the consistent use of statistical methods throughout Capsugel, a partnership was established over the years with the University of Tennessee. Employees were sent to three week training sessions called "Productivity through Quality". This way the company could deepen the overall understanding of statistics with regard to process and quality improvements. Several important tools that were taught were about checking for variation within and between; short term and long term. Furthermore this standardized training gave a common ground for investigation and communication. Reaching a critical mass was very important so the University of Tennessee was asked to design a special training just for Capsugel. For the first time in history the company was using SPC (Statistical Process Control) charts.

In 1987 Capsugel was trained by Bill Diamond on Design of Experiments (DOE), especially on how to set up, run and interpret DOEs with the proper number of trials. One of the most simple, yet powerful tools was the Analysis of Goodness (ANOG). This is a technique for interpretation of results by looking for patterns.

Again, each introduction of these new techniques can be tracked in Figure 39. The number of major defects per 100,000 capsules could be lowered below 20.

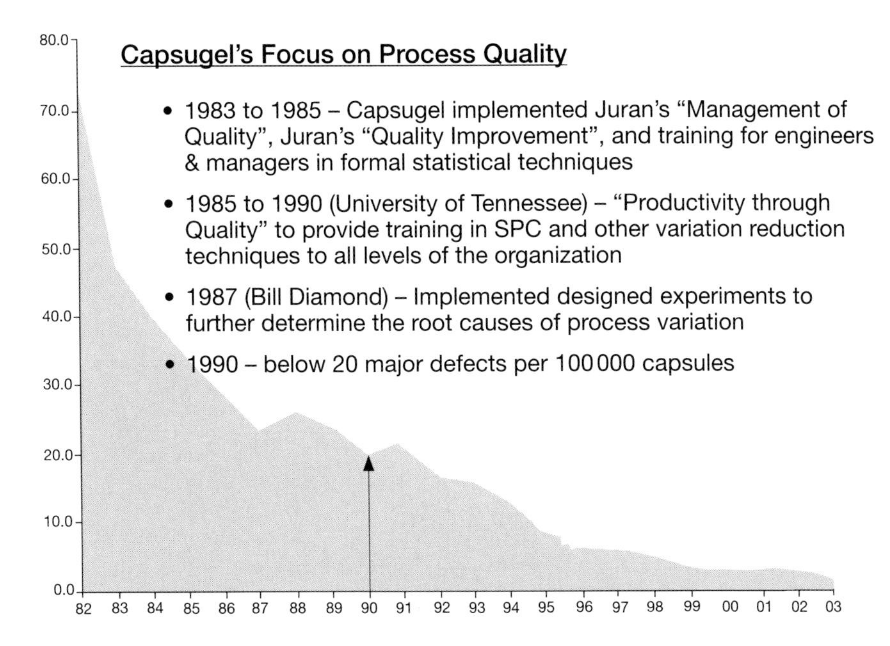

Figure 39: Capsugel's quality improvements 1983-1990.

About 13 years ago Capsugel introduced the Yearly Quality Summit Process. Every year top managers from the regions meet for 3-4 days to discuss quality from the point of view of the customers, of the competition as well as of the company itself. Looking at the feedback from customer satisfaction surveys and benchmarking data it is to decide where the biggest issues and opportunities are. Global Quality initiatives were sanctioned in the same meeting.

Since then Capsugel has also focused on mechanical innovations to increase hard capsule manufacturing reliability and developed formal affiliate quality plans.

In the 1990s, the idea that sampling would give good information about the quality was no longer effective. The company needed something better to predict quality. Engineers at a plant in Belgium developed a CAQ (Computer Aided Quality) system to assist in prediction of quality. It has been effective in combining some sampling with process monitoring to predict quality. Computer Integrated Manufacturing as well as CAQ resulted in major advances in global standardization in melting, manufacturing, and printing. Furthermore the automation of gauging systems improved dimension measurements and quality feedback to production operators. As Capsugel is a global company and statistical data has to be available at every plant of the world, state-of-the-art information technology enables the globalization of the total quality system.

As shown in Figure 40, the improvements in the 1990s again could significantly improve Capsugel's quality performance. In 2000 the defect rate was lower than 5 defects per 100,000 capsules.

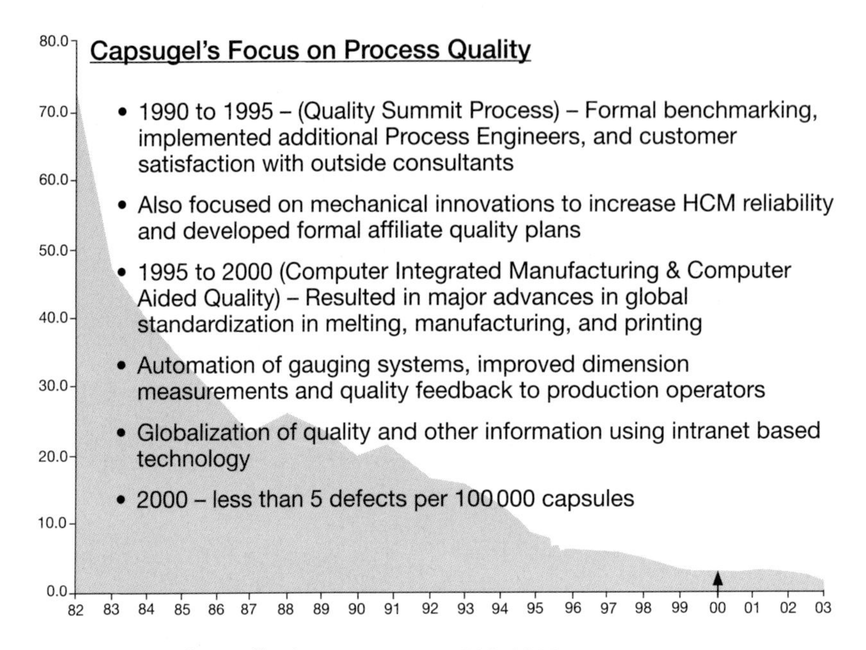

Figure 40: Capsugel's quality improvements 1990-2000.

Until the year 2000, the success story was mainly driven by three factors:

- changing the mindset throughout the whole company towards a culture of change,
- providing the employees with relevant statistical techniques and
- building up process knowledge.

In this period Capsugel could significantly reduce its cost of quality. Output more than doubled since 1982. At the same time the number of employees working in inspection could be reduced – at a single plant down to 10 employees in contrast to the year 1982 when an average of 150 employees per plant worked in inspection.

Early success played a key role in Capsugel's improvement process. Achievements in the early stages were permanently communicated throughout the company. This way the employees believed in the new "culture of change" and were motivated to contribute new quality improvements. It is obvious that the reduction of the defect rate continually slows down as one gets closer to the zero defect rate. This is obvious in the flat curve progression between 2000 and 2003 in Figure 40. At the same time the number of success stories became less and less. Hence, the management had to react: on the one hand to enable further improvements, on the other hand to reinforce employees' motivation with regard to process quality.

Since 2000, advances in visioning technology provided product quality data far beyond visual inspection. At the moment Capsugel is introducing a Quality Information System for real time decision making in quality. This system will incorporate new sensors to help identify process and mechanical control on the machine.

6-Sigma – further deepen process knowledge

In order to reinforce the motivation of its employees the management identified a need for new "breakthroughs" in the quality level at the Annual Quality Summit in 2003. During 2004 Capsugel and experts were exploring a Capsugel specific 6-Sigma approach. The next step was to assess how the 6-Sigma program should be implemented in the company. Basically three different options were investigated by Capsugel:

1. Option 1: A full 6-Sigma "culture change" approach similar to companies like GE
   - Estimate 1 % of 2500 Capsugel colleagues (additional 25 persons)
2. Option 2: Capsugel 6-Sigma team that would consist of 6 additional engineers reporting directly to a central 6-Sigma organization
   - 6 additional headcount + global coordinator
3. Option 3: Incorporation of 6-Sigma into the existing organization by identifying 6 Black Belts reporting to the local affiliates with direction from a steering committee.
   - Global coordinator + 6 Black Belts in 4 geographic regions

Finally option three was identified to be the appropriate model for Capsugel's company structure. As the management is aware of the fact that employees can only be motivated to do something new if they are provided with the necessary background, know-how and tools in order to understand and live it, the main focus in the beginning is on teaching the employees. The senior management team got a one-half day overview for the Executive Level Team. The 6-Sigma Management Team and Steering Committee was taught in a three and a half day workshop. After studying the background and objective of Capsugel's 6-Sigma initiative, the team got familiar with 6-Sigma tools and methods such as mind mapping, questioning a process, process study and metrics. The goal of this workshop was to define roles and responsibilities for the management teams, Steering Committee, local site management, and Black Belts. Over and above that, the team identified Black Belt projects by condensing an initial pool of projects into long term and further into short term (training) projects. Black Belt training and development cover a five-month period. The training includes both in-class training and site work on their assigned "training project". The training is heavily based on the application to specific projects so that at least one-half of the training days will be spent working on the Black Belt projects. Site support for application of class concepts would be a critical part of the application of the knowledge presented during the class. Using the 6-Sigma approach Capsugel worked on improving process and product quality by looking for sources of variation, understanding what these are, and making some changes in a process to sustainably reduce variation.

Lessons learned

In conclusion process understanding through data was what Capsugel made successful. Before this change, managers had plenty of instances where they thought that one thing was the root cause. But when they got the data and did the investigations they found just the opposite was the root cause. So one of the most important lessons is that statistically gained data in analysis, resulting in process knowledge, is extremely important to make the right decisions. Consequently today all claims have to be supported by valid and challenged statistical data – capital expenditures, project initiation, process change request, etc. In order to ensure that all sources of variation are considered, decisions have to be backed up by trials in another affiliate. The acceptance of this culture was straightforward. Those who "got it" and utilized the new tools were promoted, those who did not were left behind.

But employees can only build process knowledge by using statistical data if they are provided with appropriate statistical techniques and tools. Common language is essential in this change process. A company needs to get to critical mass that is provided with the same statistical know-how as quickly as possible. Capsugel chose a training partner and "stuck" with this partner for the whole training process. Training and re-training of operators is essential. The use of common statistical tools that are derived from a common training program ensures similar evaluations and analysis across affiliates. Standardized training is the key for this. But not only the employees have to be taught. Top management has to be educated to ask the right questions at the right time and top management has to be involved in the process, in training, in asking questions, in the behaviors.

To achieve a culture of change communication is essential. But communication is not enough. To promote cultural change, management must be consistent in its actions. If decisions are made on the basis of SPC, they should be implemented immediately. Then, using the cost of quality concept, the direct link between improvements to upfront process and improved product quality has to be communicated. Sharing success stories across affiliates fosters more success.

As this case study shows, companies do not necessarily need a master plan for implementing Operational Excellence as long as they consistently act upon the principle of "questions lead, answers follow", especially because there is not just one single perfect roadmap for solving all problems. Different tools are needed for different problems. The case study further underlines that building process knowledge and improving product quality is a continuous process.

IV.3 Case Study: Maximizing Equipment Effectiveness at Reckitt Benckiser[17]

Marek Szwejczewski, Keith Goffin, and Malcolm Wheatley

The name Reckitt Benckiser may not at first strike a familiar chord, although the company's products are to be found in almost every household in Europe – and further afield, too. But, of distinction Reckitt & Colman's Hull factory won the process industry category in the 1999 Management Today/Cranfield School of Management Best Factory Awards with a compelling performance. And one that the subsequent merger with the Netherland's Benckiser in December 1999, which created a GBP 3.1 billion giant with 20,000 employees spread across 170 countries, can only enhance.

17 The case study was written with the support of the Department of Trade and Industry, London (UK). The case is taken from: Process Innovation in UK Manufacturing: Best Practice Makes Perfect, by M. Szwejczewski, M. Wheatley, and K. Goffin (published by the Department of Trade and Industry, London, DTI/Pub 5468/15k06/01/NP, June 2001).

It is the employment numbers that first alert one to the remarkable transformation that the factory has achieved. "Once, almost 6,000 people worked here," muses supply chain director, Alan Brooke, of the Hull factory. Whole multi-storey buildings now stand empty, and the number of employees (including non-manufacturing personnel) now totals less than 900 – yet the products that they produce are to be found on pharmacy and supermarket shelves on five continents.

What, then, was the cause of this contraction in numbers? Not retrenchment, or farming out production to low-cost Eastern European economies. Instead, it is the result of an obsessive focus on slick supply chains, improved machine efficiencies, and an enormous degree of automation, all made possible through exploiting to the full the sheer volume of sales achieved by the factory's clutch of major brands.

Take for example the product Lemsip, a cold cure found within most households' medicine cabinets. The factory produces 100 million sachets a year; sometimes churning out a million sachets a day – as it did at the high of the flu season in January 1999 and 2000. Or familiar analgesics such as Disprin, of which more than 600 million tablets are produced each year.

Equally prolific is the output of the constipation and bowel regularity treatment Fybogel. From unpromising-looking sacks of raw material containing an obscure water-absorbing fibrous Indian plant called Ispaghula, the Hull operation produces some 300 million Fybogel sachets a year, making it, according to Brooke, the fourth most frequently prescribed medicine in the National Health Service.

Manufacturing excellence

As its filling and packaging lines prove, the factory has proved adroit at exploiting these volumes to achieve rarely encountered levels of manufacturing excellence. This contrast with other factories is stark: over the years, it has become something of an axiom among the judges of the Management Today/Cranfield School of Management Best Factory Awards that the factories' high-speed filling lines are often to be seen jammed-up, under repair, being switched from one hard-to-fill product to another, or otherwise not engaged in filling.

But this is patently not the case at Hull, where the lines just seem to keep running – period. And running, what is more, in highly concentrated areas of space: the world's total production of Lemsip, for example, comes from a floor area of just 174 square metres. Where once whole floors full of people packed products by hand, tightly-crammed machinery does the job today.

So it comes as no surprise to learn that the measure of Overall Equipment Effectiveness (OEE) favoured by the plant is a particularly tough one, with few allowances made for extenuating circumstances. Should a line fail (an extremely rare event), then flashing status lights send people scurrying to rectify problems, and reasons for downtime are meticulously posted and scrutinized. In 1998, the company's Australian factory closed, reveals Brooke, so efficient had the Hull operation become, together with savings from high volume procurement, that even bottles of Dettol could be shipped to Australia more cheaply than they could be manufactured there.

Yet the driving force behind all this manufacturing excellence is surprisingly hard to pin down, and not what might be imagined. Clearly, many of the factory's products are sold with the benefit of retail price maintenance, thus restricting downwards price pressure. Generic-equivalents and supermarket own-brands pose a threat, certainly, but the strength of brands such as Dettol, Lemsip and Disprin provide a formidable shield. Instead, the impetus comes from price rigidity within elements of the market – although medicines such as Gaviscon and Fybogel are prescribed by doctors, and purchased by pharmacists and hospitals. "It's 23 years since the NHS accepted a price increase on Gaviscon," says Brooke.

Consequently, the Hull factory's manufacturing excellence has been driven by factory management in a series of what Brooke terms "squeeze projects", designed to wring cost out of well-established and mature product lines. Take a series of supply chain initiatives in the late 1990s, for example, which powerfully transformed efficiencies not only within the supply chain, but also within the manufacturing operations themselves. "We have a lot purchasing spend concentrated on a few suppliers," observes Brooke, "A little leverage goes a long way."

Take the active ingredient in Gaviscon, for example – the indigestion reliever whose NHS price has stayed frozen for 23 years – and which is produced from seaweed-based alginates by a Norwegian firm called FMC BioPolymer. Building on the already close links between the two companies' research and development teams, the Hull factory proposed to BioPolymer a joint initiative to take cost out of supply chain, with the benefits being shared between the two businesses. "We wanted to work right back to the seabed, stripping cost out as we went," says operations manager, Mark Dean-Netscher.

And it is not rocket science – it is attention to detail, time and time again. The resulting efficiencies largely stemmed from common sense and a willingness to view the supply chain as a whole; and sharing the economic gains with partners, rather than as a series of initiatives carried out by Reckitt Benckiser. For some years, for example, FMC BioPolymer had been required by Reckitt to hold stock in the UK in order to improve volume flexibility and response time. The principle was right, the two companies' executives concluded – but the idea of a separate warehouse was wrong.

Instead, the relatively small physical quantity of material could piggyback on the massive warehousing economies of scale at Reckitt's European distribution centre at Bawtry. Better still, it then transpired that Reckitt trucks made regular journeys to Norway with finished goods, returning empty, just as BioPolymer's trucks returned empty from delivering to Bawtry. Why not use the empty leg to carry alginates to Bawtry, or finished products to Norway?

Even better, why not take advantage of Reckitt's enhanced purchasing power with ferry operators such as P&O to secure lower freight charges – even on the rapidly diminishing number of trips made by BioPolymer and Reckitt trucks? Best of all, adds Dean-Netscher, the management effort involved in bringing about these improvements has been relatively modest: "It's all done by teleconferencing and once-a-year meetings," he says.

A similar project was targeted on achieving improvements in the delivery of plastic bottles to the Dettol lines. With seven different bottle sizes, and an annual production volume of seven million liters, the quantities of bottles that the plant required were huge – but so too were the resulting inventories of empty bottles in the incoming goods warehouse. The problem: the contract was shared between two suppliers, who each delivered in quantities of a full trailer load.

What the plant wanted instead, product supply leader Mike Kaslow explains, was to work more closely with one supplier, instead of two, and to receive just a day's worth of bottles at a time, in the precise mix of bottle sizes that the filling lines would use. Moreover, with the precise mix of matching caps, too. The supplier could continue to manufacture the bottles and caps in the batch sizes that best suited their own production requirements – but Reckitt only wanted them delivered against a specific day's filling requirements. "We'd not only reduce our inventory in financial terms, but also free up a lot of warehouse space as well," says Kaslow. "Empty bottles take up a huge amount of space."

But as Kaslow and supply administration manager Sue Cecconi began to work with the chosen suppliers, they realised that there was a bigger prize within their grasp. Like most bottle-filling processes, the Hull bottling lines' first operation was to "scramble" the incoming bottles, which had been delivered on pallets in the normal orientation (with the necks uppermost) in order to feed them into the lines neck downwards, so as to ensure that any debris or dirt would fall out. Scrambling operations, explains Kaslow are typically slower than the associated filling rates – and so act as a bottleneck – but also often add unsightly scuff marks to the soft plastic.

Eliminating cost from the supply chain

The opportunity that the Hull managers had spotted was to induce the winning supplier to change the final stage of the bottle-blowing process, so as to place the finished bottles on thick cardboard sheets, already orientated neck downwards. That way, explains Cecconi, no dirt or debris could enter the bottle – and there would be no need for the slow scrambling and re-orienting operation. But this not only stripped cost out of the process: it actually added productive capacity. For with the bottleneck removed, the lines could be speeded up to around 200 bottles per minute – "an unheard-of speed," enthuses Kaslow. Focusing management attention on bottlenecks might not be rocket science, but it does bring results.

Today, bottles arrive from the bottle-manufacturing supplier in Norwich twice a day, at 8 a.m. and 8 p. m., following receipt of the schedules of requirements from Hull just the day before. The same, truck brings caps, as well. These come from another company, says Kaslow – "but that's the bottle supplier's problem to sort out, not ours." Even better, adds Cecconi, the empty trucks also deliver finished goods to the Bawtry national distribution depot as they return home. The cost? A mere 15 mile detour. "Once you sit down with suppliers and really look for ways of eliminating cost from the supply chain, it's surprising how many breakthroughs you can find," sums up Kaslow.

But what of manufacturing operations inside the factory? Twenty years of automation had seen huge gains achieved in productivity, observed Brooke, but the sheer scale of these had probably blinded management as to the actual efficiency of the automated process. This started to change when the factory decided to take advantage of accumulated reductions in floor-space, brought about by the smaller footprint of automated operations, and condense its manufacturing operations into just two buildings. With no spare space to boost short-term volumes, equipment efficiencies became critically important.

The obvious solution; implement a system of recording and improving Overall Equipment Effectiveness (OEE). "We already reported a measure of machine efficiency to group finance – but it was a 'soft' one, and gave allowances for interruptions such as planned maintenance and material shortages," recalls Brooke. "A harsher OEE measure would take away these excuses: there wouldn't be anywhere to hide."

The basic premise: multiply the theoretical maximum production per hour from each line by the 16 hours that each line ran per day, and compare this with the actual achievement, with no allowance for set-ups or disruption, or rejects. Initially, the factory captured the data manually, recording output and downtime – and the reasons for downtime – on sheets of paper by each machine. These were then entered into a spreadsheet on a personal computer to generate the OEE figure, and provide ranked sources of lost production.

This was fine as far as it went, but relied heavily on operators recording downtime correctly. Two closely-linked developments improved the process, explains site engineering Manager Garry Haswell. The first was the decision to move to an automated recording system known as ACTIVA, which improved both the capture and analysis of the data. "ACTIVA not only breaks out availability, and with it all the things that contribute to downtime, but also efficiency, which is line speed-related, to produce an overall measure of effectiveness," says Haswell, pointing to a print-out. "So, for example, an availability of 63.49 % combined with an efficiency of 66.31 % results in an overall effectiveness of 42.10 %."

The OEE results were reviewed with shift personnel and, more importantly, with the staff employed by Johnson Controls, to which the Hull factory outsourced all of its first line maintenance and changeover activities. "When we initially outsourced maintenance to Johnson we were getting too many arguments about whether lines were working well or not and whether changeovers could be completed more quickly," recalls Haswell. The use of factual ACTIVA data helped overcome these problems.

In addition, Johnson Control's engineers video-recorded and documented each changeover, developing standard procedures for them – along with an associated target time. Critically, adds Haswell, there is also an improvement target for each changeover, with a plan for achieving it, and the resources required to bring the plan to fruition.

But slicker changeovers were not the only source of improved effectiveness. As engineering support manager Barry Jones relates, projects were also targeted on improving the operation of individual lines – boosting the 'efficiency' aspect of the OEE measure. When you looked closely at what was going on, it was surprising how much slack had crept in over the years, as lines had been added-to, and new capabilities built-in he says. Certainly, a simple re-balancing exercise on the eleven year old multi-product Marchesini tablet line proved this by yielding significant improvements, forcing as many operations as possible to be carried out in parallel, rather than in series. Once again, identifying the bottlenecks and taking action to balance lines brought immediate benefits.

Philosophy of OEE

- Very self-critical but produces results
- Use analysis to determine cause
  - Equipment
  - Material
  - People
- Continually review/re-visit/re-focus
- Overall Equipment Effectiveness "Hard" Measure
  - 100 sachet/min design speed
  - 6,000 sachet/hour output
  - 16 x 6,000 = 96,000 expected over two shifts
  - 48,000 produced at 100% quality
  - i.e. only 50% efficient
- OEE = Availability x Performance Rate x Quality Rate

But further potential remained, particularly when the line operators were brought in to suggest improvements. Photocells placed at right angles to the line, for example, would occasionally interpret the gap between cardboard trays of products as indicative of no tray being present – and consequently erroneously stop the line. It was, observed Jones, a problem that operators had been living with for years. But placing the photocells diagonally instead of at right angles solved the problem for good: the photocell beam of light was always interrupted by a tray, except when one genuinely was not there.

Similarly, it was possible to fine-tune individual operations. On the tray loader unit within the line, for example, a mechanical arm pushed each tray into the plastic film in which it would be shrunk wrapped. At the point of actual insertion into the film, the speed of the push needed to be very slow, so as to avoid jams or other difficulties that would stop the line. Yet the mechanical arm as originally commissioned worked at this slow speed throughout its entire operation cycle – even when withdrawing, when the speed of the movement was irrelevant. Jones and colleague Paul Kennedy re-programmed the arm so as to initially push at high speed, then more slowly, and then withdraw once again at high speed.

Such minor tweaks to a line may not sound much – but taken together, they added up to a considerable improvement, says Brooke. Jones and Kennedy also fine-tuned the internal commands of the line's programmable logic controllers, trimming as much as three-quarters of a second from some of their cycle times, thus cutting operation times to the minimum. They also ensured that each station "stopped empty" in the event of a shutdown, which made re-starting the line much simpler and speedier. Tiny incremental improvements, to be sure – but improvements that eventually boosted throughput from 12 packs per minute to 16 packs per minute, yielding a whopping 30 % increase in capacity.

There are times of the year when that capacity is extremely useful indeed, stresses Brooke. During the peak of the annual cold and flu cycle, medicine demand massively outstrips production: the last two winter peaks, he notes, have seen three months' production of Lemsip sachets sold in a single week. So while the Marchesini line's ability to churn out additional packs of the admittedly less widely consumed Lemsip capsules comes in handy, the ability to respond rapidly to change in demand for the core sachet Lemsip product is vital.

This, as it turns out, was another aspect of the factory's operations that won plaudits from the Best Factory Awards judges. Characteristically, the approach adopted is a blend of several elements of manufacturing management, ranging from top-level forecasting and inventory planning at one end of the spectrum to detailed engineering-based improvements at the other.

Maximise production efficiencies

Broadly speaking, explained planning manager Bill Maxwell, the factory aimed to produce in excess of the level of demand in the period April to August, and to produce at least at the level of demand (or higher, if possible) during the period September to March. However, he adds, pure-and-simple inventory building is a sub-optimal solution, and so the factory has tended to build its inventory in 'campaigns'. The intention of this, he explained, was not only to maximise production efficiencies, but also to free-up productive capacity during the times of peak demand – so that during these times, the equipment would be running, more or less continuously, on the strongest selling pack sizes and flavors. To reinforce this, an additional filling line was purchased. Where there were originally two lines, one filling two sizes of Fybogel, while the other filled Lemsip, the additional line can handle both Fybogel and Lemsip, enabling the original Fybogel line to concentrate on maximising the output of a single pack size. With planned inventory buildings of Fybogel, therefore, the additional line can be switched almost entirely to Lemsip, effectively doubling capacity, while at the same time, thanks to fewer changeovers, reducing the filling cost per sachet.

Still further productive capacity is obtained through the use of labor contracts that enable filling lines to switch from two-shift working to three-shift working at short notice, in exchange for a shift premium. "Formally, the notice period is five days, but we can often switch more quickly," says Brooke. With a corps of key operatives trained to man any of the three lines, each shift can be buffered with enough temporary labor to enable two shift's worth of permanent employees to effectively cover three shifts. Weekend working at overtime rates adds still further capacity, but the overtime premium makes this a solution of last resort.

Particularly so, now that the old Reckitt & Colman is Reckitt Benckiser, one of the major changes this has brought about from a manufacturing management perspective, observed Brooke, is a much greater focus on brand profitability and brand gross margin. Post-merger, it transpires that managers imbued with Benckiser's strongly cost-driven culture are in the driving seat, giving Brooke and other senior managers a forceful incentive, through executive bonus schemes, to wring still further efficiencies from manufacturing and supply chain functions in the years ahead.

Reckitt Benckiser's Approach to Problem Solving

Determine the cause not effect

- What is the number one issue?
- What is the cause of this issue?
- Jointly determine solution
- Solve it
- Agree it is solved
- Attack the next number one issue

The continuation of a long tradition

So once-sacrosanct marketing and sales stipulations concerning things such as packaging design and specification are now under review, with marketing and sales people tasked with the same brand profitability targets as their manufacturing counterparts. "It's been an interesting time," grins Brooke, pointing to a number of areas in which manufacturing has been freed to make improvements once deemed unacceptable from a marketing point of view – shrink-wrapping cartons together, rather than putting them into trays, for example.

And with changes elsewhere, he points out, the change may not sound particularly significant – but the result has been to eliminate work contend and boost line speeds. Fewer people, slicker automation: within Reckitt's Hull factory, it is simply continuation of a long tradition.

Figure 41: Colour coded parts are held on a trolley to facilitate the quick changeover of packing lines[18].

Figure 42: Operator recording performance data for a packing line[19].

18 Photograph supplied by Jeremy Young Photography.

19 Photograph supplied by Jeremy Young Photography.

IV.4 Case Study: Achieving 6-Sigma Levels at a Pharmaceutical Plant

Bart Bastoen, Bart Dewolf, and David Hampton

The following case study describes in detail how the 6-Sigma concept has helped to fix a problem that has existed for several years. The problem has occurred at a manufacturing and packaging plant of a global pharmaceutical company. The plant delivers aseptic pharmaceuticals to more than 150 countries and employs more than 1000 people.

The company had started to implement the 6-Sigma concept a couple of years ago. The designated plant had been on the forefront of the initiative and had already successfully implemented several 6-Sigma projects. However, there was one process on the shop floor that did not fit the 6-Sigma requirements towards the robustness of the manufacturing processes at all. It was the tray forming process in which plastic foil is being heated and deformed in a mould to form plastic trays in which vials and ampoules are packed. A typical defect was that the finished tray had a hole or some other functional deformations (see Figure 43 – left: bad/right: good). On average, there was a defect rate of 400 ppm, which translated into around 3 defective products within 2 hours production time. However, some formats even had a defect rate of 20000 ppm which added up to around 240 defective trays within 2 hours production time. The worst case that could happen was a total line breakdown which resulted in downtimes that could easily add up to several hours and a significant reduction of the Overall Equipment Effectiveness (OEE).

The problem with variations in the tray forming processes existed for around 15 years. Too often people came up with "quick fixes" that did not prove to solve the problem, properly. Obviously the complexity of the problem was higher than most people had expected. There were a couple of tuning parameters at this process that directly affected the output quality.

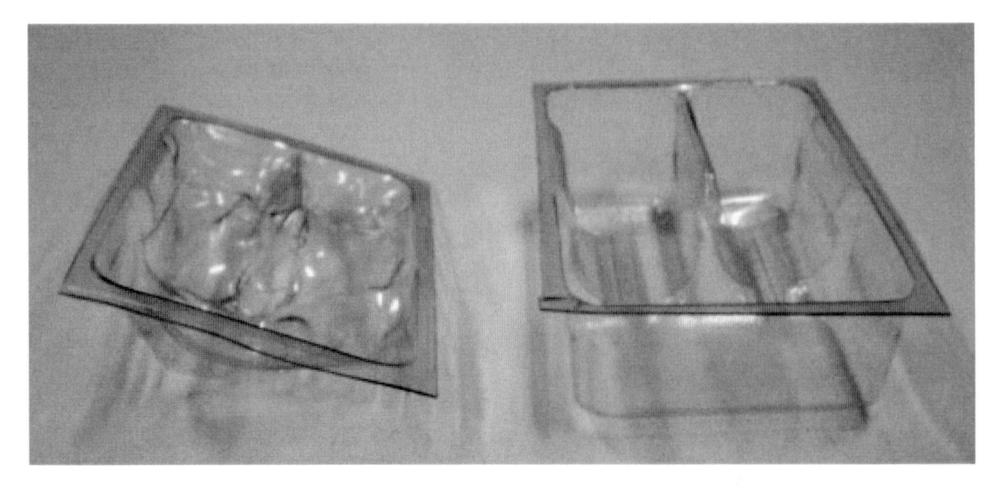

Figure 43: On the left: Example of a deformed tray. On the right: Correctly produced tray.

Hence, the right setting for each order was a very difficult task, especially as there was no detailed understanding about how specific product and process characteristics affect process quality.

At that time different teams had already worked around that issue. It literally seemed to be under a witch's spell. People had tried so much to fix the problem and to adjust the parameters of the machine. However, the problem occurred over and over again: *The machine always tended to run at normal line speed without any problems. As soon as the operator had to change from one roll of foil to another roll of foil as it was running out of foil, the problem suddenly occurred. Without changing any process- or machine-parameters, the machine suddenly started to produce defective trays or even jammed so that production had to be stopped.* As a result, people on the line tended to say *"It's the foil quality; we have to take another foil or change the supplier."* They put the defective foil into quarantine and started producing with a new batch of foil. Sometimes the new batch had also problems sometimes it didn't.

When Bart came as a new Black Belt he was eager to find a solution. Well known for being restless until not having tried everything to fix a problem, he was convinced that by fully scientifically understanding the process, one could manage to find the true root cause of the problem. Too often he had heard that people start blaming the supplier when the true root cause cannot be found.

At the plant, people did not believe that the new project that he launched was likely to succeed. People tended to think about the project as follows: *"We have sixteen years of experience with the machine and have tried to fix the problem so many times, there comes somebody with a new methodology and he wants to tell us how to solve a problem with that machine – that's ridiculous."* On the other side, by using the 6-Sigma philosophy, Bart was convinced that everybody would be forced to approach the problem in a much more structured way than before. However, this would require the full support of the project team. Bart himself understood his role not as trouble shooter that comes in to fix a problem, his role was more like a coach that comes in to support the people in applying certain tools and approaching the problem in a set-by-step way. By capitalizing on the rich process knowledge of the people at the plant and his knowledge concerning problem solving he was sure that the project was likely to succeed.

Launching the project

When Bart started the project, he tried to set-up a multi-disciplinary team. As most people thought that the problem is mainly rooted in the quality of the foil, he decided to bring in an expert with a functional expertise in material science, who could analyze the requirements concerning the foil characteristics. Apart from some functional experts from PTS (Production Technology Support), from Controlling (Plant Performance) and the Engineering department, Bart mostly relied on the experience of the operators themselves. Just the operators could provide the valuable working knowledge about the process itself and the specific problems that were typical for handling the CP (Combination Pack line: combination pack of vials and ampoules) line in the day-to-day business. Bart was convinced that each team member that he had chosen would prove to be a real contributor to the project.

After forming the team, Bart developed the charter of the project. The charter was the key document that provided a written guide to the problem and the project. The charter included the reason for pursuing the project, the goal, a basic project plan and the scope of the project. After setting up the charter, Bart started the project, based on the DMAIC problem solving model which should discipline the team to work through the problem step-by-step.

Step 1: Define – Understanding the trayforming process as a scientific experiment with 80 input variables

The first step for Bart and his team was to develop a scientific understanding about the process and try to transfer the process into a function Y = f(x) that describes all relevant relationships between the dependent output variable (Y) and the independent input variables (x) of the tray forming process. While (Y) is used to monitor a process to see if it is out of control, or if symptoms are developing within a process, the Xs are the independent inputs that cause or control a problem that occurs in the output (Y) of the process. The main question to be answered was: "What vital few process and input variables affect critical to satisfaction (CTQ)[20] *output measures of the CP manufacturing process?". To answer that question, it was important to first identify the CTQ which have a direct impact on the perceived quality of the customer. Bart and his team defined the CTQ for measuring tray quality to be the number of trays with holes and the number of trays with functional deformation. Both CTQ were supposed to be reduced to a zero defect level.*

Figure 44 describes how the zero defect requirement from the customer side was translated into critical-to-quality characteristics that could be directly measured by the project team.

While the measurement of the CTQ turned out to be quite easy, the bigger challenge that Bart and his team were facing, was to figure out all relevant input variables (Xs) that cause or control the output of the processes. To get a first overview about possible variables the team outlined the sequence of the sub-processes and each job that was performed during the tray forming process. Figure 45 describes the tray forming process.

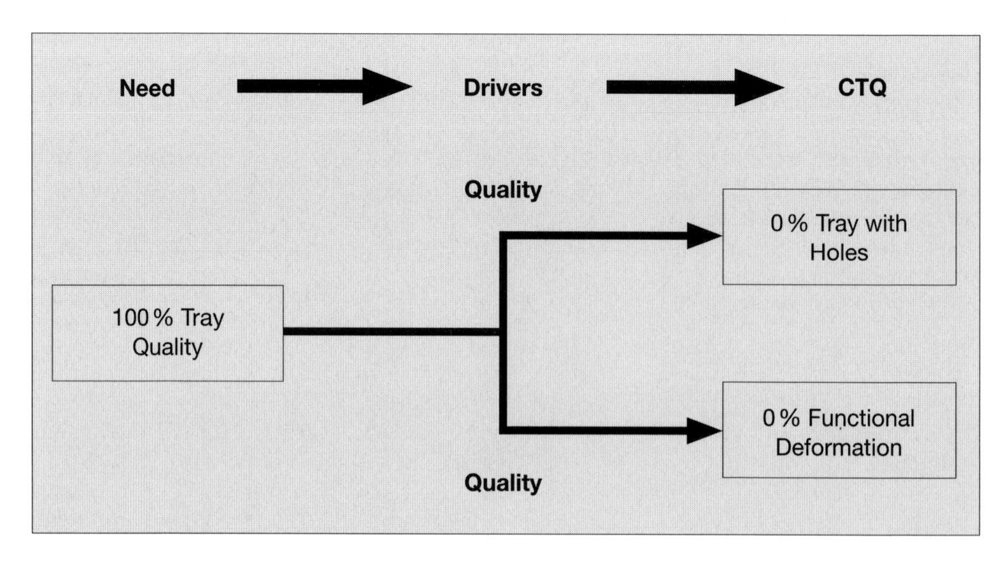

Figure 44: Example: From the Need to CTQ.

20 Critical to Quality (CTQ) describes an element of a process or practice which has a direct impact on its perceived quality.

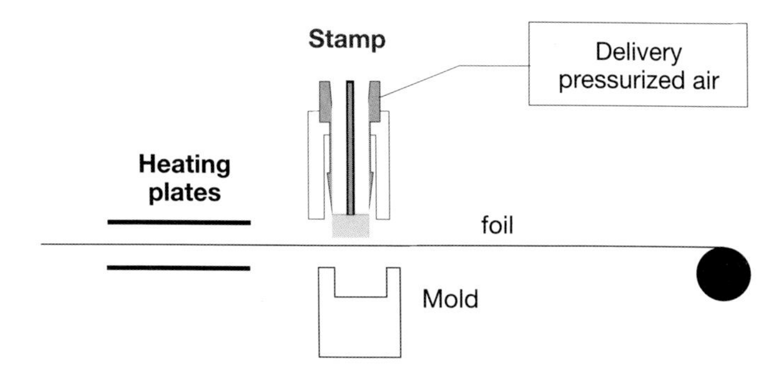

Figure 45: The tray forming process.

Two heating plates (1) heated up the foil – to a certain temperature by closing and making a contact with the plastic foil. The up-heated foil was then (2) released from the heating plates and (3) forwarded to the mould. The mould was (4) closed and afterwards (5) the stamp moved down to form the tray. The pressurised air was then (6) delivered and the stamp (7) moved up and the mould (8) opened. At last the foil was (9) forwarded and the process started again.

To further identify the various key variables, Bart and his team decided to use a SIPOC (Supplier-Input-Process-Output-Customer) and a Micro Process map. While the SIPOC map was a good tool to get a better understanding about internal customer-supplier relationships on a rather high-level basis, Bart needed a further process map to get a more detailed understanding about the process flow. Usually he went on by building a flow chart, however in this specific case he decided to use a Micro Process Map hoping to get a more detailed understanding about the technical side of the process. A Micro Process Map visualizes technically one cycle of the physical forming process described above. By accurately describing the 0° to 360° rotation of the cam,. it allowed Bart to visualize in time each specific process step. This made it possible to compare the CP process with fairly similar technical processes of other lines.

The Micro Process map provided evidence, that there were significant differences between other compared lines in terms of critical machine parameters. Figure 46 shows the results of one of the many Micro Process maps (only the first 180°) that allowed the comparison of the CP line with another manufacturing line.

After having performed the Micro Process mapping, Bart was quite sure that the different parameter settings between the CP line and the DS line could provide some answers to the problem. However, he was convinced that the differences concerning the machine parameters that controlled the cam shaft rotation did not allow to fully predict a consistent output quality of the CP process. There were still too many open questions concerning other vital factors. From other projects he remembered that one of the most valuable lessons of the 6-Sigma approach was that often the "usual suspects" (the causes you think are the root of the problem) turn out to be "not guilty".

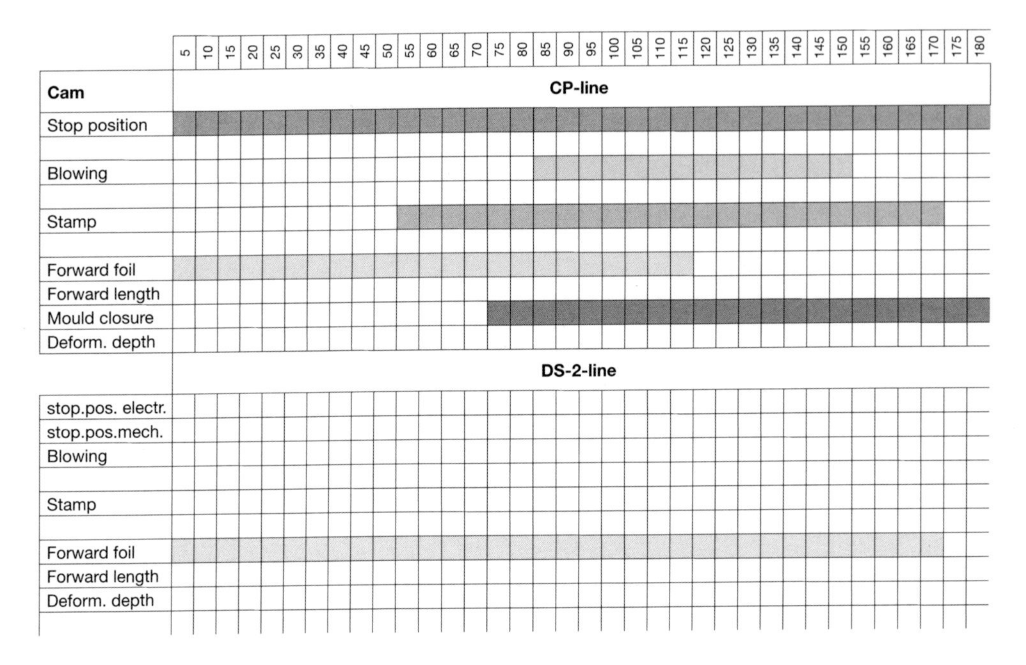

Figure 46: Micro Process maps.

The following week Bart scheduled a brainstorming session with his team. He was sure that the team would come up with a multitude of other potential root causes of deviation. Using a Cause-and-Effect Diagram forced the team to consider the complexity of the problem and to take an objective look at all the contributing factors. It helped to determine both the primary and the secondary causes of the problem.

Before constructing the Cause-and-Effect Diagram, Bart asked his team to re-examine the problem by asking several questions:

- What is the problem?
- Who is affected?
- When does it occur?
- Where does it occur?

Based on the answers to the questions Bart first constructed a high level Cause-and-Effect Diagram giving an overview of the primary causes. For each of these "prime suspects" or more technically "causal hypotheses" Bart and his team went deeper in detail. One possible root cause was the temperature of the foil during the tray forming process. By getting deeper into the details, the team identified 34 input variables that directly influenced the foil temperature. The designated Cause-Effect Diagram is illustrated in Figure 47.

Apart from the multitude of the variables that influence the foil temperature, the team managed to identify several further variables for each of the "prime suspects". At the end, the team came up with 80 input variables that might cause deviation. As a consequence, the team decided to move to the next step to set up a proper measurement system that should allow for measuring significant deviations for each possible root cause.

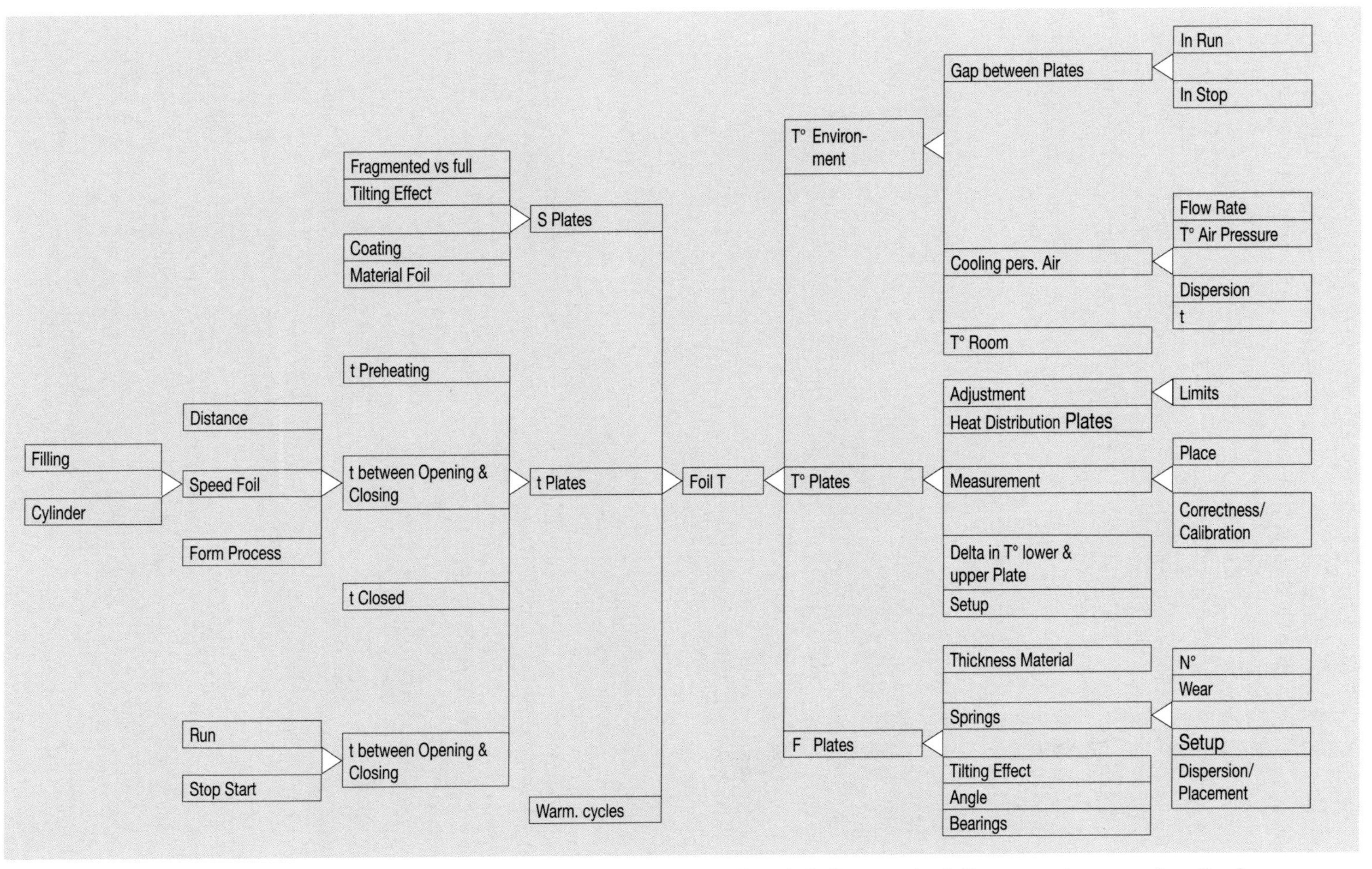

Figure 47: Cause-Effect Diagram: In this diagram 34 input variables that directly influence the foil temperature are visualized.

Step 2: Measure – Narrow down the problem to 15 possible root causes

Due to the high number of possible root causes of deviation, Bart decided to use a Pareto technique to quickly focus the effort on the key causes of the problem. The Pareto Principle states that only a "vital few" factors are responsible for producing most of the problems. This principle can be applied to quality improvement to the extent that a great majority of problems (80 %) are produced by a few key causes (20 %).

The team gathered data on the frequency of the causes. By filling the most important causes into a bar graph and calculating the cumulative percentage of all causes, Bart created some Pareto graphs to separate the important causes from the trivial ones. On Figure 48 there is an excerpt of the multitude of Pareto charts that have been made.

For Bart and his team, one of the things to figure out was whether there were significant differences in terms of the robustness of the manufacturing process when comparing the different sorts of products that were produced at different rows-(plotted on the x-axis). The Pareto charts illustrated below, show that especially row 4 of product A (running on the CP line) caused by far the biggest problems while row 5 of product D (also running on the CP line) turned out to be very robust. As a result, Bart decided to make a benchmarking between the stable running products and the highly unstable product A. By doing so he wanted to find out significant differences between the processes/formats that proved to be successful and process/formats that tended to have high failure rates. Further, he hoped that fixing the problem with product A would allow him to extrapolate the findings to all other products and by that reducing the overall defect rate at the CP line to a 6-Sigma level.

By using all parameters that have been figured out by the root cause analysis, the Pareto's and the Micro Process map, the team developed a Benchmarking form, that allowed to compare product A with the more stable running formats of the CP manufacturing process and the DS

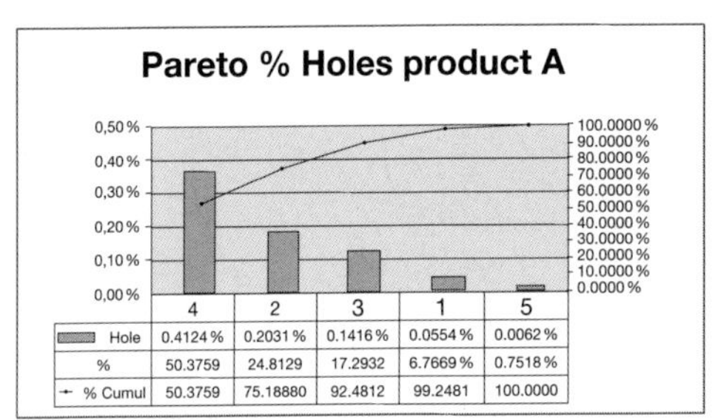

	4	2	3	1	5
Hole	0.4124 %	0.2031 %	0.1416 %	0.0554 %	0.0062 %
%	50.3759	24.8129	17.2932	6.7669 %	0.7518 %
% Cumul	50.3759	75.18880	92.4812	99.2481	100.0000

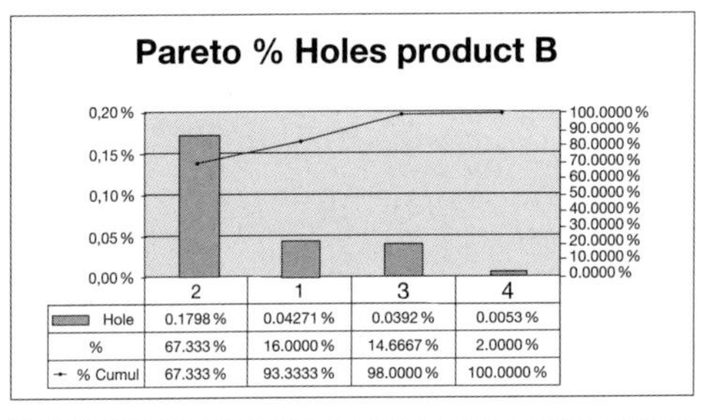

	2	1	3	4
Hole	0.1798 %	0.04271 %	0.0392 %	0.0053 %
%	67.333 %	16.0000 %	14.6667 %	2.0000 %
% Cumul	67.333 %	93.3333 %	98.0000 %	100.0000 %

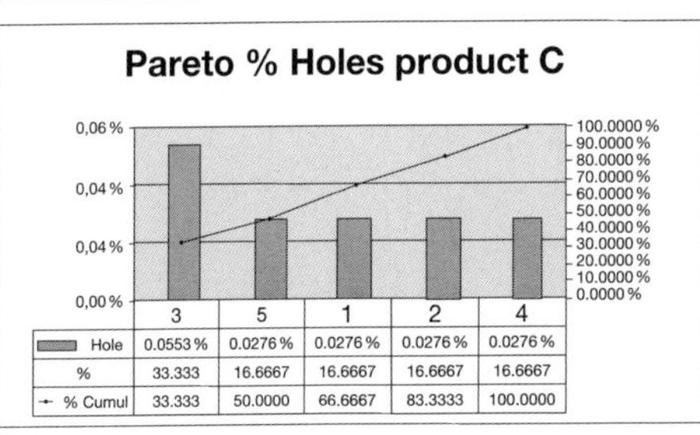

	3	5	1	2	4
Hole	0.0553 %	0.0276 %	0.0276 %	0.0276 %	0.0276 %
%	33.333	16.6667	16.6667	16.6667	16.6667
% Cumul	33.333	50.0000	66.6667	83.3333	100.0000

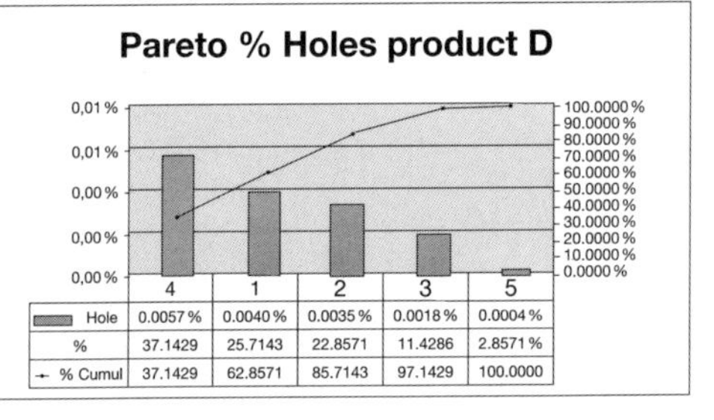

	4	1	2	3	5
Hole	0.0057 %	0.0040 %	0.0035 %	0.0018 %	0.0004 %
%	37.1429	25.7143	22.8571	11.4286	2.8571 %
% Cumul	37.1429	62.8571	85.7143	97.1429	100.0000

Figure 48: Pareto charts.

manufacturing process that was already investigated during the first benchmarking (when the cam shaft diagram of the CP line and the DS line were compared, see Figure 49) and proved to be highly stable.

So at the end, the team performed two different sorts of benchmarking. First, they performed a benchmarking within different formats on the same line and secondly they performed a benchmarking between different production lines. At the end they put together the outcomes in the benchmarking form.

Figure 49 illustrates some outcomes of both benchmarking projects.

The first form provided evidence that there was a significant difference between the heating temperature of the CP and the DS manufacturing process. Further, there were differences concerning the technical design of the process. While the heating plates of the DS manufacturing process were designed based on plain plates, the CP process was based on partially fragmented plates.

The second form provided evidence that there were also significant differences within the CP process when comparing the different formats. Based on the machine parameters, there were certain trends that could be identified based on the following parameters: (a) starting point and (b) end point of the blowing process (c) blowing time and (d) the stamp speed.

Altogether the team identified 15 potentially vital root causes that were supposed to explain most of the deviation in the output parameters.

Step 3: Analysis

To fully scientifically understand the whole process based on the remaining 15 variables, it was required to set-up a Design of Experiment (DOE). DOE is an approach for effectively exploring the cause effect relationship between numerous process variables (Xs) and the output of the process performance variables. A DOE allows you to:

- ... identify the vital few sources of variation (Xs) that have the biggest impact on the results,
- ... quantify the effect of the important Xs, including their interactions,

and by that accurately predicting the process output based on certain changes among the input variables.

A DOE is usually an "analysis of variance" because it breaks up the total variation in the data column into components due to different sources. These vector components are called "signals" and "noise." There is a signal component for each controlled variation and a noise component representing variations not attributable to any of the controlled variations. By looking at the signal-to-noise ratio for a particular variation, the analysis of variance usually provides accurate answers.

Bart was aware that the 15 variables that were still remaining would add up to run 32.768 tests (2^{15} = 32.768)[21] each sacrificing around 15 minutes production time which would translate into around 130 days of producing distressed inventory, as none of the final products would have been produced based on validated conditions[22]. However, Bart and his team decided to change some of the settings to reduce the number of required experiments:

---

21 These numbers assume that the experiment is designed as a full factorial experiment based on 15 factors, each at 2 levels which would translate into 2^{15} experiments that would have to be performed; see Annex for more detailed information.

22 As the process was validated based on the certain machine parameters, all products that would have been produced under different (experimental) conditions would have to be discarded.

Line Number	Line	Quality	Depth Stamp mold depth	Temperature	Type Plates	Tilting effect
1	Product A	b	9	188	fragmented	Yes
1	Product B	a	7	184	fragmented	Yes
1	Product D	a	10	185	fragmented	Yes
1	Product C	d	3	178	fragmented	Yes
2		good		130	Full	No
3		good		130	Full	No

Formats		Quality	Blowtime	Start Blow after Stamp	Stamp before Closing	Stamp Time	Stamp Speed	Stop Stamp before Stop Blow
Line Number								
1	Product A		48	54	24	106	450	-8
1	Product B		48	54	24	106	110	-8
1	Product D		80	38	16	16	250	0
1	Product C		80	46	26	75	125	54
2		good		1231	0	55		10 to 25
3		good		516	0	55		min 10 to 0

Figure 49: The two different formats of benchmarking on the same line.

Standardize the experiment: Based on the lessons learned of the benchmarking there were certain trends that provided as much predictive power that they did not have to be integrated into the experiment. This helped to narrow down the number of variables from 15 to 9.

Perform design changes: Further, there were certain design changes that allowed Bart and his team to eliminate certain factors[23]. This helped to narrow down the number of variables from 9 to 6.

Change the statistical method: Instead of performing a full factorial experiment, Bart decided to use a half fractional experiment[24]. This helped to further half the number of required experiments from 64 experiments to 32.

With 32 runs to perform the DOE, it was now feasible to successfully conduct the required amount of experiments. By putting the output data of the DOE into Pareto charts Bart hoped to identify the vital factors significantly influencing the output variables. Figure 50 shows the Pareto plot ranking the factors and their interactions in Bart's experiment by the strength (length) of their signals.

The main factor that proved to have the highest effect was the temperature of the heating plates and the starting point of stamping process. Especially concerning the temperature there was an almost linear relationship between a higher temperature and changes in the

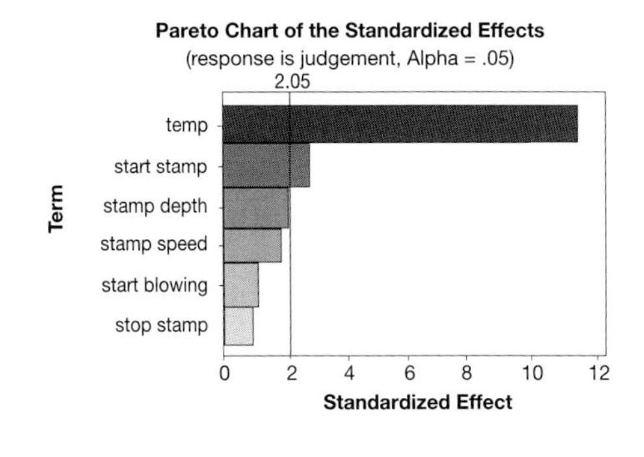

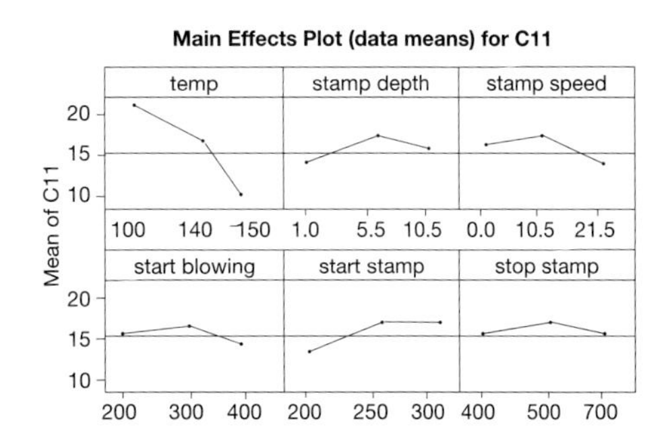

Figure 50: The Pareto ranking factors and their interactions in Bart's experiment.

23 One example was the design of the heating plate. The team was sure that the fragmented heating plates was inferior to the fully plain heating plates because the fully plain heating plates allowed for better distributing the heat on the foil.

24 The half factorial experiment is based the assumption that high order interactions (mutual interactions between three or more factors) are usually negligible as there is a diminishing return of information on higher-order interactions.

output parameters. Small changes in the temperature of the heating plates caused significant differences in the output quality and proved to be the most vital causes of deviation. However, the interaction plots showed that there are a couple of interactions between several variables. An incremental change in one parameter obviously required certain adjustments concerning other parameters at the same time.

Now Bart and his team understood why the people in the past were struggling to find the solution of the problem, even though they tried very often to reduce the temperature of the heating plates. Without adjusting other parameters at the same time, the lower temperature did not produce the desired effect. Now he could scientifically explain the interrelated relationships between the different parameters – example:

Lowering the temperature from 180°C to around 140°C in the past did not yield the desired effect as the colder foil became very stiff which in turn did not allow proper moulding anymore as the deformation time (blowing time/stamp time) was too short .

When simultaneously increasing the blowing time by a certain percentage and improving the heat exchange it now allowed to deform a colder foil while not exceeding the maximum temperature of 145°C that has proved to be the critical frontier.

As the DOE helped to accurately simulate the optimum settings of all relevant parameters simultaneously, Bart and his team could now move on the improvement phase.

Step 4: Improve

Based on the scientific understanding of the process, Bart and his team could now recommend several improvement suggestions:

1. **Suggestion: Lower the temperature**
   - Lower the heating temperature of the heating plates from 185°C to the maximum level of 145°C[25]
2. **Suggestion: Improve the heat exchange by performing design changes at the heating plates**
   - Increase the length of the heating plates by 35%-60% (depending on the type of product)
   - Change the design of the heating plates from a fractional plate to a full plate
3. **Suggestion: Adjust the control parameters of the cam shaft**
   - Increase the blowing time of the blowing cam
   - Start the stamping process earlier
4. **Suggestion: Optimize mould design**
   - Change the mould design by optimizing the air vents to make sure that:
     - air (which is caught between the foil and the mould) can escape quicker out of the mould during the deforming
     - air can enter the mould when the mould is opening in order to prevent a vacuum underneath the formed trays which damages the trays

25 Remark: Extra advantage of lowering the temperature is that the start up heating time (which differs from normal operating conditions) becomes less critical.

When the team presented the recommendations for improving the CP manufacturing process, there was no big discussion about implementing all of them. Each improvement suggestion was based on clear facts and none of the suggestions would have yielded any sustainable improvement without considering the interrelated effects between the several factors.

After implementing the recommended solutions, Bart and his team realized remarkable improvements. The CP tray forming process today runs 100% defect free as the defect rate has decreased from 400 ppm to 0 ppm and is now even below the targeted 6-Sigma level. As a result the number of disruptions has declined significantly and there is hardly any time wasted on investigations anymore.

As the solutions could be extrapolated to other formats, all formats today run without holes or deformation. However, there are further benefits that could be reaped. As the process is now well understood, variation in foil quality is today far less critical than it used to be and foil which used to be placed in quarantine can now be processed without problems. Furthermore, the sound scientific understanding about the process helped Bart and his team to significantly reduce the change over time, as the number of format parts could be minimized and the change over today requires far less fine tuning as it is not based on the traditional "trial and error" approach. The sound understanding of the process also has helped to become far less dependent on the line speed than in the past. As a result the OEE of the equipment has increased significantly.

Step 5: Control

Based on the project findings and the lessons learned out of it, Bart and his team implemented some projects to spread the knowledge throughout the company and to control the robustness of the CP manufacturing process in the future.

All findings with regard to operational issues were documented in the expert system of the packaging department that gathers all operational information to support the machine tenders in case of trouble shooting or other normal operational problems. A further knowledge sharing tool that supports the maintenance people during their maintenance tasks was also updated, so that the experiences of the project can now be shared with other technical support departments in the organization. Further, the PTS department (Production & Technical Support department) can now capitalize on those experiences when evaluating the acquisition of new machines.

Accurately documenting information helps to make information available for everybody, however it does not help to change the way how people do their daily work and approach their daily problems. Consequently, training has become the most vital part to spread the knowledge throughout the company. While it is important that the technical information about optimizing the CP manufacturing is accessible for everybody, it is even more important to change the way that people approach their daily problems. Bart realized that as soon as people have learned to tackle problems based on the structured step by step problem solving approach of the 6-Sigma concept, the biggest benefits will be those reaped in the future rather than today.

Annex: About the 6-Sigma Concepts

The 6-Sigma program was first applied by Motorola in the mid-1980s. A lack of customer orientation and considerable problems in the quality and reliability of Motorola's products led the then CEO to a reorientation of the company. Being faced at this time with the upcoming Japanese manufacturers, a benchmarking tour in Japan showed the managers of Motorola the new direction: all operations – manufacturing, service, administration, and sales – have to be focused on total customer satisfaction. From this point of view the 6-Sigma program then was not a radical innovation compared to the popular Japanese Total Quality Management (TQM) approach. What distinguished 6-Sigma was the strong orientation on the statistical measure Sigma, standing for standard deviation. Standard deviation is a statistical way to describe how much variation exists in a set of data, a group of items, or a process. The essence of 6-Sigma is to reduce this variability (see Figure 51). Based on the customer requirements and expectations Sigma is an indicator to what extent quality is reached, thus a measure of quality. 6-Sigma implies the occurrence of defects at a rate of 3.4 defects per million opportunities (DPMO). By contrast sigma levels of three, four, and five produce DPMO rates of 66,807, 6,210, and 233. The concept of opportunities-for-error was developed to account for differing complexities. An opportunity-for-error is something that must be performed correctly in order to deliver conforming product or service.

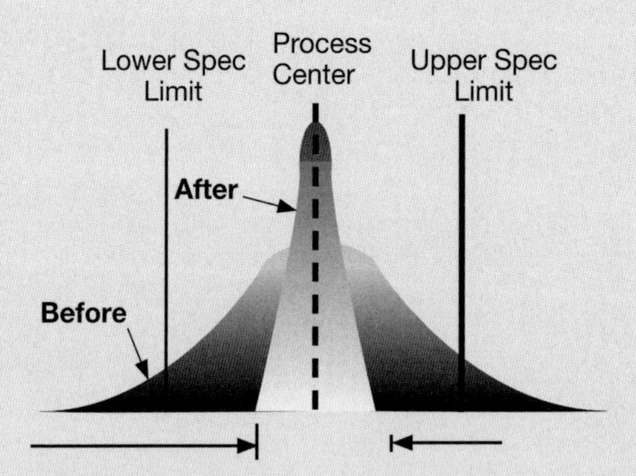

Figure 51: Principle of 6-Sigma.

Less variation provides greater predictability in the process, less waste and rework, which lowers costs, and products and services that perform better and last longer and increases customers' satisfaction. The real message of 6-Sigma goes beyond statistics. 6-Sigma is a total management commitment and philosophy of excellence, customer focus, process improvement, and the rule of measurement rather than *gut feel.*

A new noteworthy approach of 6-Sigma is the clear structuring of the quality improvement process. DMAIC (Define, Measure, Analyze, Improve, Control) is the central project management process of 6-Sigma. Each step includes specific methods, most of them adopted from the TQM approach. Moreover, DMAIC is not a linear process but an iterative one.

A further new notion of 6-Sigma are the terms Black and Green Belt, a hierarchical concept within the organization structure. The Black Belt is a full-time person dedicated to tackling critical change opportunities and driving them to achieve results. The Black Belt leads, inspires, manages, delegates, and coaches colleagues and becomes almost expert in tools for assessing problems and fixing or designing processes and products. Furthermore, the Black Belt usually works alongside a team assigned to a specific 6-Sigma project. He/she is primarily responsible for getting the team started, building their confidence, observing and participating in training and keeping the project moving to successful results. In most organizations, a Master Black Belt additionally serves as a coach and mentor or consultant to Black Belts working on a variety of projects. A Green Belt, on the other hand, is someone trained in 6-Sigma skills, often to the same level as a Black Belt. But the Green Belt still is working on an operational level, and serves either a team member or a part-time 6-Sigma team leader. Today, there are different approaches concerning the Belt concept. It is usually customized to the specific structures of a company.

Terms and tools

Cause-and-Effect Diagram (C&E)

A Cause-and-Effect (C&E) diagram is a visual tool used to logically organize possible causes for a specific problem or effect by graphically displaying them in increasing detail. It classifies the various causes thought to affect the results of work, indicating with arrows the cause-and-effect relationship among them. Moreover it helps to identify root causes and ensures common understanding of the causes.

Critical to Quality (CTQ)

Critical to Quality (CTQ) describes an element of a process or practice which has a direct impact on its perceived quality. CTQ's are the key measurable characteristics of a product or process whose performance standards or specification limits must be met in order to satisfy the customer. They align improvement or design efforts with customer requirements. CTQ's may include the upper and lower specification limits or any other factors related to the product or service.

Design of Experiments (DOE)

This is an approach for effectively and efficiently exploring the C&E relationship between numerous process variables (Xs) and the output or process performance variable (Y). What's unique about DOE is the opportunity it gives you to plan and control the variables using an experiment, as opposed to just gathering and observing "real-world" events in the manner known as "empirical observation."

Pareto

The Pareto principle states that 80% of the impact of the problem will show up in 20% of the causes. Pareto diagrams are specialized bar graphs that can be used to show the relative frequency of events such as bad products, repairs, defects, claims, failures, or accidents. A Pareto diagram presents information in descending order, from the largest category to the smallest. Thus, the diagrams are used to prioritize continuous improvement projects and team activities.

SIPOC

SIPOC is an acronym for Supplier, Input, Process, Output, and Customer. SIPOC is used in the define phase of DMAIC and is often a preferred method for diagramming major business processes and identifying possible measures. It helps to define the boundaries and critical elements of a process without getting into so much detail that the big picture is lost.

Voice of the Customer (VOC)

The "Voice of the Customer" (VOC) is a process used to capture and describe customers' needs and their perception of the product or service (internal or external). Further it is applied to provide the customers with the best in class service or product quality. VOC data e.g. helps to decide what products and services are offered, to identify critical features and specification for those products and services and identify key drivers of customer satisfaction.

IV.5 Lean Compliance: Implementing Just-in-Time (JIT) in a Regulated Environment

Bruce Ramsay

This article looks at what life science companies can do to ensure that compliance activities do not become a bottleneck when production constraints are released.

Today's Context

The race to get more new drugs to market more quickly continues. This race is a team event and all areas of a pharmaceutical company's business must be in the team – to discover more, prove more, get more NDAs (New Drug Applications), create a larger market and get the product flowing reliably into the marketplace in the shortest possible time.

The reorganization of businesses in response to change (increased regulatory intervention, an increase in availability to end-users and regulatory requirements creating pressure to conform to new systems), and in anticipation of change presents the opportunity to create the right processes with the right performance. As the need for speed has evolved, the application of relevant systems and web-based solutions to reduce the time-to-market has become increasingly business critical. This is significant to all pharmaceutical manufacturing processes, given the volume of data involved, the need for current and accurate information and the imperative of data security.

When a world-leading ethical pharmaceutical company looked at the output of one of its factories, alarm bells began to ring. The demand for the product had been established and it was way ahead of the factory's apparent capacity. But a 30% shortfall between achievable output and planned levels of production appeared to be a serious problem that could rapidly become critical. So what are the projected consequences? The answer is possibly, a failure to deliver an important drug and a multi-million dollar loss in potential sales. It was time for a serious re-appraisal of the factory's processes and procedures.

Time for a change

The output of the factory's (fictional) product, Teypro had risen steadily during the 1990's, from 82 output units (ou) in 1993 to 380 in 1997. But in recent years the growth had reached a plateau at only 400ou against a planned 490ou – the 30% shortfall that the company had identified. The plant seemed to have reached capacity. It was clear that the process of continual marginal improvement had gone as far as it could – something more central had to change and some of that change had to happen swiftly. The root of the problem had to be identified. Could a single major cause be identified, or was the shortfall the cumulative result of many individually small inefficiencies and mismatches in departmental practice?

Removing the Constraints – Quality Control and Efficient Manufacture Capacity

An analysis of the processes throughout the plant soon showed that the rate-limiting step was not manufacturing, but the activities of Quality Control (QC), Quality Assurance (QA) and batch documentation. This is not a great surprise in the ethical pharmaceutical/life science business, with its strong emphasis on quality and reliability. What was surprising, however, was the extent of the imbalance.

Of a total Teypro production lead time of 250 days, a total of 237 days – 90% – were taken up in QC and QA (Figure 52). Seven QC steps interlaced the short production stages, and regularly failed to deliver cleared product to the line as and when it was required. Where these processes were bottlenecks to the overall capacity there was an obvious major knock-on effect. Lack of QC capacity had become a serious constraint on potential production capacity gained from manufacturing improvements. Substantial amount of overtime was already being worked in many of the QC specialities and QC lead time was set to continue growing as production capacity rose.

Instead of promoting the efficient manufacture (EM) of a maximum quality product, apparent under-capacity in QC was becoming a threatening thrombosis in the arteries of production. So the focus had to be on the QC domain.

It was not a question of increasing QC capacity. An analysis of QC and EM activities showed, that Value Adding (VA) time – critical QC & EM activities that added value and were required for the prescribed tests – accounted for less than 40% of the time. Non-Value Adding (NVA) time – wasted activity that added no value to the product, such as manual duplication of forms and unnecessary movement of materials and documents between work areas – was 30%. Removing these steps, without jeopardising the quality of the tests, would reduce workload by up to 21%.

Further detailed investigation of the VA steps showed that the *number* of individual QC and EM tests per ou of Teypro could be reduced without compromising the process – in fact, by more than 25%. Many of these tests had been introduced to address a specific EM excursion or problem. However once these had been resolved the tests had not been removed but left in place resulting in an endlessly growing burden to the operation for no value. Not only were many of these tests sent as non value adding, many other VA assays where seen to be

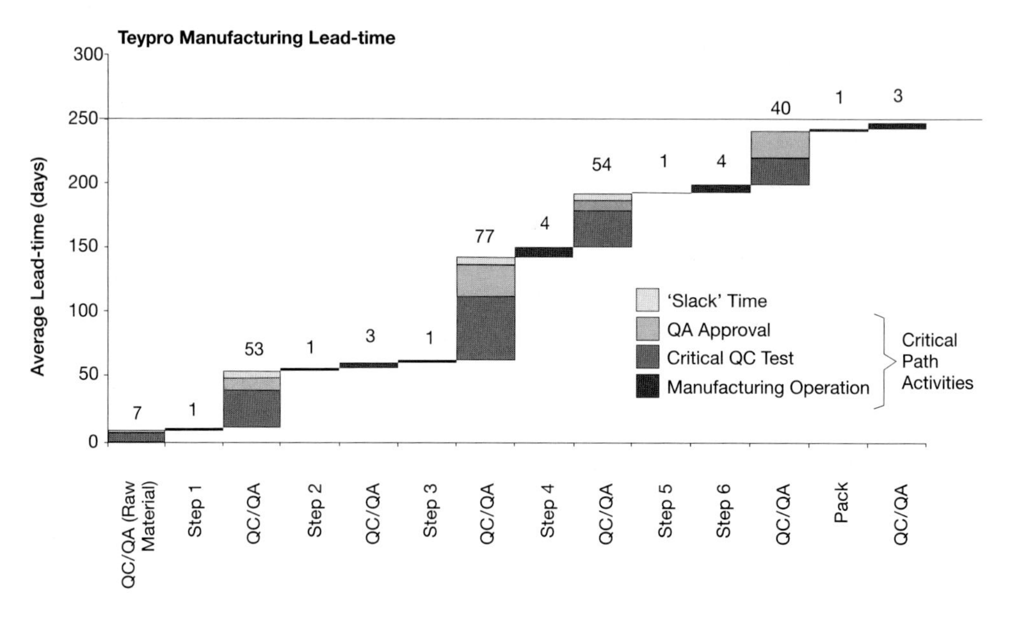

Figure 52: The current critical path activities account for 90% of the lead time.

ineffective thus a program to establish assays that gave better control and feedback to the operations and QC was initiated. Beyond this removing the unnecessary tests and assays provided an extra 12% of processing time. By reducing *both* the number of assays *and* the workload associated with each one, the business had the opportunity to increase capacity in the critical QC area by more than 30%, with the same level of resources.

Removing the Constraints – Batch Records

QC and EM capacity were not the only reason for the long lead time or the apparent capacity constraints. Production documentation was taking an average of 14 days to be processed and reach QA after the completion of each of the manufacturing operations. When the batch documentation was reviewed it was discovered that an average batch record required 10,000 data entries, of which 45% were double and triple checks not required by regulatory authorities. In addition the document was difficult to understand, despite being technically correct, as it had not been made foolproof for the operators. This in turn lead to mistakes being made, entries being missed or incorrectly entered, leading in turn to lengthy investigations by QA further extending the lead time and reducing the predictability of release. This sounds a terrible situation, but it is not atypical of life sciences operations where the tendency is for compliance requirements to be imposed upon operations without adequate consideration for the effectiveness of the method or the implications on the overall process flow. As an example in a medical device company batch record entries were found to be similarly excessive yet with some reengineering were reduced by a massive 86% for an average document.

So having recognized this problem the solution was to understand the documentation process and then to reengineer it in holistic fashion. This involved mapping the process with the users so that they could understand the NVA, and then building documentation such that built-in mechanisms made date-entry foolproof and avoided the need for double checks.

Though such detailed improvements were helpful they would not directly address the lead-time issue and still left the 'Compliance tail' wagging the 'Production dog'. The benefits were likely to decay as production capacity was released, signaling a re-emergence of the original problem before very long. A step change was needed – literally.

Simple Planning for a Simple Process

The greatest opportunity for improvement was associated with the manufacturing process itself which had a naturally smooth workflow producing a small range of very similar products in a highly regular and predictable, constantly repeated cycle that didn't and could not vary. This was the drumbeat to which all ancillary processes had to march to. The problem was that each was marching to its own, different drum.

The result? An unavoidable bottleneck in the manufacturing critical path was exacerbated by unpredictable output from QC – output was out of step with the production line. And QA, also out of step, did not clear finished Teypro so that it could be shipped out as soon as it was ready.

As a solution to their problems the business had considered introducing Advanced Planning Software (APS) to manage the apparent complexity. However, the complexity was only in the *technicalities* of production and not the planning. What was required was not a lengthy and expensive Information Technology (IT) implementation, but an elegantly simple solution to match the low-product-range, single production line environment.

The role of the stock

The chosen approach was to introduce carefully profiled stocks of material between each step. The planned levels of 'cleared' material would be based upon the volume, release cycle time, variability in both the test time and demand through the subsequent production processes. The role of the stock, and the planning process, was to ensure that there was always 'cleared' stock in front of each process – particularly the bottleneck processes – but the *minimum* level required. Once the pull-replenishment system was in place, the support departments, including QA and QC, could be integrated into the overall business output (Figure 53).

The first step was to create QC laboratory facilities with capacity balanced to the demands of production based around the *Takt* time (te = available production time divided by production volume). If the plant, operating for 24 hours, requires 80 tests to be done, and the lab works for 8 hours, then the latter must be designed to process 10 tests per hour (plus capacity buffer). Based on the Takt time, the laboratories were re-designed around the concept of a manufacturing cell (Figure 54).

Within these laboratory 'cells' the planning and prioritizing was matched to the demands of the plant. The samples for test would arrive in the lab (directly from the plant, many times a day) and be booked-in on a simple visual priority board. Different tests would have different priorities. The lab technicians would work on a simple first-in-first-out (FIFO) principle, always taking the next sample from the longest queue. Assuming the laboratory capacity is well-designed and linked to plant demands then the tests would flow easily. Simple prioritization rules linked to the inventory levels in the plant would over-ride the FIFO principle on an exception basis. No complex and expensive APS was required – just a well designed process and simple controls.

By simplifying the test process, and reducing the number required, to increase QC capacity and introducing a simple but well balanced pull-replenishment planning process the business is able to increase capacity and reduce throughput lead-times from over 250 days to approximately 160.

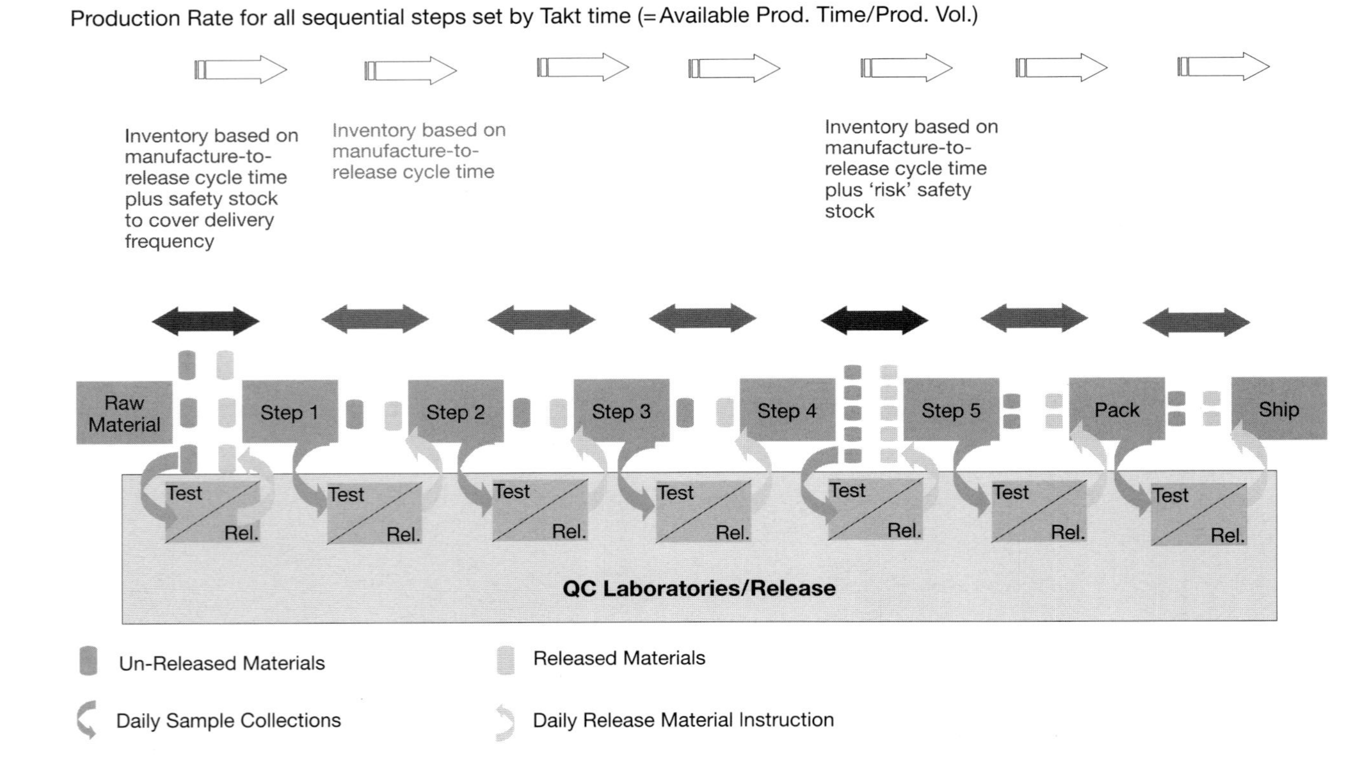

Figure 53: Introducing inventory between steps and pull – replenishment planning.

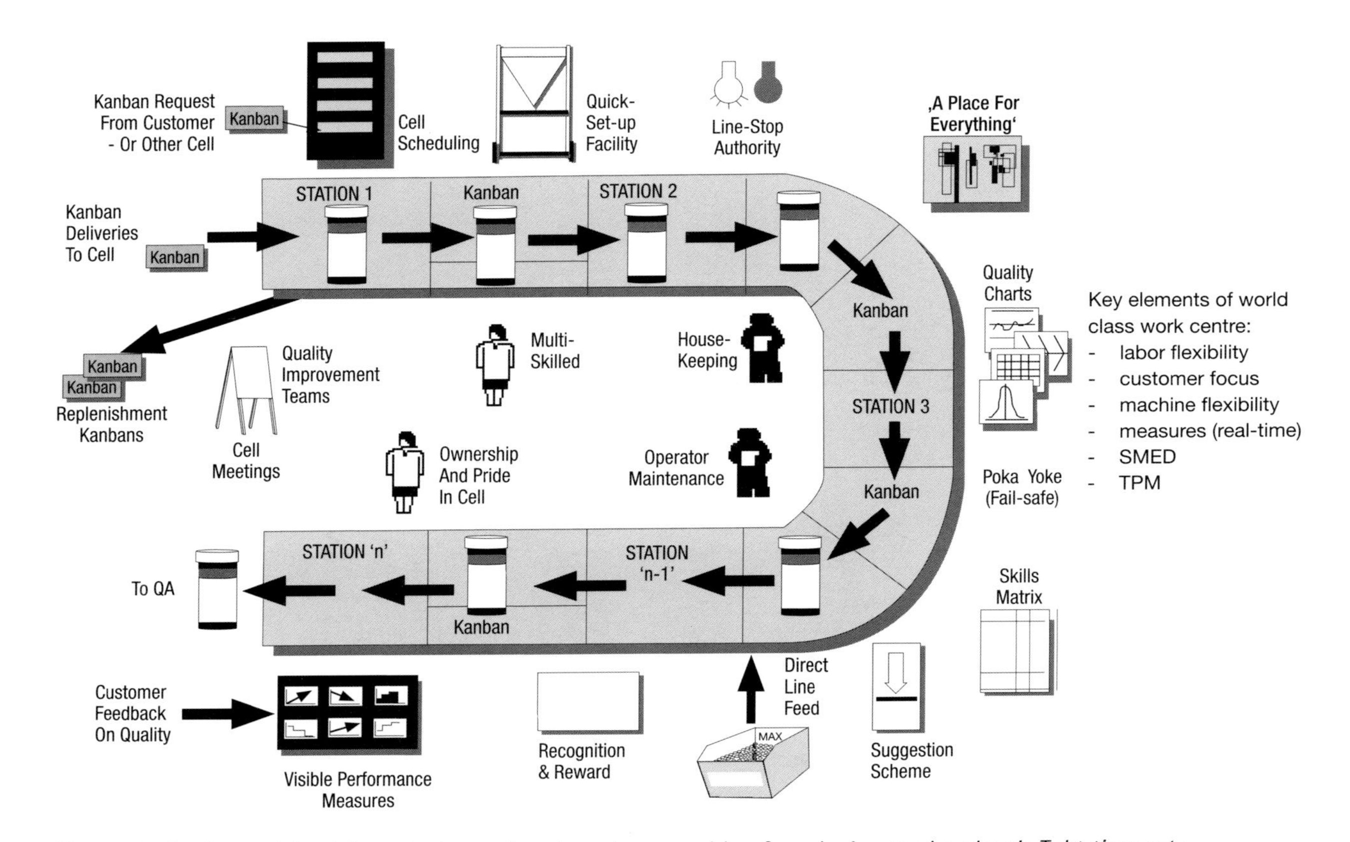

Figure 54: Laying out the labs as balanced work centers capable of producing to the plant's Takt time rate.

Eliminating the QA Lead Time

The changes described above relate only to production and QC activities. After the completion of the assays, and batch records the paperwork passes through QA for approval to proceed to the next stage. Many of these assays are critical for final release, but not for production to proceed where there is a very high track record of complying with control limits. By simply allowing a *few* of the longer critical-path assays to be passed for production *prior* to QA approval, overall lead-times could be further reduced. The approvals could still be completed within the overall lead-times, which could fall a further 30% to approximately 115 days.

Installing parallel operation

The reluctance to allow material to proceed to subsequent production stages was based upon uncertain outputs from a newly developed process. As control of the process improves, it becomes possible to allow material to proceed when just a small selection of the assays are complete. Clearly all assays will be completed and QA approved before the batch is released to the market. In fact, full approval will be maintained before the material passes into the critical bottleneck process – the business cannot risk production time on 'failed' batches. By moving towards this fast track operation the business has the opportunity to further reduce overall lead-times down to less than 80 days.

The way forward

The proposal was re-engineering QC, batch records and QA into a system, running in parallel with Production wherever it can could reduce a static and excessive 250 day Teypro production lead time by 176 days – a reduction of 70%.

The key to the change was in understanding the process and challenging the fundamental principles on which it is based. In the pharmaceutical industry the solutions to complex problems are often as complex as the problems themselves. The technology in this industry should be focused on the critical, direct, value adding steps in the production process. All support activities should be simplified as far as possible. Look for the elegant approach that allows a step change in performance in a short period of time for minimal levels of investment.

The historically high margins in the industry have allowed this 'expensive' approach in the past. As the market changes, the industry will have to look more and more to other industries for solutions to its business problems. If computers and cars can be manufactured from thousands of components in minutes, why does it take months to produce basic pharmaceutical products?

IV.6 The Role of Management Quality in the Context of Operational Excellence

Christoph H. Loch and Stephen E. Chick

Many examples of management quality and excellent manufacturing are reported in Loch et al. (2003) Most come from the automotive, electronics, and machinery sectors. We are, therefore, sometimes told that management quality does not apply to other sectors in the same way because competition in these three sectors is "special" (pharmaceutical plants have rarely participated in this cross-industry benchmarking opportunity). We now give an account from a basic, and often viewed as unsophisticated industry. RDME, a small manganese ore-to-iron converter in Dunkerque, France, applied management quality with great success (and was an IEA prize winner in 2002). They demonstrate that *any* plant can apply management quality, if the management team is decisive and willing to invest the effort.

Background

In 1999, CVRD, the largest Brazilian iron ore company purchased 100% of a troubled ferromanganese plant located in Grande-Synthe, near Dunkerque, France, to establish RDME. The plant, which contains the largest ferromanganese furnace in the world, was built by the French firm Usinor in the early 1990s. The plant had been losing money, and the plant facility and surroundings had been degraded. Price competition had taken a significant toll on the operation.

Manganese (Mn) is critical for steel production; manganese steel is used in cars, large household appliances and many other daily goods. Manganese is a greyish metal with properties similar to iron, occurs in a number of minerals, and is exploitable through rocks and fines. Approximately 90% of the worlds demand for Mn ore ultimately is used by the steel industry. Of that, approximately 84% is used in alloys. Fines must be processed by sintering before being processed in a furnace.

The furnace at Grande-Synthe produces 120,000-140,000 tons per year of ferromanganese alloys. Four times per day, 100 tons of liquid ferromanganese alloys pour from the base of the furnace. After cooling, the ferromanganese is fractured into pieces before shipping via truck or train to clients. In addition to alloys, rich slag is skimmed off the ferromanganese alloys that flow from the furnace. In addition to FeMn alloys and slag, the furnace also releases gases, which are cleaned and burned. The average holding time of materials in RDME's furnace is 16 hours.

Management Quality: Changing Processes and Management Methods

Upon arrival at the plant in 1999, the new CEO of RDME Luis Carlos Nepomuceno and his Industrial Director were faced with a rundown plant, a de-motivated workforce, and financial troubles during the same time they intensively learned the French language. The plant had received ISO 9002 certification in 1996, but processes in general were not operated in a standardized fashion, and there were a number of environmental concerns to address. These issues were tackled immediately with measures aligned with the firms priorities for technological investment; training of personnel; action for cleanliness, the environment, and safety; and process standardization.

But the management team also put a clear expansion strategy in place and began to execute it, sometimes opportunistically exploiting opportunities as they presented themselves. The strategy formulation both ran parallel to and guided operational improvements.

Strategy

Manganese and ferromanganese alloys are commodity products – beyond the chemical composition, there is simply nothing there that distinguishes one producer from the other. However, RDME has successfully managed to acquire a reputation for reliability – they deliver consistent and reliable product quality, and they deliver quickly and on time.

Quick delivery is related to RDME's location in the centre of industrial Europe. However, RDME has worked hard to move from arms length, spot market type of interactions with customers to longer-term relationships, for example, through ongoing operational relationships between RDME and the customer directly. Part of the offering is a logistics service that allows RDME to deliver product just-in-time to the customer's steel plant. No competitor offers this type of service.

Longer term relationships offer a win-win situation to sides, helping RDME to understand what the customers and need and flexibly adapting the product mix and shipping conditions, and protecting the customers from short term price swings. As a result, RDME won the large UK steel company Corus as a customer (who had never worked with CVRD before), and also expanded its customer base into Spain, Italy, and Eastern Europe.

The strategy called for aggressive expansion not only to new customers, but also to new products and markets. New markets were opened by the acquisition of a furnace in the small town Mo I Rana in Northern Norway, on the Arctic Circle. The smelter was bankrupt and about to be closed down; only a core team of 20 people was still there, the other 60 had been let go, and the end for those 20 was also in sight. The acquisition required a conversion from chrome production, and was an opportunity not seized by competitors. With help from the Norwegian community, the acquisition was cheap, and it enabled RDME to expand in Europe as well as in the US market.

The second business expansion went on line in 2004. RDME constructed a calcium-silicon (CaSi) cored wire facility. Cored wire refers to a hollow wire that is produced from a steel band that is mechanically coiled (bent) around crystallized powder such as manganese silicon (MnSi) and other compositions. This facility rounded out the bundle of services and flexible offerings that strengthened RDME's long-term value proposition to its customers.

Improvements in Technology and Processes

Environmental and safety improvement initiatives included changes to the physical infrastructure, recycling and worker safety programs, and ISO14001 certification.

Quality function deployment (QFD) and the 5S concepts were deployed in a form customized to local conditions (the "5 actes" in RDME's terminology). Most significantly, the 5S concepts were not only applied to workstations, but to the entire facility. Environmental efforts included cleaning up messy fines, and the refurbishing of the exterior and interior of buildings. The short paved road leading from the main offices to the furnace and sinter plant "used to be a dusty or muddy field worn from heavy vehicles" that was not clean for plant visits, but "now allows for clean, safe access to the facilities."

RDME also invested in new technologies at a pace of EUR 2-4 million per year. For example, SAP R3 software was implemented to standardize procurement. The control system (hardware and software) was repeatedly upgraded, to make the furnace the most automated of its kind in the world today (Figure 55). Two operators per shift (three eight-hour shifts) are sufficient

Figure 55: Inside the IT-Cockpit: One person a time is able to monitor and control all the operations.

to monitor and control operations 24 hours per day. The furnace was revamped and relined in the Spring of 2004 a major upgrade was completed that took 3 months. As a result, its uptime is expected to go above 99%. The cooling system was upgraded, and an improved off-gas washing system installed, which reduced emissions and improved efficiency simultaneously.

The improvements included investments in safety; for example, several certifications were achieved (ISO 9001 version 2000, OHSAS 18001), which included a number of procedure changes. As a result, the plant has worked over 2000 days without a single accident. During the furnace relining, 140 people from 40 companies worked for 75000 hours without a serious accident. The 5S programs helped lead to ISO14001 Environmental certification in September 2001, a first for a ferro alloy furnace, followed by the UJC Environmental prize in November 2001.

Participation

Engineering improvements relied significantly on employee participation at all levels. Ideas from suggestion boxes chosen for implementation were moved forward with significant direction from the suggestor, usually the person responsible for the process. Ideas from suggestion boxes that were not chosen for study involved management describing why the idea would not be pursued with the employee that suggested it.

Improvement projects ebb and flow; but in the long run average-out to an acceptable level. The engineering manager estimates that every employee spends about 30 minutes per day, representing about 6% of work time, on improvement activities that are non-productive in the very short term. Although the big improvements stem from engineering-driven changes, the continuous improvements efforts by all employees do contribute significantly, perhaps around 30%, to the overall productivity progress. This is remarkable – again half as many improvements come from many operator ideas as from big engineering improvements.

Training and Development

Employees were offered technical training, and language courses. Exchange programs were set up for visits between CVRD in Brazil and RDME in France lasting a week, 3 months or a year. A strong mentorship program linked employees to others to improve process knowledge and workforce renewal. A results-participation scheme provided reinforced the motivation for the workforce.

Training (9 days per employee and year in Grande-Synthe, corresponding to 8% of total salary costs, which is high in comparison to other companies across industries) includes on the job training, job rotation, visits to Brazil (for managers and high-level technicians), as well as specialized technical training courses. As the HR manager comments, "We were 'franco-français', but now we have a more international outlook. For example, 25% of our people have taken a course in English or Portuguese."

Communication

The new style of communication was characterized by Mr. Nepomuceno as requiring "Big ears and a small mouth". By 2001, office space was significantly reorganized, so that many walls were removed. The few offices with walls maintained an "open door" policy, which was perceived to be key to resolving problems before they became crises. Internal newsletters and magazines were established.

This was further extended and made extremely visible with the construction of a new administration building: offices were completely abandoned; now, everyone sits in an open space, not even separated by cubicle walls, including top management. Everyone can see everyone else all the time. "This was difficult, as it does not correspond to traditional French management culture. But people have accepted it, and now it feels good because we can very easily communicate with one another."

Personnel Policies: People at the Centre

The emphasis on teamwork, and the recognition of the contribution of all employees, is pervasive and consistent; it has become part of the company culture. It starts at the top when Luis Carlos Nepomuceno states that "Good motivated people are the way to success"; and lives the motto in his behavior. Moreover, it continues when the engineering manager, Marcelo Rocha, goes to talk to the control operators at the furnace. The atmosphere is one of pride, where everyone is willing to take an extra step on their own initiative.

In addition to the further evolution of culture, new official reward schemes are being introduced. For example, a profit sharing ("intéressement") based on company results, combined with group-based and individual bonuses. In addition, every employee is assigned a "Godfather", a more senior mentor who helps him or her in career planning. Also, everyone has a yearly performance review and goal setting conversation with his/her superior. And employees have the possibility of progressing in their career if they so desire – for example, the CFO started as a purchasing clerk. HR has databases with career status, development needs and succession planning for every employee.

In this atmosphere, the collaboration with the unions has become constructive and collaborative (although not without challenges). Marcelo Rocha comments, "Before I came here, I did not believe that it was possible to be open and listen to the workers, undertake measures to the environment, AND be highly productive, all at the same time. The key is motivated people – it IS possible to constructively work with people here. At home, people do not have the mindset to change. This is one of the main lessons I will take home with me."

The good working atmosphere was rewarded with external recognition in December 2004. RDME was awarded 11th rank in the journal *Management* competition of the "Best Places to Work" in France. Prizes 1 to 3 as the most attractive employer went to Johnson, Microsoft and Pepsi. RDME was ranked ahead of well-known companies such as Deloitte, Novartis, Computer Associates, Auchan and Bosch. This is a spectacular success for a small subsidiary of a Latin American company in an industry that is often perceived as dirty and the opposite of *sexy*. It attests how far the company has come in motivating employees with an attractive work environment. The annual turnover rate of employees remained at 1% in 2004.

Lessons from RDME

RDME's clear strategy of growth in Europe, part of the internationalization strategy of CVRD, has taken advantage of market opportunities. They gained competitive advantage through consistent product quality, the reliability of deliveries, and productivity. Location also played a role both because of port access for the delivery of raw materials, but also for distribution to customers.

The strategy combines an overall vision with flexible execution that opportunistically exploits opportunities as they present themselves. Examples include innovations in the sinterization process to convert unused stockpiles of fines into usable raw materials for sinter and alloys. The expansion into Norway allowed entry into the US market, circumventing an embargo of Latin America imports. Finally, the expansion into cored wire was achieved with a subsidy plus bank loans, to obtain a self-financing operation that provides an additional service to their clients.

The operations strategy for achieving these gains put people at the center. Luis Carlow Nepomuceno explains, "Good people lead to a better bottom line. Openness and training lead to motivation which leads to continuous improvement. Improvement leads to a better bottom line, growth, and job satisfaction. High-quality automation adds to productivity improvement." Luis and the rest of the management consistently sought win-win situations in the relationships with all stakeholders: customers, employees, unions, suppliers and the community.

For a plant in a basic materials industry that is flat overall, the results are impressive. Employment was doubled from 97 to 197 in Europe including Norway), revenues have almost tripled in 6 years, and profitability has become attractive. Part of the revenue increase comes from recent steel price increases, but also from productivity (e.g., 25% in the furnace, almost double in the sinter plant) and winning new customers and markets.

Discussion and implications

Our results confirm that TQM practices, implemented as a series of "programs," do not necessarily provide competitive advantage. However, we have argued with our concept of management quality that one does not need to retreat to intangibles such as "culture" and "openness" (Powell 1995) in order to understand manufacturing excellence. Our results point to a more operational and actionable path to competitive advantage.

1. Management quality: mobilize the capabilities of all employees

TQM practices must be elevated from the status of shop floor tools to that of a broad set of management practices, which we refer to as *management quality*. Management quality must be applied across the key business processes (strategy deployment, supply chain, product/process development) in the plant and at the interfaces to the rest of the organization.

Management Quality combines knowledge (process mastery and measurement) with a mobilization of the employees. As one plant manager put it, "It is our job to develop and tap into the intelligence of our employees." Plant management gives knowledge, and points the direction, but the initiatives come from the shop floor (participation). This is what unleashes improvement. *Everyone* participates and contributes (at least a large majority of employees – experience suggests that almost always 5-10% of basic operators cannot be mobilized).

2. Improvement never stops

Our results, unlike those of previous studies, suggest that process improvement is not a TQM program to be implemented alongside others, but an *outcome* resulting from the dynamics of decentralization, strategic vision, employee initiatives, and understanding of the process drivers. Manufacturing management quality does not lead *directly* to business performance, but *through an improvement track record.*

In this context, we sometimes hear from less successful plants, or from skeptics, the objection that improvement *must*, at some point, run into a limit, or into decreasing returns. "When your quality is already at 50 ppm, it becomes harder to improve!" This is a self-defeating fallacy that the winning plants impressively refute. They never stop improving. When one measure (such as quality) is exhausted, they attack other measures: be it cost, speed, product quality, or customer service and satisfaction. There are always ways to improve in ways that are meaningful to the customer. Improvement, in the best plants, becomes a way of life, and a way to never become complacent. The operators do not sigh, "We've done improvement program X, and now they want us to change AGAIN!", but they accept that standing still means falling behind. The improvement mindset is at the heart of excellent management.

3. Systemic practices

The six dimensions of manufacturing management quality (delegation, integration, communication, participation, employee development, and measurement) are *systemic*; that is, their full benefit is only felt if they are applied consistently together. This finding is consistent with and extends a previous observation: Lieberman and Demeester (1999) found that inventory reductions in the Japanese automotive industry drove about 10% of labor productivity improvements between 1965 and 1991; the remaining improvements had to come from a combination of other measures. Our study outlines what this combination of measures is and how they interact to support one another.

The system character of management quality represents *protection from imitation*, as the majority of the six dimensions must be implemented before benefits accrue, which requires organizational vision and stamina. The difficulty of implementing the system of practices is illustrated by the fact that no plant was able to execute all dimensions at once. Moreover, it is possible to do "too much of a good thing" – too much communication may cause information overload, and thus hinder improvement. Some dimensions also present the manager with trade-offs: close integration of the plant with new product introduction causes disruption (i.e., lower improvement rates) in the short term, but it helps the improvement of the product introduction process, and thus future plant growth.

Indeed, discussions with plant managers at the IEA plants we visited provide consistent anecdotal evidence that it takes 3-4 years of persistent effort to arrive at a self-reinforcing level of management quality. Our observations at the plants visited also indicate that none of them simply took TQM tools (such as SPC or 5S) "off the shelf", rather they adapted them to local "ways of doing things" and to particular process demands in the plant. Speeding up the implementation of management quality requires:

- Getting the manufacturing strategy aligned with the business
- Getting the structure of the basic business processes right

- Installing a powerful measurement system for understanding quality and productivity drivers
- Cascading down the strategy to the shop floor, communicating the vision, and being consistent and trustworthy to establish trust
- Reaping the first benefits to establish momentum
- Further communicating and being consistent – trust is hard-won and easily lost.

4. Learn from others

The comparison of different sectors points to the *limit of protection from imitation:* the automotive and electronics industries are at present leading in the application of management quality in the factory, and high manufacturing management quality is essential in order to gain high improvement rates and plant growth. We believe this reflects the higher *competitive pressures and the diffusion of best practice* (Stalk Jr. and Webber 1993; Womack et al. 1990). For factories in less advanced industries, this means that it is worthwhile looking over industry boundaries and to learn from others, even if the technology and detailed processes are not comparable, as the management practices may well be applicable.

For the leading plants, this means quite clearly that no competitive advantage lasts forever. Once the source of advantage from a management method is understood, it can, in principle, be imitated, even if its systemic nature makes imitation slow and costly. Over time, "best practice" spreads, first within an industry and then across industries. Several managers of the plants visited were aware of this and thus determinedly seeking further improvements in order to stay ahead. Relentless improvement is the only defense that works in the long run.

Another consistent observation indicates that the best plants, while always observing others and learning from them, never simply imitate what they find. They always adapt whatever practice they adopt to their local environment and their specific needs. This includes modifications of procedures, of the groups of workers involved, the set of precise qualifications, and even the names of the procedures and concepts. Modifying the practices serves two purposes: first, it provides flexibility in responding to the specific situation of the plant, and second, it increases the ownership and the buy-in of the workforce, because it is named by them and, thus, theirs.

5. Pursue growth

We provide additional evidence that *volume growth is a good measure of plant success,* especially in international multi-plant companies. Sister factories typically compete against one another for volume. This makes plant growth an accurate indication of plant performance, measured almost independently of the growth of the company overall. Other measures (such as costs or plant profits) are subject to distortions from transfer pricing and allocation rules. At the business unit level, in contrast, profitability seems a more appropriate performance measure.

The findings from this study have served participating factories in our competition as compasses for further improvement efforts. The study has improved their (and our) understanding of how competitive advantage arises from detailed manufacturing management practices. Our experience suggests that the results are as relevant for pharmaceutical plants as for other sectors. Of course, all practices must be adapted and modified to fit the specific needs of pharmaceutical processes, but that is normal, and learning from others (within an industry and from other industries), combined with modification, is a key driver of improvement, as our discussion point 4 above emphasizes. It is in that sense that we hope that the Management Quality concept is useful for the companies participating in this book.

IV.7 Stages of Operational Excellence

Michael Kickuth and Thomas Friedli

Whilst chapter III just gave some insights of the effectiveness of certain principles like TQM or TPM, it did not provide a complete answer concerning the dynamic effects between those principles. However, we can also present evidence – through statistical data – that Operational Excellence represents a system of interlocking parts. An operations improvement program that solely concentrates on one aspect – e.g. inventory reductions – will not yield significant operational improvements. To give an example: one of the best predictors for a high level of continuous improvement (measured as the number/quality of suggestions per employee) was the level of implementation of JIT-practices of a pharmaceutical plant. At first sight, this looks like a coincidental correlation between two independent factors. However, both factors are highly interrelated. A reduction in buffer stocks between manufacturing processes (measured as work in process stock) has to go hand in hand with the development of continuous improvement capabilities in the form of empowered/self directed work team capable of problem solving. Thus, the problem solving capabilities that arise as a result of empowered work teams can help boost performance by identifying root causes of quality problems and unstable running machines; and thus help to reduce safety stocks (measured as work-in-process stocks). The relationships between those factors are significantly correlated and show that an effective production system is an interrelated system of various aspects of Operational Excellence.

First, an Operational Excellence initiative should start with programs related to improving dependability of the core manufacturing processes. For example, reducing the percentage of un-planned maintenance, and capitalize on stable running machines could be a first step. Learning more about the process and reducing variances (e.g. by implementing process management tools as presented in the 6-Sigma case study) could help to build in quality to the manufacturing processes and thus break up the vicious circle of high costs of prevention vs. high costs of failures and compliance. This research data provides evidence that companies that extensively make use of process management tools (e.g. statistical process control, flow charts etc.), have lower cost of compliance, while mutually having moderate cost of prevention (e.g. Cost of QC/QA). Companies that have managed to develop a comprehensive internal process management system could proceed with their Operational Excellence program by integrating customers and suppliers into their quality system.

As soon as companies can capitalize on stable running equipment, stable running manufacturing processes and reliable and integrated suppliers, a JIT-program could help to reduce buffer stocks and increase the flexibility. An effective management system has to support those manufacturing programs. While first it is important that the workforce understands the mechanism of a preventive maintenance philosophy, employee development in the next stage should focus more on quality improvements and ways to reduce variances in the manufacturing processes. In the last stage, employee development should foster ways and techniques to reduce set-up times and reduce non-value adding activities in the manufacturing processes.

The data provides strong evidence that an Operational Excellence initiative that first starts to tackle effectiveness issues and afterwards shifts its efforts to increase efficiency is much more likely to proceed than a program that is started *vice versa*. While the Pfizer case study has presented a successful example on how to develop sustainable process improvements by

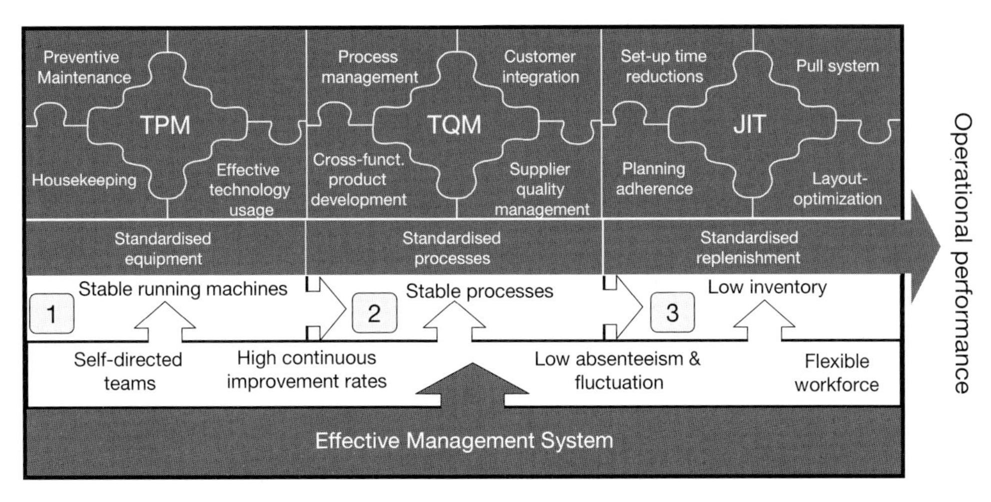

Figure 56: Stages of "Operational Excellence".

considering those interrelated effects, there are also some more statistical causal relationships that also show that there are key stages of Operational Excellence.

Having a closer look at the sample that we have analyzed, it is interesting to find out that the group that we called the JIT Performers also have a significantly higher performance concerning maintenance- (TPM Performance) and quality performance (TQM Performance) figures than the rest of the sample. However this does not work *vice versa*. Being a TPM Performer does not help to predict a high JIT performance which shows that achieving a high JIT Performance requires a much higher level of implementation of different principles of Operational Excellence than just maximizing the equipment effectiveness.

As a consequence, a jigsaw puzzle of "Operational Excellence" could look like illustrated in Figure 56.

The Operational Excellence Framework: Getting from Stage 1 to Stage 3

Based on the jigsaw puzzle described above, we would like to provide a short overview on how an Operational Excellence initiative could look like.

Stage 1: Increasing TPM-Performance

An important aspect that provides evidence, that an early implementation of TPM principles make sense, has already been presented previously: as quality performance is highly correlated with the robustness of the equipment, TPM could be a useful principle to first increase equipment reliability before starting to reduce other process variances. The next reason why an early adoption of TPM tools could make sense is rooted in the nature of the principle. Many practices under the "TPM umbrella" are fairly easy to implement and do not require strong analytical skills and a long training curriculum. In the early phase, a TPM program should just bring production and maintenance people together in teams (teamwork) to stabilize conditions and halt deterioration of equipment. Second, by effectively developing and sharing responsibility for the critical daily maintenance tasks, production and maintenance people should allow people to improve the overall 'health' of the equipment. Through autonomous maintenance, operators should learn to carry out important daily tasks that maintenance people rarely have time to perform. These 'housekeeping' tasks include cleaning and inspecting, lubricating, precision checking, and other light maintenance tasks. Easy to learn tools like 5S will help the operator to structure the Housekeeping programs.

However, before starting a TPM program it is important to set up a proper measurement system for getting a harsh OEE measure. As also presented in Reckit Benckiser case study (page 87 ff.), too many plants that we have visited have OEE measures that give allowances for a lot of interruptions such as planned maintenance and material shortages. As a result a proper OEE should allow for:

- ... determining root causes of low equipment effectiveness. Or at least enable the plant management to figure out whether a low OEE is a result of low equipment performance, availability or quality rate. One approach that has been presented in the Reckit Benckiser case study is to split up the OEE as follows: *OEE = Availability * Performance rate * Quality rate*
- ... tracking the level of unplanned maintenance. The level of unplanned maintenance is one of the key performance indicators for assessing the level of implementation of a TPM program. This is also strongly supported by our data. As a high level of unplanned maintenance directly affects product quality performance indicators; the level of unplanned maintenance should be tracked carefully as it provides some evidence whether a "preventive maintenance culture" has already been established.
- ... achieving clarity concerning the "effective" capacity of the overall plant. As future capital investments have to be planned on real- and not budgeted capacity, a proper OEE will allow for driving down capital investments in the future. With an average OEE of 35% in the sample, a lot of future volume growth in the pharmaceutical industry could be absorbed by freeing-up productive capacity.

While the Reckit Benckiser case study presented very vividly how to increase equipment efficiency by optimizing the OEE, it does not seem to be the appropriate strategy in general. The data provides evidence that a high level of unplanned maintenance correlates with high equipment utilisation rates. This indicates that plants operating at peak capacity may potentially encounter more equipment and process problems and thereby affect product quality. As a consequence, we would again recommend to first tackle effectiveness issues of TPM (e.g. driving down the level of unplanned maintenance) and afterwards starting to maximize the OEE; because otherwise a trade-off between either having high utilisation rates or having stable processes would result. During our plant visits we realized that many companies tend to put the TPM paradigm into the "efficiency tool box" as to their mind the primarily goal of TPM is to maximise the OEE. Having a closer look to the founders of the TPM philosophy (the Japanese Institute of Plant Maintenance), this is not true, as they define TPM as follows: *"TPM is designed to maximize equipment effectiveness, by establishing a comprehensive productive-maintenance system during the life of the equipment, whilst spanning all equipment-related fields".* When the JIPM started to promote the TPM philosophy it was sometimes also called "Quality Maintenance", which also shows that the philosophy behind TPM is (in the short term) much more focused on the effectiveness (reliability) of the equipment than on pure efficiency issues. At least in the short term, this should be considered when rolling out a TPM program.

Stage 2: Increase TQM performance

In the instance where equipment reliability has already increased significantly, the next objective of an Operational Excellence program would be to reduce other root causes of process variability to minimum level. While we have not used the term 6-Sigma in our reference model, all of the process management tools under the "6-Sigma umbrella" that have been presented in the 6-Sigma case study, can also be assigned to the process management tool box of the TQM philosophy. The data provide strong evidence that "state of the art" process management in the pharmaceutical industry can yield high quality performance without further increasing the level of end-process quality inspections. Starting to optimize processes without having a sound understanding of sources of variability, and robust estimates of variability is difficult. Moreover, in the absence of good information, attempts to adjust a process can potentially create new problems. According to the FDA, a manufacturing process is generally considered well understood when (a) critical sources of variability are identified and explained, (b) variability is managed by the process, and (c) product quality attributes can be accurately and reliably predicted over the design space established for materials used, process parameters, environmental and other conditions. The ability to predict, then reflects a high degree of process understanding (FDA 2003a).

For developing a sound understanding of the process, one possible way would be to use the DMAIC problem solving model, borrowed from the 6-Sigma concept, to adequately approach the problem *per se*.

1. Define the problem from the eyes of the customer
It is important to have common mindset concerning the "nature of problem" and scope and the objective of the related project. The team must grapple with an array of questions: "What are we working on?" "Why are we working on this particular problem?" "Who is the customer?" "What are the customer's requirements?" "How is the work currently being done?" "What are the benefits of making the improvements?"

2. Measure the problem
Gather data to validate and to quantify the problem. The 6-Sigma case study has presented a very good example on how linking relationships between the input and process activities and the outcomes of a process. While most of the companies tend to have information about the final product quality and the quality of the incoming raw material, few have adequate information about the process itself. Process and a select few input measures should be targeted to begin getting data on potential causes. Hence, during this phase, visualization and prioritization techniques (e.g. cause-effects diagrams, affinity diagrams, Pareto analysis etc.) should help to identify all relevant potential root causes and to pinpoint the location of sources of problems. Once the project team has determined what to measure, the data collection can start. Various tools like data collection forms, control charts or frequency plots can help to make the data collection more structured.

3. Analyze the problem
In the analysis phase the team has to develop theories of root causes, confirm the theory with data, and finally identify the root causes of the problem (Rath and Strong 2000). While during step two, the task of the process optimization team was to collect data, the team now has to figure out which sources of variability can be regarded as critical and directly influences the quality of the products. The case study has presented an example of how a theory of root causes can be developed by applying the tool Design of Experiments (DOE). DOE tends to be easier to apply to technical processes (e.g. a manufacturing line like presented in the case study) than to people as the design of "real world" tests can be tough when the variables are based on people behavior. However, the current PAT initiative opens the door for designing proper experiments in the pharmaceutical industry much easier than in the past.

4. Improve and Control

Based on the current "Change control" cGMP regulatory concept, a pharmaceutical manufacturer is empowered to make changes based on the variability of materials and processes and optimization of the process from learning over time (FDA 2004). As a result, the DMAIC problem solving model helps to manage changes according to the "Change control" cGMP regulatory guidance. For many company "of process testing" is synonymous with process control. However, tests at the end of a process do not provide any direct means to keep a process under control. For getting those information it is important to develop thorough process capability indices based on the findings of the analysis phase that allow to track the robustness of the processes more or less in real time.

Furthermore, the case study has presented very vividly that it is not just important to make changes and improvements, it is also important to leverage the knowledge and extrapolate the findings to other situations. Hence, control does not just mean to tightly monitor process variation in accordance to the new process understanding, it also means to control the improvements efforts and to identify further improvement opportunities.

Whilst process management is obviously one of the most important elements of the TQM reference model, other elements like cross-functional product development or supplier quality management should also be considered in the long-run. However, the 6-Sigma case has illustrated that it makes sense to first develop a proper process understanding in the manufacturing function before rolling out a TQM or 6-Sigma initiative to other functional areas (e.g. R&D) or suppliers. In the designated case study, it prevented Bart and his team to quickly jump to a solution and blame the supplier for its low quality while not having figured out the true source of variation. Further, it helps to develop a much better understanding about the required characteristics of the incoming materials and by that helps to build up a better supplier management based on true requirements rather than rough estimates.

Stage 3: Increase JIT-Performance

Based on truly robust and highly capable processes and equipment, the focus of optimization in stage 3 can now switch towards efficiency issues. Efficiency issues comprise all sorts of other waste besides high scrap rates (which should be already covered in stage 1 and 2). According to the Toyota Production System, these forms of waste are: waste due to overproduction, waste due to high inventories, waste due to excess material movements (e.g. unnecessary material handling), waste due to long waiting times and waste due to non-value adding activities. The statistical data provides evidence that JIT performers (those companies that have performed well concerning all JIT performance measures) have already implemented a multitude of other principles of Operational Excellence (e.g. TPM and TQM principles) which in fact leads us to the assumption that achieving a high JIT-performance should be considered as a long term goal of Operational Excellence initiatives rather than a starting point. This hypothesis is also strongly supported by our personal perceptions when performing the plant audits. The statement of one production manager who is in charge for optimizing the European plant network of a global pharmaceutical company that we would judge as fairly advanced compared to most other plants and companies that we have visited, underlines that hypotheses: *"We have done a lot of work in the 80s and 90s to reduce our process variances and to optimize our equipment effectiveness. I would say that this is not a major concern for our operations today. The main problem today is matching demand variability with capacity throughout our operations. We have to drive down inventories to now achieve true cost reductions".* The Pfizer case study also provides a very good example that an Operational Excellence program should not start with efficiency issues first. Further, it gave some guidance on how to integrate a TQM or 6-Sigma program with a Lean- or a JIT-program. One good starting point could be to widely analyze the value stream by designing a value stream map of the plant. As the value stream map expands the view to take in all process details – inventory levels, batch sizes, equipment efficiency, staffing etc., it allows to get a much broader view than most process management tools under the TQM/6-Sigma umbrella can provide:

1. Mapping the value stream

- Identify all external and internal customer-supplier relationships between incoming materials and the plant's customers.
- Identify all value adding activities (manufacturing, critical QC time) and non-value adding activities (warehousing, batch documentation, unnecessary material movements) and visualize these activities according to overall cycle time, manufacturing operation time and slack time. Deviate the flow-level as a ratio between the manufacturing operation time and the overall cycle time based on each API or respectively finished goods.
- Optional: In the case where cycle time reductions and inventory reductions are the focus of optimization, the value-added costs have to be visualized. To visualize the value added costs, each value step of the designated products has to be ranked according to the material costs (e.g. costs of raw materials than can be attached to the product) and the activity based costs (costs that have occurred due to manufacturing operation time, which can be directly attached to the product) throughout the manufacturing process.
- As a result the flow level or/and the visualization of the value added costs can provide answers on how to optimize the cycle time or/and inventory related costs.

2. Reducing and standardizing set-up times

The value stream map often allows identifying crucial bottlenecks in the manufacturing process. To smooth the manufacturing process, performing set-up time reductions can yield significant improvements in the value stream. Based on our experience, a common bottleneck at a manufacturing plant is the packaging line. JIT-Performers (companies that have performed better than average concerning inventory related performance figures in our study) have on average 40% shorter set-up times at their packaging line than the remaining companies in our sample[26]. As the packaging line is the last step in the manufacturing process of a secondary manufacturing plant, it strongly determines the Takt time of the upstream processes of the plant. Hence, set-up time reductions at the packaging line can yield significant improvements of the overall cycle time on the shop-floor. One experience of our plant audits was that it is not just the average set-up time that highly determines other upstream processes, but it is also the average variability of the set-up time that has an impact on other processes. Without exception, there was none plant that we have visited where we would say that machine set-ups are already standardized. However, implementing work leveling *(Hejunka)* throughout all manufacturing processes requires robust and standardized processes as buffer stocks have to be reduced to a minimum level to allow the identification of potential root causes of deviation and to match daily demand with the daily production volume. Based on the high variability in set-up times that we have seen, it is not possible to smoothly level production capacity throughout the whole manufacturing process. A typical example of our plant audits that illustrates the high variability in set-up times is presented in Figure 57.

26 Average set-up times JIT-Performer: 57 min; Average set-up times JIT-Non-Performer: 90 min.

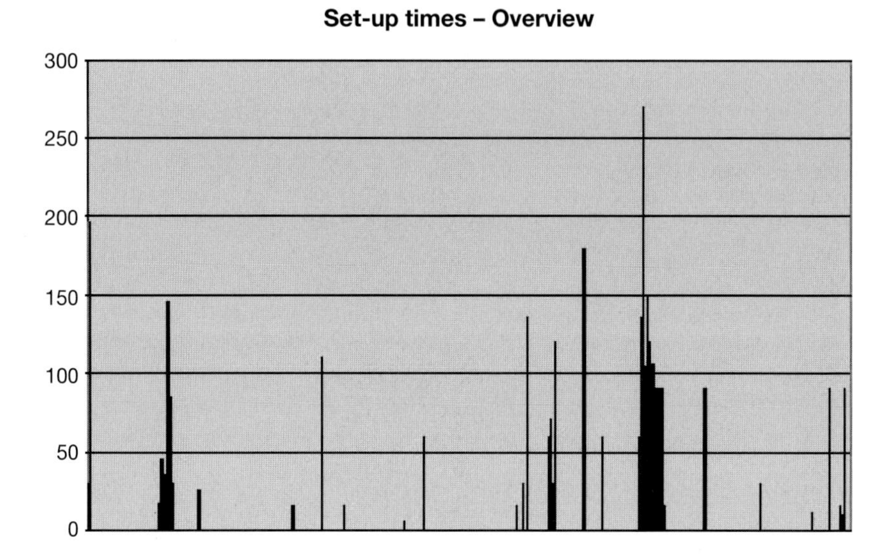

Figure 57: Variability of set-up times at a packaging line of a pharmaceutical plant.

The example provides evidence that set-ups are not standardized. Based on the different sorts of set-ups that typically occur at a packaging line (typically between 3-5 different sorts of changes), it should be possible to identify certain "set-up patterns" that occur quite frequently (e.g. 30 min. set-up, 45 min. set-up etc.) in a standardized manner. However, in the picture above it is not possible to identify that kind of pattern. By identifying the root causes of deviation, the process engineer at the designated plant could now try to figure out the vital factors of deviation by for example applying some of the process management tools presented in the 6-Sigma case study.

3. Optimizing the plant layout

Based on the collected data, JIT Performers have implemented a couple of projects to optimize their plant layout. A first step for optimizing the plant layout can be the classification of products according to their processing and routing requirements. A lot of data required for that analysis is also required for performing a value stream analysis (e.g. manufacturing operation times, slack times, flow level etc.), but most of the information should already be available. The JIT case study gave a good example on how a traditional pharmaceutical manufacturing line was redesigned around the concept of a manufacturing cell. By doing so, the layout enabled the plant to drive down cycle time by making each work centre capable of producing to the plant's Takt time rate.

4. Drive Pull production

While few companies have already implemented pull production, the data provide evidence that pull production can also yield significant improvements in JIT-performance in the pharmaceutical industry. On the basis of the reduced set-up times, it should now be possible to further drive down the average lot size and by that trying to match the daily production plan with the daily demand requirements. Trying to balance the capacity of each production step with the daily demand requirements now finally requires definition of a Takt time that determines the cycle time of each production step. Often the implementation can be simple

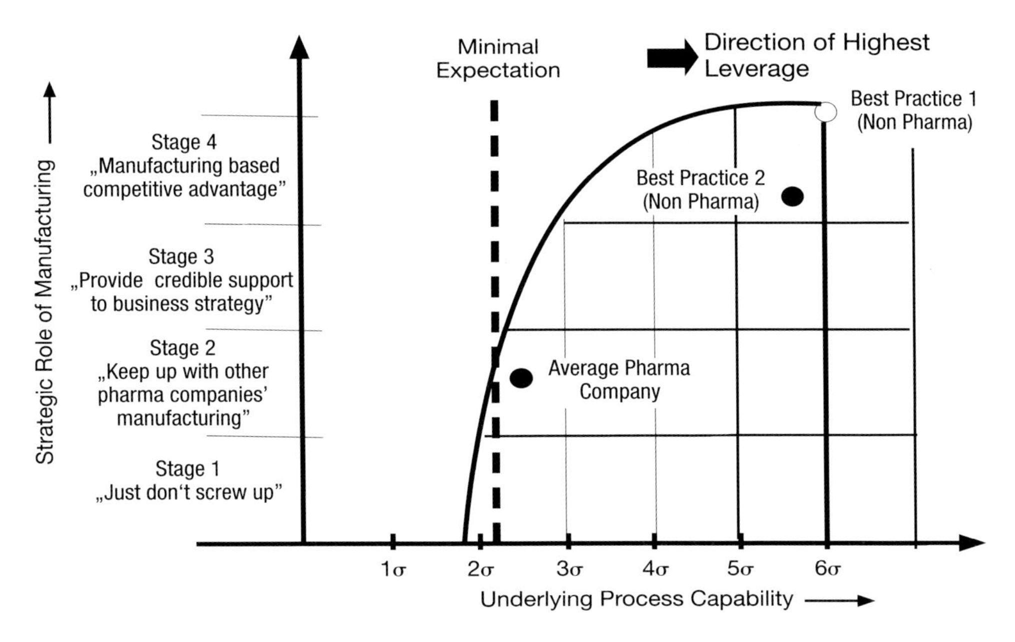

Figure 58: Current status of the pharmaceutical industry (Source: Raju 2003).

replenishment principles like *Kanban* or FIFO lanes to allow level the capacity between the different production steps. A problem that many of the plants we have visited are facing is the synchronization of the manufacturing process with the QC/QA process, as presented in the JIT case study. As most "white collar QC/QA departments" today still understand themselves as a control function rather than a support process for the "blue collar manufacturing process", the implementation of a pull production first requires a cultural shift.

Conclusion: Drive Operational Excellence and understand Operational Excellence as a system of interlocking parts

We are convinced that a structured way of how to roll out an Operational Excellence program will accelerate the improvement process of the pharmaceutical industry. Chapter III and IV provide strong evidence that most of the principles of the Toyota Production System also work in the pharmaceutical industry. Even more surprising based on our experiences and data is that there are certain principles that should get even more attention than in many other industries. Regarding the very high level of "Cost of Non-Quality" (e.g. Low yield due to high process variances, very high cost of non-compliance[27]), it is surprising that the pharmaceutical industry is lagging behind most other industries even with regard to the robustness of its processes. According to C. K. Raju the average underlying robustness of manufacturing processes of the leading top five pharmaceutical companies is far less than 3-Sigma in terms of process variance (see Figure 58). Hence, the impact of rolling out a

27 E.g. in 2001 Schering-Plough had to pay a USD 500 million settlement to the FDA because four plants failed to meet the FDA standard.

TQM/6-Sigma program should have an even bigger impact on the operational performance than in many other industries. No wonder that the biggest difference between low and high performing plants in our survey is in terms of Cost of Quality and the highest cost savings potential can be realized by improvements in that area.

However, we also presented evidence that Operational Excellence represents a system of interlocking parts. Companies that will try to catch up with companies from other industries by quickly driving down inventories and removing waste along the value chain will face severe challenges, as certain restrictions have to be considered.

Based on those restrictions, we have described one possible way of becoming excellent by defining three "stages of excellence". Whilst not arguing that there is just one way of organizing an Operational improvement program, there are, however, certain contingencies between the different principles of Operational Excellence that restrict or reinforce the implementation of Operational improvement programs. This outcome is consistent with the (sometimes) painful experiences that the automotive industry has gained a couple of years ago. Today's integrated production systems in the automotive industry include identical practices, methods and tools that have previously been used ten years ago. What is new is not the knowledge about single methods like *Kanban*, value stream mapping or *Poka-Yoke*, what is new is more the understanding about the multiple dimensions of Operational Excellence that reinforce one another and produce their powerful effect; but only if used as a system. If the pharmaceutical industry does not want to experience the same fall backs like the automotive industry it has to develop a much broader understanding about the multiple dimensions of Operational Excellence than it has today.

The Pharmaceutical Plant of the Future

Michael Kickuth and Thomas Friedli

The objective of this chapter is to provide answers to the following questions:

- What are the relevant industry forces that will shape the structure of the pharmaceutical industry in 2020?
- How will those forces affect the pharmaceutical operations?
- How should companies respond to these forces?
- What should drive pharmaceutical companies to become "operationally excellent"?
- What could the plant of the future look like?

This chapter has been developed on the basis of interviews with high-level executives and academics of the research driven pharmaceutical industry, the generics industry, the contract manufacturing industry and academia.

Special thanks for making valuable contributions go to Dr. Daniel Vasella (Chairman & CEO Novartis), Dr. G. K. Raju (Executive Director, Pharmaceutical Manufacturing Initiative, Pharmi, MIT Program on the Pharmaceutical Industry, Massachusetts Institute of Technology), Dr. Hermann Allgaier (CEO Merckle Biotec), Harald Doerenbach (Siemens VDO Automotive AG), Dr. Christian Ewers (Schering AG), Mark Levin (CEO Millennium Pharmaceuticals), Dr. Jürgen Werani (Europe Area RFT Leader, Pfizer).

V.1 The Pharmaceutical Industry in 2010

The economics, business, regulatory and technological environment in the pharmaceutical industry is undergoing rapid changes and uncertainty. The time of steadily growing revenues and margins in pharmaceuticals and healthcare products is history.

There is a strong consensus among the interviewees that the challenges described in chapter I will have a significant impact on the way pharmaceutical companies will operate in the future. These challenges are:

1. Declining R&D productivity
2. Changing market conditions
3. Increasing Competition
4. Increasing costs and low operating efficiency

While chapter I was more about the challenges of the pharmaceutical industry today, this chapter should provide some answers on how the pharmaceutical industry will respond and especially about the implications for pharmaceutical technical operations. Hence, it is important to figure out the possible structures of the pharmaceutical company of the future and by that to define the role of pharmaceutical operations tomorrow.

The structure of pharmaceutical companies in the future – virtually outsourced or vertically integrated?

Mr. Bell from Arthur D. Little is comparing the pharmaceutical industry of today with the oil industry in the 1960s to 1970s. In the 1960s, the oil industry was dominated by a small number of fully integrated companies. This integration covered all segments of the value chain from exploration to sales and marketing of the finished goods. The oil price crash of 1986 split the ends of the integration cord, which would unravel by the mid 1990s. The result today is a separation in the upstream (exploration & production) and downstream (refining and sales & marketing) portions of the value chain (Bell 2003).

To his mind as well as Mr. Osterwald (COO, NextPharma) the same process has already begun in the pharmaceutical industry. An ever-increasing number of companies entered the game by playing in very specific portions of the traditional value chain. The number of these so called "activity specialists" has exploded in the last decade, while the number of integrated pharmaceutical companies has steadily declined over the same period.

There are certain factors that support this "Outsourcing scenario". In recent years, the outsourcing market has grown significantly along all segments of the pharmaceutical value chain. Today, industry estimates of the CRO (Contract Research Organizations) business in 2002 ranged from USD 7.8 billion to USD 9.7 billion, corresponding to a 19% to 22% share of total pharmaceutical and biotech development spending (Reuters 2001). The market is expected to grow to a USD 36 billion market in 2010 (Reuters 2001). The global outsourcing market for production services is now about USD 8 billion and the contract manufacturing industry is growing at 10% annually (Bell 2003). Initially the contract manufacturing market provided mainly primary production services but areas of growth have expanded to include secondary production as well. Even Marketing & Sales which has traditionally remained the bastion of the integrated pharmaceutical companies is beginning to yield specialized companies offering contract sales services to the pharmaceutical industry. In recent years, this market has grown rapidly with growth rates of about 35% to a USD 1.5 billion market in 2001.

Besides the rise of the activity specialists, Bell assumes that another sort of company will gain momentum, which he calls the market specialist. Market specialists are nearly integrated through the entire value chain in defined, lucrative markets, such as dermatology, hormones etc. They specialize on a certain market segment and do not face any oligopoly in either production or marketing and sales as they can perform any activity in-house.

While Bell assumes that the pharmaceutical value chain will be far more disintegrated than in the past, however there are also some indications that the value chain of tomorrow will look pretty much like the value chain of today. Daniel Vasella predicts that Big Pharma will remain integrated in the future:

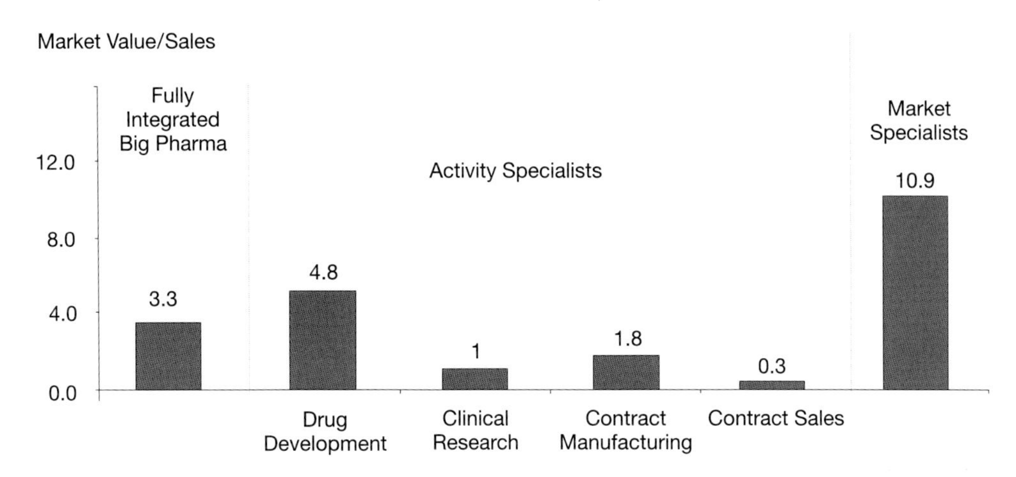

Figure 59: Overview of different business models and their average market valuations (Source: Arthur D. Little).

"We cannot afford to lose control of critical processes like development or manufacturing as pharmaceutical companies are exposed to much higher risks than most other industries. Many people cite the automotive industry as a role model for outsourcing. However, especially in the field of electronics there are some indications that the automotive OEMs have lost too much control towards their suppliers. This cannot be a role model for the pharmaceutical industry. If you have a look at how the pharmaceutical industry has developed in recent years, most companies that have started as specialists are moving towards vertical integration which shows that there is not a general tendency towards disintegration. Furthermore, I do not know any reason why a company like Novartis with fairly high economies of scale should not be able to manufacture drugs cheaper than a contract manufacturer."

This assessment of the future structure of the pharmaceutical industry fits pretty much with the strategy of Millennium Pharmaceuticals, a former bio-tech start-up that currently transforms itself from a pure bio-tech research player to an integrated pharmaceutical company. When Mark Levin, CEO of Millennium Pharmaceuticals, was asked why he thinks the pharmaceutical industry is still vertically integrated while most other high-tech industries tended to break down into a few separate, largely independent industries, he answered: *"It's because there's still only one valuable product you can sell: the pill or serum that the patient takes. The discrete stages that specialist companies can carve out ultimately do not carry enough of the product's value, so margins tend to be quite small. Say I find a protein for obesity, that target is still USD 500 million away from doing anybody any good. [...] I am not saying that you can't make a good business by being a niche player – there are, for instance, very profitable companies that just do preclinical and even clinical testing. But no company will ever create any serious long-term value in our industry by staying in just one or two stages of the value chain"* (Champion 2001).

While there seems to be no consensus about the future of the activity specialists that are primarily focused on certain processes, Daniel Vasella agrees that focussing on specific markets will pay off. However, he stresses that a big pharma company that is positioned as a multi niche player which is specialised on several specific markets will be in an even better position than a pure smaller market specialist as there are still synergies on which a big pharmaceutical company can capitalize on.

Figure 59 shows that the market is already beginning to reward the market specialists while the activity specialists and the fully integrated big pharma companies are priced significantly lower. Just, taking the market value of today's pharmaceutical companies, the most successful business model of the future is likely to be the integrated market specialists; that is focusing on a specific market niche.

V.2 Implications for Manufacturing

Based on the future structure of the pharmaceutical industry and challenges described in chapter I, there are certain implications that will affect pharmaceutical manufacturing:

Changing market conditions – flexibility is key

Changing market conditions, the rise of multi-niche products and the rise of bio-tech will add further complexity to the supply chain and demand much higher flexibility than today. The rise of multi-niche products will increase the complexity of manufacturing products. While blockbuster products demanded high-volume plants that supplied the market with a single product on a huge scale, multi-niche products will require a more flexible production. Yet, the data that was presented in chapter III provides evidence, that most plants lack the flexibility to produce different products or switch swiftly from one product to another to meet fluctuating demand as long set-up times and production runs are quite common.

Furthermore, biotechnology will revolutionize the production of specialized medicines and diagnostics. As disease and illness are usually caused largely by damage at the molecular and cellular level, biotechnology and nanotechnology is supposed to build a broad range of complex molecular machines ensuring medicine intervention in a sophisticated and controlled way at the cellular and molecular level. The biological differences in patients and the relevance of human genome to inherited and acquired diseases will be a key factor in prescribing medicines. This will allow targeting of medicines to effectively cure illnesses. While the technological advances are promising from a patient's perspective, they sound like a nightmare for a site-manager who is responsible for producing customized medicines. This will lead to a situation in which medicine will have to be produced on a one-piece-flow philosophy which is far away from producing medicines today. Hence, flexibility will become the key success factor for delivering custom-made healthcare solutions for patients.

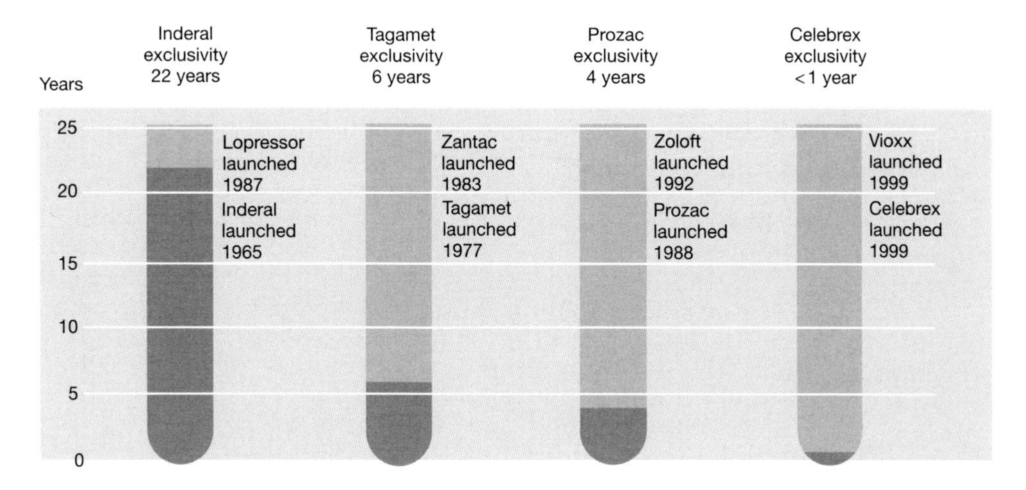

Figure 60: Period of exclusivity (Source: CapGemini, Economist Intelligence Unit, 2004).

While these requirements towards an increased flexibility of manufacturing medicines can be traced back to the changing market conditions, there are also some financial constraints that force pharmaceutical manufacturing to become more flexible. With set-ups costs of around USD 500 million to build a biotechnological plant, no pharmaceutical company will be able to afford an investment in a facility with utilization rates of around 30 %, which is not uncommon today. Hence, flexibility in design to accommodate multiple products will become crucial for operating in the field of biotechnology.

Increasing Competition – Increase operational efficiency while not sacrificing effectiveness

With increasing market competition and lower growth rates, there will be an increasing cost pressure on pharmaceutical companies. In the pharmaceutical industry, world-wide sales have grown at an average annual rate of 11.1 % from 1970 to 2002 (PhRMA 2003), today, these double-digit growth rates are strictly incorporated into the industry's overall growth expectations. However, as most of the industry expects the growth rates to decrease, a main leverage for maintaining current high company valuations is, to improve the return on sales while at least maintaining the capital employed. The three largest leverages for increasing profitability in the pharmaceutical industry are: Marketing, R&D and manufacturing. There are two factors that indicate to us that neither marketing nor R&D costs will decrease, and thus help to cope with combating the challenge. Some 67 % of all companies that we asked expect their R&D budgets to keep rising. Simultaneously, the average period between the launch of an innovative pharmaceutical drug and the launch of its "me-too" product has declined (see Figure 60).

The shorter this exclusivity period becomes, the more emphasis will be put on pushing new drugs into the market. Hence, we do not expect significant cost reductions in the field of R&D and marketing. One of the main leverages for increasing return on sales will be an increase in operating efficiency. *"In the past companies have seen manufacturing simply as a matter of compliance with regulatory requirements, rather than an opportunity to cut costs. Today things have changed. Operating efficiency now has become a major issue for pharmaceutical companies"* says an executive manager of a pharmaceutical company.

However, especially for R&D driven pharmaceutical companies a strategy that is purely based on increasing operating efficiency will not pay off. Rather than just driving down costs, manufacturing also has to fit a specific strategic role to support the needs of the different market segments and to support the business strategy. With more and more "me-too" products rushing faster into the market, a rapid scale-up will become even more important for several reasons. It enables a company to penetrate the market quickly, gain broad market acceptance, and begin to accumulate experience with high-volume production. As a consequence, pharmaceutical companies will have to push their launch sites even more to accelerate their time to peak sales. That trend will also drive companies to simplify manufacturing processes in the early stage of the product life-cycle. For example, AstraZeneca has established the round white 7-mm tablet as its default standard for new products because it is predictable and quickly scales up from pilot to production (Kager and Mozeson 2000). However, when markets mature, process innovation will become key and complexity will increase. One example of a mainly saturated market is the pain reliever market. Consider McNeil Consumer Products' gel-cap version of its pain reliever Tylenol. A distinctive manufacturing process provided an easy to swallow product, and because the process was proprietary, the product was the only one in its class with that feature. As a result the gel cap strengthened Tylenol as a brand. Bayer's Aspirin brand has managed to still capture a significant market share in the pain reliever market by pursuing the same strategy and offering various formulation forms. However, as a result this will add even more complexity to the pharmaceutical supply chain.

New process technology and business needs could enable new manufacturing related business models

While there is obviously no consensus concerning successful future business models, we think that there are certain business models that could arise due to unique manufacturing capabilities that a company possesses. With more products that are getting stopped in manufacturing due to the inability of pharmaceutical companies to produce the product robustly, activity specialists to build up a business model which is based on fundamental process design changes that would lead to unique manufacturing capabilities.

One company tried to fundamentally change today's process design by promoting a process technology that enabled it to spray the API on a paper and by that managed to reduce significantly manufacturing costs. At the end, the company failed as the presentation of the API was too far away from today's usual forms of presentation and the company did not manage to make the drug look like common drugs that are on the market. Further, due to the specific market and institutional structure of the Healthcare industry, there was no way to reward the company for its efforts to enhance product functionality and reduce manufacturing costs. Further potential business models that could arise due to the high attractiveness of the biotechnological market can be found in the bio-generics market. The market of biotech products is faced with an increasing interest not only from a medical point of view. The market is growing faster than the pharmaceutical market and, currently, takes in more than 10% of the total pharmaceutical revenues. Forecasts predict that in 2010 more than 50% of all newly approved pharmaceuticals will be of biotechnical origin. Moreover, the market of biopharmaceuticals is not only a growing market but also a very lucrative market, as there are some products having a gross margin of about 80% and more.

The growing number of expiration patents also opens a wide range of opportunities for the generics market. However, the market is different from the classical generic business.

The cost for developing a generic biotechnological drug costs up to 10 times more than the development of a chemical based new drug. With total costs of between USD 40 and 80 million, the production of bio generics is highly complex and requires high capital investments. The manufacturing process is very critical to the effectiveness and quality of the products as the composition of the biopharmaceuticals varies easily. Since numerous patents not only protect the product itself but also the process of manufacturing, the development of a generic drug is often even more difficult.

Taking into consideration the differences mentioned above, it gets obvious why the development of bio-generics is much more risk- and cost-intensive than the generic development of chemical based pharmaceuticals. This fact implicates that the market of bio-generics and classical generics will differ in many ways. The old generic approach will not work. The market will be ruled by a few big and, in particular, financially strong pharmaceutical companies which are able to provide the high costs and technologies for the development. Consequently, the bio-generic market will not be a highly fragmented market consisting of many small generic companies as we can see today in the classical generic market. Furthermore, smaller companies with focus on bio-generics development need to partner with champions in marketing and sales. Since the production process is highly complex a successful business model should be based upon vertically integrated control over its value chain. Companies specialized on a particular level of the value chain will at least be a rarity in the bio-generic market.

V.3 How To Respond?

By analyzing the current challenges the question arises how to respond. Besides optimizing processes and launching an Operational Excellence program there are a number of structural changes that could help pharmaceutical companies to cope with those challenges:

1. Define the strategic role of manufacturing

First, pharmaceutical companies have to define the strategic role of the manufacturing unit. Kasra Ferdows, Professor for Global Manufacturing at Georgetown University notices that many pharmaceutical and biotech companies face the dilemma that there is usually no clear role for manufacturing. They do not know how far and how deep their company should get involved in coordinating its internal and its extended supply chain. To define the strategic role of manufacturing he proposes a simple framework that should provide answer to two major questions:

- What is the company's proprietary production know-how?
- How important is superiority in production and logistics to meet the company's strategy?

Figure 61 shows the simple framework for how these factors affect the decision.

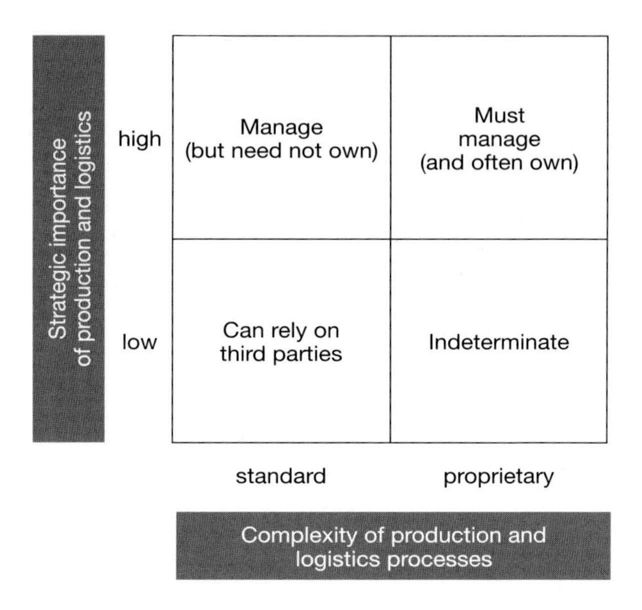

Figure 61: The structure of the supply chain under regard of its strategic role.

If the production processes are standard in the industry, and if the company is not competing on the basis of superior supply chain performance, then much of the management of the supply network can be easily outsourced. For example, McDonald's can easily outsource supply of promotional toys. Production processes of these toys are seldom proprietary, and superiority in production and logistics of toys is not part of McDonald's competitive strategy. For these products, McDonald's operates in the bottom left quadrant of Figure 61. But for its main business, McDonald's operates in the top left quadrant. It has sophisticated systems for managing the supply chain for its hamburgers (all the way to cattle farms), French fries (all the way to potato seeds), buns, ketchup, and other food items. Even though it does not own the farms, cattle, and factories that produce its food items and packages, it is heavily involved in coordinating these supplies.

When a company possesses significant proprietary knowledge in its product design and production processes and competes through superiority in the management of its supply chain, (operating in the top right quadrant), then it has no choice but to develop the ability to manage its dispersed manufacturing. Often it must also own the manufacturing assets to protect its proprietary know-how. Seagate Technology, the world market leader for disk drives, is an example of a company that is using superior management of its production and logistics value chain as an effective competitive weapon. Seagate is more vertically integrated than its competitors and is deeply involved in managing its supply network.

Most pharmaceutical companies that we have seen lack a common understanding about the strategic role of their manufacturing unit. They state that their competitive strategy is based on innovation and marketing and do not regard manufacturing as a strategic asset. However, they are still vertically integrated and have not aligned their operations strategy with their competitive strategy.

2. Reconfigure the plant network

In the past, if a pharmaceutical company wanted to sell its products in a foreign country, it would often have to make concessions. Among those was building a manufacturing plant in the country, staffing it with local workers, and entrusting it to a local manager, who in most instances, acted autonomously, accountable only to top- and bottom-line performance. As a result of such regulatory and governmental constraints, pharmaceutical companies saw a proliferation of their plants and distribution centers around the world. Rather than having a plant network that was build up on an overall operations strategy, the network was more like a loose confederation with far more facilities and capabilities than needed. As the global situation has changed, and many regional plant barriers have disappeared, these plant networks do not comply anymore with today's changing requirements towards flexibility and efficiency. G. K. Raju states that pharmaceutical companies increasingly have to question themselves why they are manufacturing in a certain country. The more pharmaceutical companies will raise that question, the more will countries like China and India be taken into consideration. As long as gross margins on drugs are as high as today, questions on intellectual property are overriding the question of manufacturing costs. With lower gross margins sticking to the products, this might change in the future. However, especially in the case of India, manufacturing costs are just one issue. With its history of more than 30 years of "process patents"[28], India nurtured a pharmaceutical industry which is very competitive with regard to process innovations. Hence, Indian companies are not just cheap, they are often also very advanced on the process side of drug development and manufacturing.

Even though emerging off-shore opportunities for building up manufacturing capacities abroad might look promising, many western pharmaceutical companies are facing a situation of excess capacity. Especially in the field of chemical production there is a lot of excess capacity. Mergers and acquisitions have led to varied portfolios, manufacturing redundancies and excess capacity. Some global pharmaceutical companies like GlaxoSmithKline have already restructured their manufacturing operations and have reduced their number of plants significantly. While some companies prefer to sell their plants to contract manufacturers, some prefer to close plants as they are especially afraid of transferring valuable knowledge to buyers from India or China. *"Those companies that are most interested in buying excess production capacity in Europe from us come from India. However, we do not want to nurture potential future competitors"* says one executive manager of a pharmaceutical company that is currently restructuring its production network.

Summarizing the current situation, one major structural change should be the centralization of supply chain management. No longer will an individual manager make a unilateral decision about building a new plant. Thinking globally, the company will design its manufacturing operations to support overall needs. Furthermore, companies can optimize their sourcing and achieve better economies of scale. Each plant within in the network has to play a certain role within the plant network which is derived from the overall operations strategy of the company.

However, this approach does not mean that each plant in the network is dedicated to a certain product. This approach usually does not fit with today's changing requirements towards flexibility. Again the configuration of the plant network should start by answering two basic questions:

---

28 In 1970, India introduced „process patents" which, unlike patents in the US or Europe, allowed innovators to protect the way they made drugs, rather than the molecules themselves.

- What is the primary strategic reason for the factory's location?
- What is the scope of its current activities?

Based on the answers of these questions, managers can use a framework Kasra Ferdows (1997) developed to categorize plants and to determine how to expand their roles (see Figure 62).

According to this framework, foreign factories can fall into any of the six categories. ① An *offshore factory* is established to gain access to low wages or other factors integral to low-cost production. Its responsibilities are limited to the low cost production of specific items that are then exported either to further work or for sale. Such a factory is not expected to be innovative, its managers follow the instructions, methods, and plans handed down to them, and they rely on others to provide the expertise in new processes, products and technologies. ② A *source factory* also is established to gain access to low-cost production, but unlike an offshore factory it has the resources and the expertise to develop and produce a part of a product for the company's global markets. ③ A *server factory* is a production site that supplies specific national or regional markets. ④ A *contributor factory* both serves a local market and assumes responsibilities for product customization, process improvements, product modifications, or product development. ⑤ An *outpost factory* is established primarily to gain access to the knowledge and skills that the company needs. ⑥ Finally a *lead factory* has the ability and knowledge to innovate and create new processes, products and technologies for the company (Ferdows 1997).

When performing the plant audits, we observed that there were several indicators that provided evidence that few pharmaceutical companies have already structured their plant network based on a thorough overall operations strategy. One plant of a European pharmaceutical company that we have visited explained us that they had to handle very complex processes as they were producing solid forms for the European and for the Japanese market. However, the management complained that the customer requirements and the requirements in terms of QC/QA for the Japanese market are totally different. Therefore, the company had to set up a totally different QC/QA process for products for the Japanese market that was causing a lot of trouble as the process and planning complexity exploded.

Furthermore, some employees even had to be trained in Japan to perform certain jobs. Even though, building up a dedicated *server factory* in the Japanese market might not be an answer, the question arises whether a local contract manufacturer could not perform that process cheaper and better.

3. Make or Buy or Ally: Define the role of suppliers and contract manufacturers

The example of the European pharmaceutical company struggling to meet the requirements of the Japanese market shows that the time of doing everything by itself is over. However, based on the statements of Daniel Vasella and other executives we talked with, the big pharmaceutical companies remain very concerned with controlling supply.

Obviously there will not be a fundamental shift towards strategic outsourcing of certain functions that are not regarded as core competencies Martin Joyce, president of the Pharmaceutical Outsourcing Management Association (POMA) agrees with that opinion: *"We are seeing more vividly that truly strategic outsourcing never really took hold in the industry"* (Kager and Mozeson 2000). Another executive of a big pharmaceutical company we talked with stated: *"I see this [outsourcing] rather opportunistic. In case that there is an opportunity to capitalize on external capacity or capabilities we are making use of it. However, I do not believe that there is a general tendency towards strategic partnerships with external suppliers."*

Offshore Factory

An offshore factory is established to produce specific items at a low cost items that are then exported either for further work or for sale. Investments in technical and managerial resources are kept at the minimum required for production. Little development or engineering occurs at the site. Local managers rarely choose key suppliers or negotiate prices. Accounting and finance staffs primarily provide data to managers in the home country. Outbound logistics are simple and beyond the control of the plant's management.

Source Factory

The primary purpose for establishing a source factory is low-cost production, its strategic role is broader than that of an offshore factory. Its managers have greater authority over procurement (including the selection of suppliers), production planning, process changes, outbound logistics, and product customization and redesign decisions. A source factory has the same ability to produce a product or a part as the best factory in the company's global network. Source factories tend to be located in places where production costs are relatively low, infrastructure is relatively developed, and a skilled workforce is available.

Server Factory

A server factory supplies specific national or regional markets. It typically provides a way to overcome tariff barriers and to reduce taxes, logistics costs, or exposure to foreign-exchange fluctuation. Although it has relatively more autonomy than an offshore plant to make minor modifications in products and production methods to fit local conditions, its authority and competence in this area are very limited.

Contributor Factory

A contributor factory also serves a specific national or regional market, but its responsibilities extend to product and processes engineering as well as to the development and choice of suppliers. A contributor factory competes with the company's home plants to be the testing ground for new process technologies, computer systems, and products. It has its own development, engineering, and production capabilities. A contributor factory also has authority over procurement decisions and participates in the choice of key suppliers for the company.

Outpost Factory

An outpost factory's primary role is to collect information. Such a factory is placed in an area where advanced suppliers, competitors, research laboratories or customers are located. Because every factory obviously must make products and have markets to serve, virtually all outpost factories have a secondary strategic role – as a server or an offshore, for example.

Lead Factory

A lead factory creates new processes, products, and technologies for the entire company. This type of factory taps into local skills and technological resources not only to collect data for headquarters but also to transform the knowledge that it gathers into useful products and processes. Its managers have a decisive voice in the choice of key suppliers and often participate in joint development work with suppliers. Many of its employees stay in direct contact with end customers, machinery suppliers, research laboratories, and other centers of knowledge; they also initiate innovations frequently.

Figure 62: Categorization of plants and determination of how to expand their role (Source: Ferdows 1997).

While obviously Big Pharma will not give up manufacturing as a whole and concentrate on R&D and marketing, there is a growing tendency towards outsourcing of certain products. The sales volume, margin and the phase of the product life cycle of the product will determine the decision. The earlier a product is in its life cycle (especially with a blockbuster drug), the less the company will want to share the technology or the secrets of the product.

Besides late-stage products, niche products that demand a truly proprietary capability that Big Pharma does not want to build up have traditionally been the growing segments in the contract manufacturing market.

However, lessons from other industries show that outsourcing does not inevitably mean losing control of its supply chain. While Toyota has pretty much the same degree of company internal value-adding like its competitors, it does not face the same problems (e.g. in the field of electronics). By building supplier *Keiretus,* close knit networks of vendors that continuously learn, improve, and prosper along with their parent company, Toyota managed to control its value chain without doing everything in-house. According to Liker and Choi (2004) they build their supplier relationships by following six distinct steps: First, they understand how their suppliers work. Second, they turn supplier competition into opportunity. Third, they supervise their suppliers. Fourth, they develop their supplier's technical capabilities. Fifth, they share information intensively but selectively. And sixth, they conduct joint improvement activities (see Figure 63).

While most of the pharmaceutical industry has not yet started to optimize their internal processes, building up a *Keiretsu* and trying to expand continuous improvement to its suppliers does not make sense. However, we met one global pharmaceutical company that was already using its Operational Excellence Black Belts for optimizing their supplier's processes and was already closely cooperating with its contract manufacturers willing to expand the Operational Excellence initiative throughout the whole supply chain. The basic rationale behind that decision was that this company did not want to just force its suppliers to annually drive down their costs, but help them to achieve cost targets that were based on the realistic assumptions about cost savings potentials due to inefficiencies in their manufacturing processes. By doing that, the company could also start unleashing the cost saving potentials that were hidden in the 40% material costs that used to be taken as granted, before. Furthermore, the company did not lose control of its supply chain and developed a better understanding about its suppliers' processes, thus starting started to build up a mutual relationship that was based on continuous improvement and trust.

This approach is already pretty close to what Toyota is doing with its suppliers. In 1988 when Toyota decided to make cars in Kentucky, it picked Johnson Controls to supply seats. Johnson Controls wanted to expand its nearby factory, but Toyota stipulated that it shouldn't, partly because an expansion would require a large investment and eat into the supplier's profit. Instead, the Japanese manufacturer challenged Johnson Controls to make more seats in an existing building. That seemed impossible at first, but with the help of Toyota's Lean Manufacturing experts, the supplier restructured its shop floor, slashed inventories, and was able to make seats for Toyota in the existing space. That experience helped the American vendor understand that it was not enough to deliver seats just-in-time, it had to use a system that would continually reduce its costs and improve quality (Liker and Choi 2004).

4. Create a learning factory

Before starting an overall Operational Excellence initiative one of the most important issues will be to transform a traditional pharmaceutical plant into a learning factory. Herein lies one of the great contributions of Japanese manufacturers over recent decades: the view that process improvement and development is key to industrial competitiveness.

Products and services are only the outpost of ongoing business processes or "ways of doing things". Competitiveness must thus be rooted in a superior ability to run these business processes. Furthermore, "best-practices" diffuse over time, making process improvement an ongoing competitive requirement. Pushing this argument to its conclusion, sustainable competitiveness must, then, be rooted in a superior ability to improve one process faster and better than one's competitors (Loch et al. 2003).

Conduct joint improvement activities.
- Exchange best practices with suppliers.
- Initiate Kaizen projects at suppliers' facilities.
- Set up supplier study groups.

Share information intensively but selectively.
- Set specific times, places, and agendas for meetings.
- Use rigid formats for sharing information.
- Insist on accurate data collection.
- Share information in a structured fashion.

Develop suppliers' technical capabilities.
- Build suppliers' problem-solving skills.
- Develop a common lexicon.
- Hone core suppliers' innovation capabilities.

Supervise your suppliers.
- Send monthly report cards to core suppliers.
- Provide immediate and constant feedback.
- Get senior managers involved in solving problems.

Turn supplier rivalry into opportunity.
- Source each component from two or three vendors.
- Create compatible production philosophies and systems.
- Set up joint ventures with existing suppliers to transfer knowledge and maintain control.

Understand how your suppliers work.
- Learn about suppliers' capabilities.
- Go see how suppliers work.
- Respect suppliers' capabilities.
- Commit to coprosperity.

The Supplier-Partnering Hierarchy

Figure 63: The Supplier – Partnering Hierarchy (Source: Liker and Choi, 2004).

Many managers that we talked with during our plant audits told us that it is not possible to set up a thorough continuous improvement process in the pharmaceutical industry. *"With highly complicated internal change procedures that take some 30-40 days to change a process, a Kaizen process which is build on incremental changes will never pay off,"* said a production manager. Obviously, the high-level of regulation has hindered pharmaceutical companies to continuously improve their processes. However, we sometimes had the impression that many pharmaceutical production managers use the high level of regulation as an excuse for not having achieved any significant process improvements over the years.

First, many of the changes that are typical for a *Kaizen* process are as incremental that they would not need any official regulatory change. Often, process changes are more about better ergonomics and the worker usually can just save a couple of seconds e.g. in the way how he is handling the material. Most of those changes would not cause any regulatory change procedure as they are very incremental. Spear presents in his case study "Learning to lead at Toyota" how an American manager has experienced the different philosophies between American companies and Toyota concerning the way of how to incrementally improve processes when he had to optimise processes at a Toyota manufacturing plant in Kentucky:

"Of course, many people trying to improve a process have some idea of what the problems are and how to fix them. The difference with the Toyota Production System – and this is the key – is that it seeks to fully understand both the problem and the solution. For example, any manager might say, "Maybe the part rack should be closer to the assembler's hand. If we move it here, I'll bet it'll save a few seconds off the cycle". Were he to try this and find that it saved six seconds, he would probably be quite pleased and consider the problem solved.

But in the eyes of the Toyota manager Takahashi such a result would indicate that the manager did not fully understand the work he was trying to improve. Why hadn't he been more specific about how far he was going to move the rack? And how many seconds did he expect to save? Four? If the actual savings is six seconds, that is a cause for celebration – but also for additional inquiry. Why was there a two second difference? With the explicit precision encouraged by Takahashi, the discrepancy would prompt a deeper investigation into how a process worked and, perhaps more important, how a particular person studied and improved the process."

The small case study shows that many changes that are typical for process optimization at Toyota are much more incremental – and more structured – than most western manager would expect. As a result many process changes would not cause any trouble with the FDA.

Second, even those process changes that require an official regulatory change procedure can be handled much better than in the past. One company that we met had anticipated that the old system of "changing things" does not fit the requirements of today's environment. Before starting to improve its manufacturing processes, the company realized that it had to improve its change process first. With an internal change procedure that took around 30 days to get an approval, the company was far away from a situation that could have nurtured any continuous improvement thinking within the company. By analyzing its change process it realized that there was so many manual duplication of forms and unnecessary movement of documents between the different work areas that it could finally reduce its change process to one day. By doing that it was able to implement a change process which was not far away from change procedures of other industries.

Third, some of the changes the FDA recently launched with their 21st century cGMPs as described in chapter I will hopefully help to free-up the industry from prescriptive rules and help to foster continuous improvement.

While the process of changing things is important, the challenge to create a culture of change is even more demanding. Prof. Loch states that: *"A company might change a strategy in a matter of weeks, a supply chain (e.g. in the form of a set of contracts with suppliers and distributors) perhaps in months. New products can often be introduced in a year or less, but people working in plants some of them for decades) have traditionally needed several years to change.*

To his mind, plants that he regards as world class are those that are not static but constantly changing, dynamic and creative: *"A theme common to the best plants is speed of change. When returning after three years, many of them have completely changed, running their processes differently and making different products. [...] Routine work is done by machines or in low-wage countries, workers in first and second world factories adjust, monitor, and improve processes. We have observed how "lowly assembly line workers" spend a third of their time problem solving and improving operations. This trend will increase even further in years to come."*

However, as already presented in chapter III this is a true weak point of the pharmaceutical industry as a whole. Only a few plants in the pharmaceutical industry can be regarded as "learning factories". This status is not just reflected by very low average numbers of suggestions per employee in the pharmaceutical industry; this is also one of the major findings of our plant visits. Talking to one manager in charge for continuous improvement at a big pharmaceutical company who just came back from a plant visit to the AUDI plant at Ingolstadt (Germany) he told us: *"When I compare the pharmaceutical industry with the automotive industry, there was one thing that was for me most impressive: The way how people are managed and organized: People are empowered and problem solving is delegated to the shop floor. Shop floor workers are spending a lot of time for problem solving and the way how workers approach problems is done in a very structured manner. While on the one hand there is a lot of responsibility shifted to the shop floor there is a lot of standardization and structure with regard to working shifts and procedures on the other hand. Furthermore, it is interesting to find out how employee development is seen as an essential tool to foster employee participation and flexibility. Workers are usually striving to become multi-skilled and to continuously improve processes as this is linked with their salary and their personal development. For each new job, there are internal assessment centres and candidates are assessed very carefully. Workers are really regarded much more like assets."*

5. Increase flexibility by optimizing processes, people skills and technology mutually

At the beginning of this chapter we predicted that in future, flexibility will be key. However, we have not provided any answer how to cope with that challenge. While there might be still some high volume plants that will produce easy to manufacture 7-mm tablets with volumes of some 100 million tablets a year, especially the lead plants (see Figure 63) in the plant networks will have to handle much more complexity than in the past. This will be one of the biggest challenges of the future. Driving down set-up times by implementing a JIT program and having a flexible multi-skilled workforce that can perform different tasks could be a first step. However, appropriate technology has to be developed mutually. Today's process and information technology often does not support the rising requirements towards flexibility in the pharmaceutical industry. Due to several reasons today's multipurpose equipment usually does not fit this requirement. Ewers et al., already showed that multipurpose equipment even reduces flexibility when compared to dedicated equipment (Ewers et al. 2002).

As dedicated and standardized and modularized equipment reduces the capital investments compared to multipurpose equipment, it allows to produce much smaller batches and by that increases the average cycle time As a result much smaller capacity is required and capacity

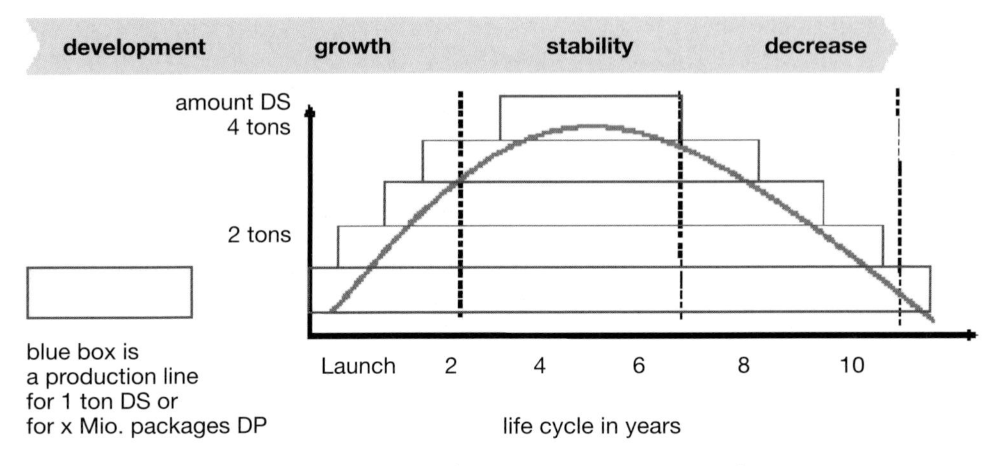

Figure 64: Modular growth of capacities (Source: Ewers, Schering AG).

can be expanded in smaller incremental steps which further reduces the required capital investments which then accelerates the scale up of new products as no more engineering and validation is required. When the product matures and the demand decreases, standardized and modularized equipments also allow much quicker capacity adjustments as excess modules can be assigned to other products. Ewers estimates that by designing manufacturing processes based on standardized and modular dedicated equipment it would be possible to double the capacity of most products in less than one year while reducing the overall capital expenditures significantly. Figure 64 illustrates how modularized and standardized equipment easily allows adjustments to capacities according to market changes over the life cycle of a drug.

This experience is pretty close to the experiences that the discrete industry has gained by the mid of 1980s when a lot of western manufacturers tried to implement Advanced Manufacturing Technologies (AMT) to enable flexible automation. However, Jaikumur summarized the experiences of those projects as follows: *"With few exceptions, the flexible manufacturing system installed in the United States show an astonishing lack of flexibility* (Jaikumar 1986)". One severe problem of those technologies was their huge upfront capital investments that forced the companies to a much higher asset utilization. As a consequence, flexibility sometimes became technically feasible but did not prove to be financially attractive. *"Rather than functioning as sources of competitive advantage, large asset bases increasingly tie a manufacturer to obsolete strategies, allowing innovative competitors to swarm in* (Wise and Baumgartner 1999)". Having a closer look at automation in the pharmaceutical industry, there will certainly be some dimensions where at automation will also play a certain role to increase flexibility. According to G. K. Raju, this especially affects areas where automation helps to reduce batch-sizes or to increase process understanding (e.g. on-line measurement and control).

Hence, the equipment design of tomorrow has to be based much more on flexibility, on lower capital investments and on quick changeover and real-time quality control than on pure volume. To our mind, a higher Overall Equipment Effectiveness can be often be easier achieved by trying to reduce overall downtime than to increase the theoretical technical output of the equipment.

When performing our plant audits, we have seen too much process equipment that does not support quick changeover or quick fixes at all. It was not uncommon to see an operator at a high volume line who was struggling at least two minutes to open a cover tray which was fixed with four screws to release a jammed package and to continue production.

As a consequence, tomorrow's equipment has to be designed more customer-oriented, standardized and modularized. Equipment vendors have to be integrated into process development to allow for a much higher usability, standardization will help to increase reliability while modularization will allow for more spending flexibility as extra modules can be added to adapt to demand changes. Furthermore, by delivering manufacturing facilities in a standardized and modular concept pharmaceutical plants will be able to do as much validation ahead of time.

Modular processes combined with modular and exactly specified products will allow for flexible and rapid response to a specific customer demand. Mini-plants, which are small manufacturing cells within one plant, will become more widespread as standardization and modularization will drive down the minimum efficient scale of the manufacturing process. *"To use a biological analogy, the cell is an extremely efficient and flexible production system* (Loch et al. 2004). *It derives its performance from tight process control (hardwired in its DNA) and from using a small number (about 30) ubiquitous, general purpose materials (types of molecules) that are assembled into a large variety of proteins, lipids, etc., and recycled and shared across species"* (Loch et al. 2003). The Siemens VDO Automotive AG plant in Babenhausen, winner of the Best Factory of the Year Award 2003, has proved that a factory layout which is based on standardized manufacturing cells can cope with the ever increasing various customer demands. Its plant layout is divided into thirty manufacturing cells each serving a different customer or different customer needs. While the customer demands are totally different the layout of each manufacturing cell is based on standardized modules that can be configured customized by using an IT based "Process Design Guide" (which is the "DNA" of the factory) that allows for optimizing each cell according to the specific customer need. While sophisticated IT is used to configure the plant layout, there is not much IT used to operate each cell as material planning in each cell is done by following standardized replenishment signals that are based on standard lot sizes and "physical" *Kanbans* (however, the optimum lot size and *Kanban* have been calculated by the Process Design Guide upfront).

This example also leads the way to the next enabler which is information technology. Today's IT Systems also usually do not fit an increasing flexibility. This is true for most of industries (not just the pharmaceutical industry). Most ERP systems are still based on a MRP II logic that tries to optimize equipment utilization at first and does not support a pull production philosophy. The Siemens VDO Automotive AG example provide some evidence that tomorrow's IT systems also have to be much more decentralised than they used to be in the past. Otherwise they do not fit with the changing requirements of today's environment.

V.4 The Plant of the Future

In the following section we would like to give an outlook how a plant in the year 2020 could look like, assuming that the pharmaceutical industry will develop in accordance to the scenario described above.

The pharmaceutical world

The pharmaceutical market in the year 2020 is dominated by a limited number of large companies that have emerged through mergers, consolidations and acquisitions. In contrary to these companies there are some niche players that have captured high market shares in specific market segments which are not covered by the big companies.

The activity specialists have followed different strategies: Some have transformed themselves into fully integrated pharmaceutical companies and are now producing generics or ethical drugs and some have expanded their activities towards a global scale, operating as a full-service provider for the big pharmaceutical companies as well as some of the market specialists. The successfully operating activity specialists have managed to prove the ability to leverage resources of its customer and to gain speed and efficiency in the process. Some activity specialists have developed truly proprietary, performance enhancing capabilities and have successfully capitalized on that niche market.

Consolidation has affected the generics industry, too. Some global generics companies have successfully expanded their market presence to a global scale and managed to build up strong brand positions. Especially the global generics companies have managed to capture a significant share of the bio-technological market by successfully producing and selling bio-generics based on proprietary process knowledge.

Main regulations are globally harmonized in a science and risk based way in cooperation with the industry. While the global regulators have started to develop a much broader perspective towards quality, regulators asses product, process and to a certain extent also the quality of the company.

The market for pharmaceutical products has expanded to a USD 1000 billion[29] market. With new consumers mainly in China and India, the market presence of the global pharmaceutical companies has expended widely from US/Europe to the Asian market.

Sophisticated customers are demanding tailored products but a major part of the market share remains focused on traditional products.

Manufacturing has a specific strategic role to support the needs of the different market segments. Companies have a significant manufacturing presence in locations such as China and India. Due to the lack of intellectual property security, many of the plants in those markets still serve as offshore or server factory. However, there are also some Contributor and Lead factories in China and India.

29 Based on the assumption that the projected growth rates for the period from 2005-2010 can be extrapolated for the period between 2010-2020.

As most trade restrictions have been loosened, the location of manufacturing facilities is much more aligned with a specific strategic role that the factory has to fulfill. However, external factors like tax, education, infrastructure and remaining trade restrictions still have a high influence on the decision process where to locate a manufacturing facility.

The products

The products and the way in which they are provided to the customer are designed to satisfy the customer's individual demands.

The products manufactured can generally be described as follows:

1. High volume standard products to address common diseases

While the number of high volume products that are produced on a huge scale in a fairly standardized manner has decreased, there are still some products that address common diseases. As there are still communalities in diseases across many people without big differences between certain groups of people, there is still a market for blockbuster drugs that exceed the USD 1 billion annual sales volumes. These products are provided directly to the customer and are widely available via the internet and other web based systems. The products are fully traceable and therefore the level of counterfeiting in this area has been virtually eliminated. A full follow-up service is also available to the customer and this service allows the company to ensure the success of the products provided.

2. Medium volume standard products to address multi-niche markets

Due to the lack of drugs that address common diseases with an annual sales volume of more than USD 1 billion, most pharmaceutical companies have thus started to question the traditional blockbuster strategy and have started to offer 'multi-buster' drugs, a series of personalized therapies that are able to dominate a certain targeted disease area. Consequently, the new 'multi-buster' strategy requires targeting increasingly differentiated markets with specialized therapies. These products are provided through the same distribution channels like the high volume standard product. However, the manufacturing of these products require a different plant design that is more based on flexibility issues, as it will be required to produce a number of different multi-buster drugs within one plant.

3. Tailored compositions

For patients requiring multiple medicines, combination dosage forms are now available. The traditional solid oral dosage form of supplying one type of medicine in a bottle proved inconvenient for patients requiring more than one medicine and therefore the need to combine medicines into one dose was developed. This combination therapy has many advantages, it simplifies the business of medicine purchase and usage for the patient, improves patient compliance as appropriate quantities are ingested at the appropriate time. Very individual drugs are currently being developed based on genome. These medicines are designed for a small portion of the population and are specially designed medicines for individual patients. The drug delivery systems are also specific to the patient needs, for example, we have many new slow release formulations designed to be specific the personal needs of the patient.

4. Products for different segments of population

In many cases medicine combinations are manufactured, packaged and targeted at specific groupings in terms of age, illness grouping etc.

Innovative drug delivery systems and adjustable drug delivery systems are available in addition to the traditional delivery methods (e.g. pulmonary delivery systems).

Real time diagnostics systems are provided to the customers together with medicines to enhance the use of the products for the patient's benefit.

The plant design

Each plant has a strategic role within a plant network. Besides the strategic role, plant networks will be configured based on the level of flexibility that a plant has to provide. Hence, there are still plants operating that directly provide standardized mass volume output and other plants that have the mission to provide personally tailored healthcare solutions that cure and improve life quality. These two sorts of plants are structured in a totally different manner. Besides that, plants are more integrated than today. Integration refers to the following issues:

1. Integration between primary and secondary manufacturing

Due to the ongoing efforts of reducing batch sizes, re-designing plant networks and the rise of bio-technological products, a strict separation between primary and secondary manufacturing does not exist anymore.

2. Integration between manufacturing and development

Due to the higher focus on process innovations and the increasing requirements with regards to quick scale-ups, there will be a lot less disconnection between the manufacturing and the development organizations.

3. Integration between manufacturing and QC/QA

Advancements in the field of Process Analytical Technologies, the changing customer focus that increasingly concentrates on the internal or external customer rather than the "FDA customer" will enable pharmaceutical companies to integrate much of the Quality Control function into the manufacturing processes. Parametric release has become an industrial standard.

As many QC/QA functions as possible should be directly integrated into the manufacturing cell. All remaining QA functions are regarded as support processes that act in accordance to the process flow. This allows for significant reductions in cycle time.

4. Integration between the "thinking" and the "doing" organization

The section "Create a learning factory" has already leaded way. Organizations that have transferred themselves into excellent organizations have put their improvement efforts on a much broader basis than in the past. Hence, most of the improvement efforts now come from the shop floor rather than the plant management.

The high-volume plant looks quite similar to the pharmaceutical plant of today. However, there is a much higher level of automation. The use of continuous processing is common and gives the plant a greater degree of control and flexibility. Batch size is defined by time and not by volume.

However, there is a big difference between the low-volume plant and today's plants. Plant design is based upon small, flexible, standardized, modular manufacturing cells. Process modularity allows differentiation for, and focus on, the needs of various customers served (e.g. a specific regional or specific demographic market).

Dedicated manufacturing units manufacture highly potent products. These units are specifically designed to handle high potent products with no exposure to the operating personnel or the environment.

Suppliers

As a lot of innovation now comes from the process side, some suppliers have managed to achieve a preferred supplier status – making them also responsible for driving process innovation. With those suppliers, pharmaceutical companies are now frequently performing joined process optimization projects. As those suppliers are also operating on a global scale and have a global network of facilities, supply risks could be reduced and working arrangement creates an environment of 'mutual accountability'. Best-practices are exchanged and the production systems and philosophy between the pharmaceutical company and preferred suppliers are closely aligned. The suppliers involved in the supply of materials have the same approach to quality standards as those of the buyer company. The suppliers are fully integrated into the manufacturing process including planning and control systems.

This close working relationship allows minimum stock level as the philosophy of 'just in time' applies, and guarantees superior Quality Assurance and Customer Service.

In some cases, suppliers manufacture early stages of the products and where they form part of the production process, they are located close to the primary manufacturing facilities.

While manufacturing is still one of the core activities of the big pharmaceutical companies, more non-strategic activities are outsourced to preferred suppliers. Due to the close relationship with those suppliers, the big pharmaceutical companies are still the focal point of the supply chain.

To provide a full healthcare solution to customers, joint ventures and partnerships with other pharmaceutical companies are common, particularly when the use of special technologies is required for manufacture, application and/or presentation of product (e.g. Consumer Health Care).

Purchasing focuses on global contracts, thereby ensuring supply, the combining of volume, value for money, the use of supplier and information pools.

People and organization

The plant of the future is run by operations personnel with a high standard of technical training and know-how which allows them to thoroughly understand manufacturing and business processes. Due to their high level qualification, they can perform a variety of jobs which makes them flexible and adaptable. As they have been trained in diagnostic skills, they are familiar with problem-solving techniques and capable of tracking an issue to its root cause instead of resorting to quick fixes. A change of mindset that has taken place over the years enables them to anticipate issues and deal with them proactively. Excellent communication skills and the ability to use and manage all types of information and data are of paramount importance.

Employees are organized in self-managing teams where members assume responsibility for their own job and are, at the same time, mutually accountable to each other. Although this concept places high demands on the team members, it is very rewarding as it encourages a sense of ownership and identification with the common task.

The teams greatly benefit from the diversity of their members. These are encouraged to continuously learn and improve their qualifications so that they are able to keep pace with technological development, but also to enhance interpersonal and conflict-solving skills. Flexible working time models give individuals greater freedom to pursue a healthy work-life balance and allow teams to act with greater agility and provide excellent service to both their internal and external customers.

Customer orientation is a key objective of the organization of the future. To ensure the highest level of customer service, of both reliability and flexibility, plants are broken down to sub units or "mini plants". These sub-units are organized as process oriented teams, empowered to act at their respective levels of competency. They are an important, well-integrated link in a smooth supply chain delivering either customized solutions or standardized low-cost goods.

The organization of the plant of the future is characterized by flat hierarchies. It had to be changed from function oriented to process oriented to do justice to both the high level of technological development and the rapidly changing conditions and demands. Top performing process oriented teams are agile and flexible enough to quickly respond to these conditions and demands. This also means that decisions have to be made fast and at plant level, based on sound data and risk assessment.

Information systems

The Siemens VDO case already provided some evidence that tomorrow's IT will be less centralised than today. Tomorrow's IT has to support the changing requirements. As already presented in the case of Siemens VDO Automotive AG, one of the most sophisticated part in terms of IT support could be rooted in the decision support to quickly design optimized cell layout that allow for short cycle time, while each cell is still operated mainly manually based on simple replenishment signals. This will allow for high flexibility and adaptability.

Assuming that the whole supply chain will work like a biological cell, decentralization will also become more widespread throughout the supply chain. As a result we assume that information will be shared much more closely and timely than today while each unit within the supply chain will mainly optimize itself on the basis of consistent real-time information and centrally dispersed information concerning possible supply chain constraints. This information will be provided by the focal point within the supply chain which will most likely be the pharmaceutical company. Hence, constraint based intelligent planning software has to be able to provide such information on a real-time basis.

Decentralization will also drive the rise of Auto-ID technologies (e. g. RFID) as they will ensure those closed loop supply chains by attaching the required information to each product. This will ensure a much better and less centralized IT architecture than today and support supply chain wide data integration. However, Enterprise Application Integration (EAI) software that will be based on a global standard will allow the integration of most strategic suppliers into the corporate IT systems. Most transmission protocols will also be easily translated into the required format by using this EAI software.

Process and technology

Intelligent equipment is widely used and the use of smart instruments is now standard which gives beneficial real-time information and minimizes manufacturing down time and cost.

Partnerships exist with main equipment suppliers. Dedicated autonomous software has been developed to allow the exchange of information between the equipment used and the operations systems.

Manufacturing processes are highly predictable and the chemistry is known, understood and monitored using inline Process Analytical Technology. Knowledge has moved from empirical to science-based.

The process knowledge allows smooth transfer of products from development to production and ensures full control of all parameters which in turn assures the quality of the products. The focus has in general moved from compliance to a quality culture.

Issues can be prevented from occurring and the need to react to issues is a rare occurrence ensuring products are manufactured right first time.

Biotechnology and nanotechnology are widely used, particularly in the manufacture of specialized medicines.

In areas of gene therapy, treatment of diseases, understanding the function/structure of biomolecules, biotechnology has provided huge advancements in improvements in patient health.

The biological differences in patients is now a key factor in prescribing medicines and the relevance of human genome to inherited and acquired diseases, allows targeting of medicines to effectively cure illnesses.

Disease and illness are caused largely by damage at the molecular and cellular level. Nanotechnology has allowed us to build a broad range of complex molecular machines ensuring medicine intervention in a sophisticated and controlled way at the cellular and molecular level.

The area of biotechnology has revolutionized the production of specialized medicines and diagnostics (FDA 2004).

Appendices

Questionnaire

Please refer to the following pages 172 to 185 for appendices A to H.

A. General questions

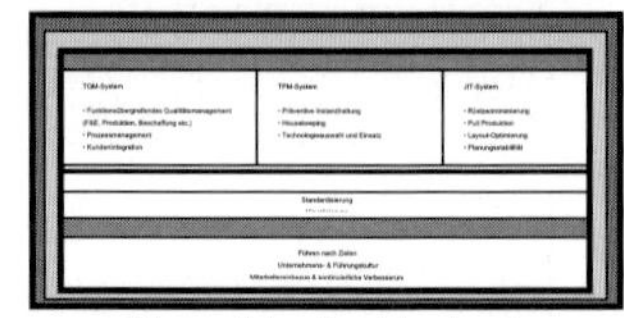

Please, click on the picture to zoom

	Contact information	
A01	Family name	
A02	Given name (s):	
A03	Position or Role:	
A04	Company name:	
A05	Production site:	
A06	Telephone:	
A07	Fax:	
A08	E-Mail:	
A09	Address:	

All data should refer to the year 2003. If the data is not available yet, please take data from 2002!

	How many production sites does your company have?	
A10	Number:	

	What was your sales revenue in 2003?			
A11/A12	Currency	▼		(in Millions)

	Please fill in the cost structure of your company as a percentage of sales (Approximate figures are sufficient):	
A13	R&D:	
A14	Manufacturing Costs:	
A15	General & Administration costs:	
A16	Sales & Marketing costs:	
A17	Margin:	
A18	Total:	**0%**

	Compared to your competitors, indicate the development of your company on the following dimensions within the last 3 years ...	Significantly Lower		Average		Significantly Higher	Don`t know
A19	... Marktet share:	○	○	○	○	○	○
A20	... Sales growth:	○	○	○	○	○	○
A21	... Return on sales:	○	○	○	○	○	○

	Please indicate your company type	
A22	Pharmaceutical company with R&D	○ yes ○ no
A23	Generics manufacturer	○ yes ○ no
A24	Contract manufacturer	○ yes ○ no
A25	Miscellaneous:	

Business environment

For the pharmaceutical industry, how would you classify the expected rate of change of the following dimensions within the next years?

	Dimension	Definition	Strongly decrease		Stagnate		Strongly increase	Don`t know
	Dynamism							
A26	Growth	Expected growth opportunities	O	O	O	O	O	O
A27	Production technology	Changes because of new production technologies	O	O	O	O	O	O
A28	Rate of innovation	Rate of launches of new drugs on the market	O	O	O	O	O	O
A29	R&D spending	R&D expenditures as a percentage of sales	O	O	O	O	O	O
	Heterogeneity of customer preferences							
A30	Customer preferences	Changes due to growing diversity of customer preferences	O	O	O	O	O	O
	Hostilty/Rivalry							
A31	Customer-driven	Changes due to increasing bargaining power of customers (e.g. increasing bargaining power of health insurances)	O	O	O	O	O	O
A32	Supplier-driven	Changes due to increasing bargaining power of suppliers (e.g. increasing price pressure of raw material suppliers)	O	O	O	O	O	O
A33	Existing competitors	Changes due to increasing rivalry among competitors (e.g. rivalry due to increasing market concentration)	O	O	O	O	O	O
A34	New entrants	Changes due to new market entrants (e.g. Start-ups in the field of Biotech)	O	O	O	O	O	O
A35	Substitution	Changes due to increasing substitution of original products (e.g. Substitution through generic products)	O	O	O	O	O	O
A36	Regulatory environment	Changes due to new regulatory requirements (e.g. FDA)	O	O	O	O	O	O

Business strategy

Rate the following competitive initiatives and how important they are in meeting your business strategy

		No importance		Important		Very important	Don`t know
	Price						
A37	Increase operating efficiency	O	O	O	O	O	O
A38	Achieve competitive pricing	O	O	O	O	O	O
A39	Achieve high economies of scale within procurement	O	O	O	O	O	O
A40	Reduce product costs (e.g. reduce complexity of the products)	O	O	O	O	O	O
A41	Achieve costs reductions through process innovations	O	O	O	O	O	O
	Differentiation						
A42	Effectively managing your brand	O	O	O	O	O	O
A43	Pursue innovative marketing strategies	O	O	O	O	O	O
A44	Intensify advertising and product communication	O	O	O	O	O	O
A45	Develop and launch new products	O	O	O	O	O	O
A46	Gain control of distribution channels	O	O	O	O	O	O
	Focus						
A47	Increase proximity to customers	O	O	O	O	O	O
A48	Address niche markets	O	O	O	O	O	O
A49	Produce individual products (e.g. special pharmaceutical forms)	O	O	O	O	O	O

B. Type of production site

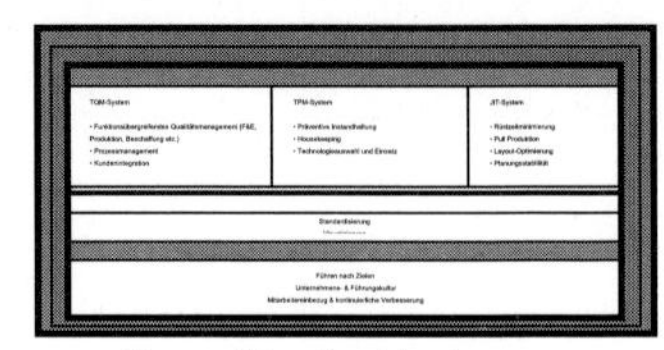

Please, click on the picture to zoom

Manufacturing strategy

Indicate the degree of emphasis which your manufacturing plant places on the following activities

		No importance		Important		Very important	Don`t know
	Increase of Flexibility						
B01	Reduce cycle time	○	○	○	○	○	○
B02	Reduce Set-up time	○	○	○	○	○	○
B03	Increase flexibility of machines and labour	○	○	○	○	○	○
B04	Accelerate new product introductions (scale-ups)	○	○	○	○	○	○
	Increase Quality						
B05	Reduce process variance through statistical process control	○	○	○	○	○	○
B06	Increase supplier quality performance	○	○	○	○	○	○
B07	Reduce scrap rates	○	○	○	○	○	○
	Increase Service Level						
B08	Reduce lead time	○	○	○	○	○	○
B09	Increase on-time delivery rate	○	○	○	○	○	○
	Reduce costs						
B10	Reduce stock	○	○	○	○	○	○
B11	Increase asset utilisation (e.g. machines)	○	○	○	○	○	○
B12	Increase employee productivity	○	○	○	○	○	○
B13	Increase capital investment productivity	○	○	○	○	○	○

	Indicate how your production site is organised	
B14	○ Cost-center	○ Profit-center

	Indicate the proportion of products manufactured at your plant	
B15	Original (ethical) products:	%
B16	Generics:	%
B17	Contract manufacturing:	%

	Indicate the different types of products produced at your plant			
B18/B19	Synthetic products:	%	Phytopharmaceutical products:	%
B20/B21	Bio-technological products:	%	Other products:	%

	Headcount structure		Headcount structure concerning volume dependability	
B22	API production:		Note: Volume-dependant relates to the number of actively working employees that have a direct impact on the produced volume	
B23	Pharmaceutical production:			
B24/B25	Packaging:		**Volume dependant employees**	
B26	Quality control/Quality assurance:		that are distributed as follows:	
B27/B28	Maintenance:		Productive	
B29/B30	Material management (Procurement/Logistics):		Service	
B31/B32	IT-Support:		Quality control	
B33	Miscellaneous (Selling, general & admin. staff):			
B34			**Non volume dependant employees**	
			which are distributed as follows:	
B35			Service	
B36			Quality control	
B37/B38	Overall (number of employees at the site):	0		

	Procurement and supplier structure (supplier count: number of suppliers for direct & indirect materials and services)			
B39/B40	Suppliers - Indirect materials:		Overall number of orders:	
B41/B42	Suppliers - direct materials:		Percentage of master agreements (%):	%
B43	Suppliers - services:			
B44/B45	Overall nr. of suppliers in the supplier base:	0	Total amount purchased: ▼	

Production structure

	Indicate the volume of bulk goods produced in 2003		
		Unit	Measure
B46	Solid forms (tablets, capsules etc.):	Pieces	
B47	Liquids	Litre	
B48	Sterile liquids	Litre	
B49	Semi solid forms	kg	
	Indicate the volume of bulk goods that were packed at your site (2003)		
		Unit	Measure
B50	Solid forms	Pieces	
B51	Liquids	Litre	
B52	Sterile liquids	Litre	
B53	Semi solid forms	kg	
	Indicate the number of packed units (boxes) at your site (2003)		
		Unit	Measure
B54	Solid forms	Packed units	
B55	Liquids	Packed units	
B56	Sterile liquids	Packed units	
B57	Semi solid forms	Packed units	

Vertical range of manufacture - Indicate the number of different operating procedures performed at your site (e.g. weighing, mixing, granulate, pelleting, packaging etc.)

B58/B59/B60	e.g. 20% of the products run through 1 operating procedure, remaining 80% of the products run through 2-5 operating procedures i.e., 20%, 80%, 0%	1 operating procedure		2-5 operating procedures		More than 5 operating procedures	

Plant Size

B61	Size of the production area :		m^2
B62	Size of the warehousing area:		m^2
B63	Overall size of the site :		m^2

	Order management structure (2003)	
B64	Number of delivered orders:	
B65	Average number of items per order:	

	Innovation structure (2003)	
B66	Number of new product introductions at the site (2003):	
B67	Number of launched stock keeping units (SKU) at the site (2003):	
B68	Number of inspections (FDA, EHS etc.) at the site within the last 3 years:	

	Age of the production technology	
B69	Percentage of machines which are less than 3 years old:	%
B70	Percentage of machines that are between 3 and 5 years old:	%
B71	Percentage of machines that are between 6 and 10 years old:	%
B72	Percentage of machines that are older than 10 years:	%

	Level of automation	
B73	Percentage of machines that are manually operated	%
B74	Percentage of machines that are operated with IT-support	%
B75	Percentage of machines that are fully automated (without supervision)	%

proceed

C. Management System

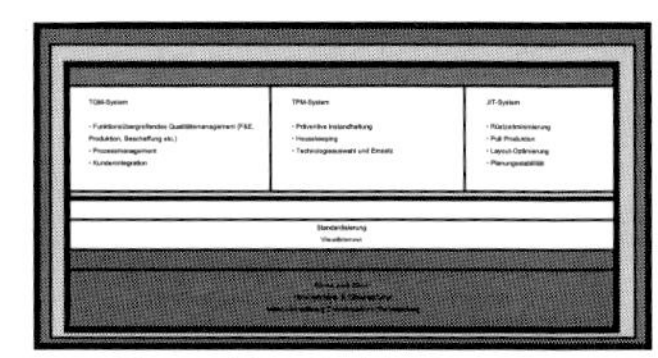

Please, click on the picture to zoom

	Direction setting	Strongly disagree				Strongly agree	Don`t know
C01	Our production site has a formal and documented strategy and strategy deployment process that is closely related to our corporate mission statement	○	○	○	○	○	○
C02	Our vision, mission and strategy is broadly communicated and lived by our employees.	○	○	○	○	○	○
C03	Goals and objectives of the manufacturing unit are closely linked and consistent with corporate objectives. The production sites have a clear focus.	○	○	○	○	○	○
C04	Goals and objectives of manufacturing and other functions (e.g. Marketing) are consistent and closely linked to each other.	○	○	○	○	○	○
C05	The overall objectives of the production site are closely linked to the team or personal objectives of our shop-floor teams and employees.	○	○	○	○	○	○
C06	I feel that manufacturing managers (Head of manufacturing, site-leader etc.) have a good understanding of how the corporate/divisional strategy is formed.	○	○	○	○	○	○
C07	I feel that manufacturing managers are an integral part of the strategy formulation process and their inputs are part of the corporate/divisional strategy.	○	○	○	○	○	○
C08	I feel that manufacturing manager know exactly what the most important criteria for manufacturing jobs are (i.e. low cost, delivery, quality etc.)	○	○	○	○	○	○

	Management committment and company culture	Strongly disagree				Strongly agree	Don`t know
C09	Plant management empowers employees to continuously improve the processes and to reduce failure- and scrap rates	○	○	○	○	○	○
C10	Plant management is personally involved in improvement projects.	○	○	○	○	○	○
C11	The company has an open communication culture. There is a good flow of information between the departments and the different management levels	○	○	○	○	○	○
C12	Employees are encouraged to bypass formal channels to get their work done.	○	○	○	○	○	○
C13	Problems (e.g. reclamation etc.) are always traced back to their origin to identify root causes and to prevent doing the same mistakes twice.	○	○	○	○	○	○
C14	We continously try to transfer central quality control activities to the operating units and to reduce the number of staff that is solely responsible for QC.	○	○	○	○	○	○
C15	The achievement of high quality standards is primarily the task of our QA/QC departments	○	○	○	○	○	○
C16	Our employees continuously strive to reduce any kind of waste (e.g. waste of time waste of production space etc.).	○	○	○	○	○	○

	Employee involvement and continuous improvement	Strongly disagree				Strongly agree	Don`t know
C17	We have implemented tools and methods to deploy a continuous improvement process	O	O	O	O	O	O
C18	Shop-floor employees actively drive suggestion programmes	O	O	O	O	O	O
C19	Our plant form teams to solve problems	O	O	O	O	O	O
C20	Problem solving teams have helped to improve manufacturing processes at this plant	O	O	O	O	O	O
C21	A signifcant percentage of income of an average production worker comes from bonus programmes due to realised suggestions for improvements	O	O	O	O	O	O
	Please indicate which of the following statements are true for your work teams						
C22	We have organized production employees into teams in production areas. Team leadership rotates among team members.	O yes O no					
C23	We have organized production employees into teams in production areas. For each team there is one dedicated team member that is responsible for supervisory tasks.	O yes O no					
C24	We have organized production employees into teams in production areas. For team leadership we have an additional supervisory level in our organization.	O yes O no					
C25	We do not organize production employees into teams	O yes O no					

	Functional integration and qualification	Strongly disagree				Strongly agree	Don`t know
C26	Employees at this plant can be deployed to different tasks	O	O	O	O	O	O
C27	Each of our employees within our work teams (in case workers are organized as teams) is cross-trained so that they can fill-in for others when necessary	O	O	O	O	O	O
C28	At this plant we have implemented a formal programme to increase the flexibility o our production workers. Employees rotate to maintain their qualification	O	O	O	O	O	O
C29	We continuously invest in training and qualification of our workers. We have a dedicated development and qualification programme for our production workers.	O	O	O	O	O	O

proceed

D. Total Quality Management System

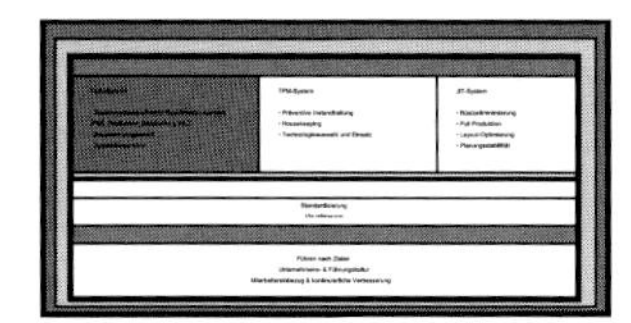

Please, click on the picture to zoom

	Process management	Strongly disagree				Strongly agree	Don`t know
D01	In our company processes are well documented. This is valid for direct processes as well as indirect processes (e.g. HR, controlling etc.).	○	○	○	○	○	○
D02	We continuously measure the quality of our processes by using process measures (e.g. On-time-in-full delivery rate).	○	○	○	○	○	○
D03	Our process measures are directly linked to our plant objectives.	○	○	○	○	○	○
D04	In our company there are dedicated process owners that are responsible for planning, management and improvement of their processes.	○	○	○	○	○	○
D05	A large percentage of equipment on the shop floor is currently under statistical quality control	○	○	○	○	○	○
D06	We make use of statistical process control to reduce variances in processes	○	○	○	○	○	○

	Cross functional product development	Strongly disagree				Strongly agree	Don`t know
D07	Manufacturing engineers (e.g. Industrial engineers) are involved to a great extent in the development of a new drug formulation and the development of the necessary production processes.	○	○	○	○	○	○
D08	In our company product and process development are closely linked to each other.	○	○	○	○	○	○
D09	Due to close collaboration between the R&D and the manufacturing department, we could significantly shorten our time for product launches ("Scale-ups") in our plant	○	○	○	○	○	○
D10	For the last couple of years we have not got any delays in product launches at our plant.	○	○	○	○	○	○

	Customer involvement	Strongly disagree				Strongly agree	Don`t know
D11	We are frequently in close contact with our customers	○	○	○	○	○	○
D12	Our customers frequently give us feedback on quality and delivery performance.	○	○	○	○	○	○
D13	We regularly survey our customer`s requirements	○	○	○	○	○	○
D14	We regularly conduct customer satisfaction surveys.	○	○	○	○	○	○
D15	We always deliver on time	○	○	○	○	○	○

	Supplier quality management	Strongly disagree				Strongly agree	Don`t know
D16	Quality is our number one criterion in selecting suppliers	○	○	○	○	○	○
D17	We use mostly suppliers that we have certified	○	○	○	○	○	○
D18	For a large percentage of suppliers we do not perform any inspections of the incoming parts/materials.	○	○	○	○	○	○
D19	Inspections of incoming materials are usually performed in proportion of the past quality performance or type of supplier.	○	○	○	○	○	○
D20	Basically, we inspect 100% of our incoming shipments.	○	○	○	○	○	○
D21	We jointly develop our processes with our suppliers to continuously improve our process quality	○	○	○	○	○	○

proceed

E. Total Productive Maintenance System

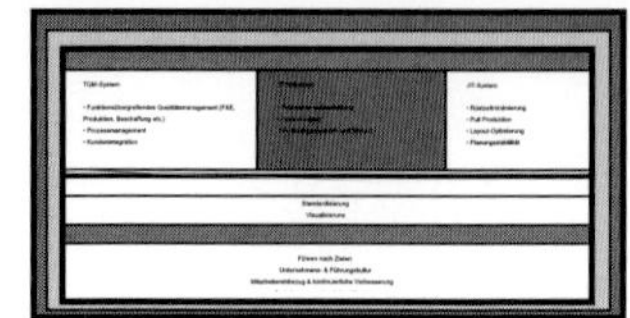

Please, click on the picture to zoom

	Preventive Maintenance	Strongly disagree				Strongly agree	Don`t know
E01	We have a formal programme for maintaining our machines and equipment	O	O	O	O	O	O
E02	Maintenance plans and checklists are posted closely to our machines and maintenance jobs are documented	O	O	O	O	O	O
E03	We emphazise good maintenance as a strategy for increasing quality and planning for compliance.	O	O	O	O	O	O
E04	All potential bottleneck machines are identified and supplied with additional spare parts.	O	O	O	O	O	O
E05	We continuously optimize our maintenance programme based on a dedicated failure analysis.	O	O	O	O	O	O
E06	Our maintenance department focuses on assisting machine operators perform their own preventative maintenance	O	O	O	O	O	O
E07	Our machine operators are actively involved into the decision making process when we descide to buy new machines.	O	O	O	O	O	O

	Technology assessment and usage	Strongly disagree				Strongly agree	Don`t know
E08	Our plant stays at the leading edge of new technology in our industry.	O	O	O	O	O	O
E09	We are constantly screening the market for new production technology and asses new technology concerning its technical and financial benefit.	O	O	O	O	O	O
E10	We are using new technology very effectively.	O	O	O	O	O	O
E11	We actively develop proprietary equipment.	O	O	O	O	O	O
E12	We rely on vendors for most of our equipment	O	O	O	O	O	O
E13	Part of our equipment is patented by the firm`s patents	O	O	O	O	O	O
E14	Proprietary process technology and equipment helps us gain a competitive advantage.	O	O	O	O	O	O

	Housekeeping	Strongly disagree				Strongly agree	Don`t know
E15	Our employees strive to keep our plant neat and clean.	O	O	O	O	O	O
E16	Our plant procedures emphasize putting all tools and fixtures in their place	O	O	O	O	O	O
E17	We have a housekeeping check list to continuously monitor the condition and cleanness of our machines and equipment	O	O	O	O	O	O
	In case you have a housekeeping checklist, please indicate which of the following criteria are on this check list.						
E18	Cleanness of facilities and equipment	O yes O no					
E19	Clear painting and labeling of machines and equipment	O yes O no					
E20	Clear labeling of aisleways, work- and warehousing areas.	O yes O no					
E21	Condition and order of tools and equipment:	O yes O no					

proceed

F. Just in Time System

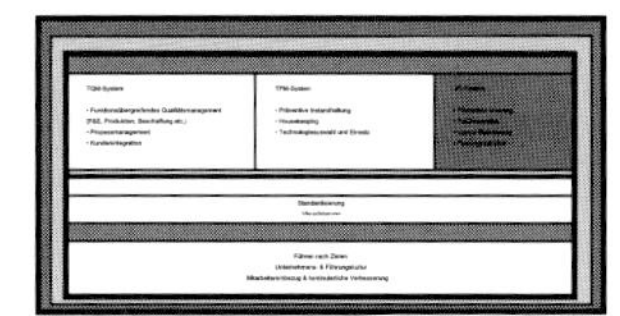

Please, click on the picture to zoom

	Set-up time reduction						
		Strongly disagree				Strongly agree	Don`t know
F01	We are continuously working to lower set-up times in our plant	O	O	O	O	O	O
F02	We have low set-up times of equipment in our plant	O	O	O	O	O	O
F03	Our crews practice set-ups to reduce the time required	O	O	O	O	O	O
F04	To increase the flexibility, we put high emphasis on reducing lot sizes in our plant.	O	O	O	O	O	O
F05	We have managed to schedule a big portion of our set-ups so that the regular up-time of our machines is usually not effected.	O	O	O	O	O	O

	Pull Production						
		Strongly disagree				Strongly agree	Don`t know
F06	Our production schedule is designed to allow for catching up, due to production stoppages for problems (e.g quality problems)	O	O	O	O	O	O
F07	We use kanban squares, containers or signals for production control	O	O	O	O	O	O
F08	Vendors fill out kanban containers, rather than filling our purchasing orders.	O	O	O	O	O	O
F09	We can depend upon on-time delivery from our suppliers	O	O	O	O	O	O
F10	We deliver our customers on a JIT-basis.	O	O	O	O	O	O

	Layout optimization						
		Strongly disagree				Strongly agree	Don`t know
F11	Our processes are located close together so that material handling and part storage are minimized.	O	O	O	O	O	O
F12	Products are classified into groups with similar processing requirements to reduce set-up times	O	O	O	O	O	O
F13	Products are classified into groups with similar routing requirements to reduce transportation time	O	O	O	O	O	O
F14	We have laid out the shop floor so that processes and machines are in close proximity to each other.	O	O	O	O	O	O
F15	The layout of the shop floor facilitates low inventories and fast throughput	O	O	O	O	O	O
F16	As we have classified our products based on their specific requirements our shop floor lay-out can be characterized as separated into "mini-plants"	O	O	O	O	O	O

	Planning adherence						
		Strongly disagree				Strongly agree	Don`t know
F17	We usually meet our production plans every day.	O	O	O	O	O	O
F18	We know the root causes of variance in our production schedule and are continuously trying to eliminate them.	O	O	O	O	O	O
F19	To increase our planing adherence we share data with customers and suppliers based on a rolling production plan	O	O	O	O	O	O
F20	We have smoothly leveled our production capacity througout the whole production process.	O	O	O	O	O	O
F21	Our plant has flexible working shift models so that we can easily adjust our production capacity according to current demand changes.	O	O	O	O	O	O

proceed

G. Basic elements

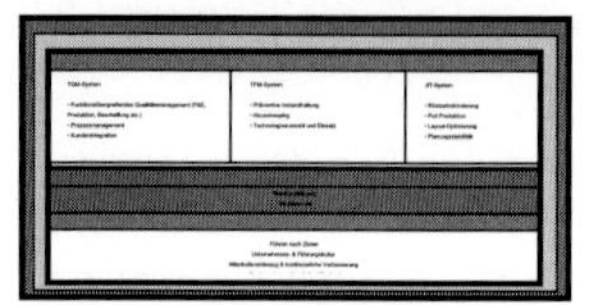

Please, click on the picture to zoom

	Standardisation and simplification	Strongly disagree				Strongly agree	Don´t know
G01	We emphasize standardisation as a strategy for continuously improving our processes, machines and products.	O	O	O	O	O	O
G02	We use our documented operating procedures to standardize our processes (e.g. set-ups)	O	O	O	O	O	O
G03	Optimized operating procedure (e.g. shortened set-ups) are documented as best-practice process and rolled-out throughout the whole plant.	O	O	O	O	O	O
G04	Standardized functional descriptions have reduced the period of vocational training for new employees.	O	O	O	O	O	O
G05	We use standardised machines and equipment (e.g. standardised machine design, standardised spare parts etc.) to achieve a high up-time of our machines.	O	O	O	O	O	O
G06	By using standardised machines and fixtures we could significantly lower our cost of materials for spare parts.	O	O	O	O	O	O

	Visual management	Strongly disagree				Strongly agree	Don´t know
G07	Performance charts at each of our production process (e.g. packaging) indicate anual performance objectivees.	O	O	O	O	O	O
G08	Technical documents (e.g. Maintenance documents) and workplace information (e.g. standardised inspection procedures, team structures) are posted on the shop floor and are easily accessible and visible for all workers.	O	O	O	O	O	O
G09	Charts showing the current performance status (e.g. current scrap-rates, current up-times etc.) are posted on the shop floor and visible for everyone	O	O	O	O	O	O
G10	Charts showing current takt times and schedule compliance (e.g. Andonboards) are posted on the shop floor and visible for everyone	O	O	O	O	O	O

proceed

H. Performance of the plant

Please indicate the sales revenue of your production site in 2003			
/H02 Currency		Tsd.	Please notice! Figures are in Tsd.

To ensure the comparability of the production sites its important that you just fill in the figures that are related to the manufacturing part of your site. In case that you also have part of your R&D, Sales, Marketing etc. at your site, please list costs related to those functions under other costs.

Cost structure		
Please indicate the accounting principles on which the data is based (e.g. US GAAP)		
Material costs		
Direct material costs (Costs for raw materials and preliminary produts)		Tsd.
Indirect material costs (Costs for operating supplies as well services):		Tsd.
Labour costs		
Direct labour costs (volume dependant employees):		Tsd.
Indirect labour costs (e.g. plant management, industrial engineering, maintenance etc.):		Tsd.
Plant, property and equipment costs		
Costs for machines & tools (incl. costs for depreciation, electricity of the machines etc.):		Tsd.
Costs for property and plant (incl. costs of depreciation and other costs for electricity, water etc.):		Tsd.
"Other costs"		
Corporate allocations (to central departments or headquarter)		Tsd.
Other costs (e.g. Sales & clerical, Marketing, R&D located at the dedicated plant):		Tsd.

Asset structure - Please indicate the following assets of your company (2003)			
Total assets		Mio.	Please notice! Figures in mio.
Machinery value (machines & other equipment)		Mio.	

Please indicate how you would rate the performance of your production site compared to the industry, based on the following criterias...

Category	Sub category	Defined as the capability ...	Significantly lower				Significantly better	Don`t know
Price	Costs	... to compete on price	O	O	O	O	O	O
Quality	Conformance	... to offer consistent quality	O	O	O	O	O	O
	Significantly lower	... to provide high perfromance products with a functionality	O	O	O	O	O	O
Delivery	Lead time	...deliver products quickly	O	O	O	O	O	O
	Dependability	... to deliver in full on time (as promised)	O	O	O	O	O	O
Flexibility	Volume flexibility	... to respond to swings in volume	O	O	O	O	O	O
	New product flexibility	...to introduce new products quickly.	O	O	O	O	O	O
	Product mix flexibility	...to produce a broad product line at your site	O	O	O	O	O	O

	Quality performance (2003)				
	Category	**Definition**	Unit	Measure	Don`t know
H22	Complaint rate (customer)	Number of complaints as a percentage of all customer orders delivered.	%		☐
H23	Rejected batches	Number of released batches as a percentage of all batches produced.	%		☐
H24	Complaint rate (supplier)	Number of rejected batches as a percentage of all batches received (from your supplier).	%		☐
H25	Costs of quality	Overall costs for quality insurance in 2003 (usually the total number from your cost center(s) QC/QA).	Costs in thousand		☐
H26	Yield	Overall scrap rate as a percentage of the total volume produced.	%	○ < 3% ○ 3-8% ○ >8%	☐

	Devlivery performance (2003)				
	Category	**Definition**	Unit	Measure	Don`t know
H28	Service level - Availability	Days per month in which requested products from your customer are available at your warehouse.	Days		☐
H29	Service level - Delivery	Number of orders shipped in time from your site (max. +/- 5 days of the agreed shipment day) and in the right quantity (max. +/- 5% of the agreed quantity).	%		☐
H30	Service level (supplier)	Number of orders shipped in time and in the right quantityto your site from your suppliers.	%		☐

	JIT performance (2003)				
	Category	**Definition**	Unit	Measure	Don`t know
H31	Volume flexibility	Freezing period in which you do not allow any changes of your production schedule.	Days		☐
H32	Production-against-schedule	Number of released production orders as scheduled as a percentage of all production orders released within your freezing period.	%		☐
H33	Batch size - Packaging	(Estimated) average batch size at your packaging production line	Packaging units ○ <1'000 ○ 1'001-10'000 ○ >10'000		☐
H34	Set-up times	Please indicate the distribution of your set up times at your packaging line e.g. 30% of your set-up times are between 15-30 minutes, 20% between 30-60 minutes etc.	< 15 min.		☐
H35			15-30 min.		
H36			31-60 min.		
H37			61-90 min.		
H38			> 90 min.		
H39	Raw material turns	Annual outward raw material movements divided by average annual raw material inventory stocks in 2003	Number		☐
H40	WIP turns	Annual outward work-in process material movements divided by average annual WIP-inventory stocks in 2003	Number		☐
H41	Finished goods turns	Annual outward finished goods material movements divided by average annual finished goods stocks in 2003	Number		☐
H42	Cycle time	Cycle time (from weighing to packaging). e.g. 30% of all products have a cycle time of approximately 16-29 days. 70% of all products have a cycle time of more than 30 days.	< 15 days		☐
H43			16-29 days		
H44			> 30 days		

	TPM performance (2003)				
	Category	**Definition**	Unit	Measure	Don`t know
	Technical capacity	*All numbers concerning capacity are measured as a percentage of the overall technical capacity of all machines based on the assumption that machines are running 7 days a week for 24 hours.*		*100%*	
H45	Available capacity	Technical capacity after deduction of all planned down-times due to maintenance works (as a percentage of the technical capacitiy)	%		☐
H46	Effective capacity	Effectively with orders occupied capacity in 2003 (as a percentage of the technical capacity).	%		☐
H47	Shift-model	Number of shifts per week	Number		☐
H48	Maintenance costs	Overall costs for maintenance in 2003 (usually the total number from your cost center "maintenance").	Costs in thousand		☐
H49	Unscheduled Maintenance	Proportion of unscheduled maintenance work as a percentage of the overal time spent for maintenance works (e.g. 70% scheduled maintenance, 30% unscheduled maintenance).	%		☐

	Management System Performance Indicators (2003)				
	Category	**Definition**	Unit	Measure	Don`t know
H50	Management Layers	Number of management levels between production workers and the highest ranking manager at the site (e.g. Worker - Supervisor - Manager of the department - Site-leader = 4 Levels)	Number		☐
H51	Group work	Percentage of production workers that are organized in teams.	%		☐
H52	Job classifications	Estimated number of different job classifications in the production department (e.g. Maintenance, process engineering, packaging etc.)	Number		☐
H53	Functional integration	Number of employees that can perform more than 3 jobs.	%		☐
H54	Suggestions (Quantity)	Average number of suggestions per employee.	Number		☐
H55	Suggestions (Quality)	Estimated total savings due to suggestions that were implemented (2003).	Tsd.		☐
H56	Employee turnover	Employee turnover at your site (comprises all kinds of fluctuations of employees: terminations, expired work contracts, retirements etc.).	%		☐
H57	Sick leave	Total time of employees absent (e.g. sich leave) as a percentage of the total working time .	%		☐
H58	Training	Number of training days per employee (all kinds of training off- and on the job)	Number		☐
H59	Level of qualification	Number of unskilled employees as a percentage of the total number of employee at your site	%		☐

You have completed the survey.

Thank you very much for your participation!

Please save the survey on your hard disk and email the file to

michael.kickuth@unisg.ch

References

Bell, M. 2003. Unravelling the Pharmaceutical Industry; http://www.adl.com/insights/studies/pdf/emerging_business_models_pharma.pdf.

Blackburn, J. D. 1991. Time-based competition: the next battleground in American manufacturing. Homewood, IL: Dow Jones-Irwin.

Caspar, L. 2003. Aufsichtsmethoden für das 21. Jahrhundert, Basler Zeitung, 208 ed.: 11-12. Basel.

Champion, D. 2001. Mastering the Value Chain. Harvard Business Review (June).

Crawford, K. M. 1988. A study of JIT implementation and operation problems. International Journal of Production Research, 26 (9): 1561-1568.

Davenport, T. H. 1993. Process innovation: reengineering work through information technology. Boston (Mass.): Harvard Business School.

De Meyer, A. 1990. Lasting Improvements in Manufacturing Performance: In Search of a New Theory. Journal of Operations Management, 9 (2): 168-184.

De Meyer, A. 1993. Quality has failed to lead to Profitability. Personnel Management, 25 (8): 14.

Delbridge, R., Turnbull, P. 1993. Turning Japanese? The Adoption and Adaptation of Manufacturing Systems in the UK. Cardiff, UK: Cardiff Business School.

DiMasi. 2001. Tufts center for the study of drug development pegs costs of a new prescription drug at $802 million.: Tufts University.

Economist. 2002. Trouble in the making. Economist, 364 (8288): 49-50.

Elger, T., Smith, C. (Eds). 1993. Global Japanization. London: Routledge.

Ewers, C., Küppers, S., Weinmann, H. 2002. Pharma Supply Chain: Neue Wege zu einer effizienten Wertschöpfungskette. ECV · Editio Cantor Verlag, Aulendorf.

FDA, U. S. Department of Health and Human Services; Pharmaceutical cGMPs for the 21st century - A Risk-Based Approach; http://www.fda.gov/cder/gmp/2ndProgressRept_Plan.htm.

FDA, U. S. Department of Health and Human Services; Summary Progress Report: Pharmaceutical cGMPs for the 21st Century: A Risk-Based Approach; http://www.fda.gov/cder/gmp/21stcenturysummary.htm.

FDA, U. S. Department of Health and Human Services; Guidance for Industry, Quality Systems Approach to Pharmaceutical Current Good Manufacturing Practice Regulations; http://www.fda.gov/cder/guidance/6452dft.htm.

FDA, U.S., Department of Health and Human Services; Innovation and Continuous Improvement in Pharmaceutical Manufacuring; http://www.fda.gov/cder/gmp2004/manufSciWP.pdf.

Ferdows, K. 1997. Making the most of foreign factories. Harvard Business Review, March-April.

Fiol, C. M. 1991. Managing Culture as a Competitive Ressourc: An Identity-Based View of Sustainable Competitive Advantage. Journal of Management, 17 (1): 191.

Hammer, M. 1996. Beyond Reengineering: How the Process-Centred Organization is Changing our Work and our Lives. London: HarperCollins.

Hammer, M. C., James. 1993. Reengineering the Corporation: a Manifesto for Business revolution. New York: HarperBusiness.

Hayes, R. H., Wheelwright, S. C., Clark, K. B. 1989. Measuring manufacturing performance, McKinsey Quarterly: 73-82: McKinsey & Company, Inc.

Hayes, R. H., Pisano, G. P. 1994. Beyond World-Class: The New Manufacturing Strategy. Harvard Business Review, 72 (1): 77-86.

Hayes, R. H., Pisano, G. P., Upton, D. M., Wheelwright, S. C. 2005. Operations, Strategy, and Technology: Pursuing the Competitive Edge. New York: Wiley.

Imai, M. 1986. Kaizen: The Key to Japanese Competitive Success. New York: Random House.

Ittner, C. D., Larcker, D. F. 1997. The Performance Effects of Process Management Techniques. Management Science, 43: 522-534.

Jaikumar, R. 1986. Postindustrial manufacturing. Harvard Business Review, November-December: 69-76.

Jones, B. E. 1987. The Manufacture of Hard Gelatin Capsules, Hard Capsules: Development - Technology. New York: Pharmaceutical Press.

Juran, J. 1986. Quality by Design: The New Steps for Planning Quality into Goods and Services (Revised edition). New York: Free Press.

Kager, P., Mozeson, M. 2000. Supply Chain: The forgotten Factor. Pharmaceutical Executive: 84-96.

Lawrence, P. R., Lorsch, J. W. 1967. New management job: the integrator. Harvard Business Review, 45 (6): 142-151.

Leonard-Barton, D. 1992. Core Capabilities and Core Rigidities: A Paradox in Managing new Product Development. Strategic Management Journal, 13 (5): 111-125.

Lieberman, M. B., Demeester, L. 1999. Inventory Reduction and Productivity Growth: Linkage in the Japanese Automotive Industry. Management Science, 45 (4): 466.

Liker, J. K. 2004. The Toyota Way: 14 Management Principles from the World's Greatest Manufacturer. New York: McGraw-Hill.

Liker, J. K., Choi, T. Y. 2004. Building Deep Supplier Relationships. Harvard Business Review, December.

Loch, C. H. 1998. Management Quality, Continuous Improvement and Growth in the Factory. Fontainebleau: INSEAD.

Loch, C. H., Heyden, L., Wasserhove, L., Huchzermeier, A., Escalle, C. 2003. Industrial Excellence - Management Quality in Manufacturing. Berlin: Springer.

Loch, C. H., Demeester, L., Eichler, K. 2004. Organic Production Systems: What the Biological Cell Can Teach Us About Manufacturing. Manufacturing & Service Operations Management, 6 (2): 115-132.

Loch, C. H., Seidel, M., Chahil, S. 2005. Quo Vadis, Automotive Industry? A Vision of Possible Industry Transformations. European Management Journal, 23 (4): 439-449.

Lockwood, G. 2003. Strategic View 2003 - Pharmaceutical and Healthcare Products Industry (Executive Summary). Lockwood Greene.

Miller, J., Roth, A. V. 1994. A taxonomy of Manufacturing Strategies. Management Science, 40 (3): 285-301.

Nevins, J. L. W., Daniel E. 1989. Concurrent design of Products and Processes: A Strategy for the next Generation in Manufacturing. New York: McGraw-Hill.

Peters, T. J., Waterman, R. H. 1982. In search of excellence: Lessons from America's best-run companies. New York: Harpers & Row.

Pfizer. 1999. Pfizer turns 150; http://www.ul.ie/~childsp/CinA/Issue59/TOC11_Pzifer.htm.

Pfizer. 2003. Pfizer Annual Report 2003: Pfizer.

Pfizer. 2004. Pfizer Annual Report 2004: Pfizer.

PhRMA. 2004. Pharma Industry Profile. In: P. R. a. M. o. Amerika (Ed.). Washington D.C.

Pisano, G., Wheelwright, S. 1995. High-Tech R&D. Harvard Business Review: 93-105.

Pisano, G., Günthardt, D. 2003. Wo sich Hollywood und Detroit treffen. Neue Zürcher Zeitung, 11.08.2003.

Porter, E. M. 1980. Competitive strategy: techniques for Analyzing Industries & Competitors. New York: The Free Press.

Porter, E. M. 1996. What is Strategy? Harvard Business Review, 74 (6): 61-78.

Powell, T. C. 1995. Total Quality Management as Competitive Advantage: a Review and Empirical Study. Strategic Management Journal, 16 (1): 15-37.

Powell, W. W., Koput, K. W., Smith-Doerr, L. 1996. Interorganizational collaboration and the locus of innovation; Networks of learning in biotechnology. Administrative Science Quarterly, 41 (1): 116-145.

Rath & Strong. 2000. Rath & Strong's 6-Sigma Pocket Guide: Rath & Strong.

Reuters. 2001. Pharmaceutical R&D Outsourcing strategies. In: Reuters (Ed.).

Reuters. 2003. The blockbuster drug outlook to 2007: Identifying, creating and maintaining the pharmaceutical industry`s growth drivers, Reuters Business Insight - Healthcare: 11-13: Reuters.

Rodengen, J. L. 1999. The Legend of Pfizer. Fort Lauderdale: Write Stuff Syndicate.

Rössl, D. 1990. Die Entwicklung eines Bezugsrahmen und seine Stellung im Forschungsprozess. Journal für Betriebswirtschaft, 2 (81-94).

Rumelt, R. P. 1991. Heterogeneity under Competition. Economic Inquiry, 29 (4): 774.

Safayeni, F. 1991. The Difficulties of Just-In-Time Implementation: A Classification Scheme. International Journal of Operations & Production Management, 11 (7): 27-36.

Schmenner, R. W. 1991. International Factory Productivity Gains. Journal of Management, 10 (2): 229-254.

Schonberger, R. J. 1982. The Transfer of Japanese Manufacturing Management Approaches to U.S. Industry. Academy of Management Review, 7 (3): 479-487.

Sirisha, D., Mukund, A. 2002. 6-Sigma at GE. ECCH College.

Skinner, W. 1969. Manufacturing: Missing Link in Corporate Strategy. Harvard Business Review (May/June): 136-145.

Skinner, W. 1974. The focused factory, Harvard Business Review, Vol. 52: 113-121: Harvard Business School Publication Corp.

Spaethe, T. U. 2001. Die Pharmaindustrie und die Biotechnologie: Analyse der Veränderungen in der Industriestruktur. Universität Regensburg, Regensburg.

Spath, D., Korge, A., Scholtz, O. 2003. Mensch, Technik und Organisation – ganzheitlich zu effizienterer Produktion, RATIO - Neues vom RKW Baden-Württemberg, Vol. 9: 9-12.

Spears & Bowen. 1999. Decoding the DNA of the Toyota Production System. Harvard Business Review, 77 (5): 96.

Stalk Jr., G. 1988. Time: The Next Source of Competitive Advantage. Harvard Business Review, 66 (4): 41.

Stalk Jr., G., Webber, A. M. 1993. Japan's dark side of time. Harvard Business Review, 71 (4): 93-102.

Swamidass, P. M., Newell, W. T. 1987. Manufacturing Strategy, Environmental Uncertainty and Performance: A Path Analytic Model. Management Science, 33 (4): 509.

VFA. 2005. The Pharmaceutical Market: Verband Forschender Arzneimittelhersteller e.V. (German Association or Research-Based Pharmaceutical Companies).

Vocke, R., Jäger, M. 2004. Supply Chain Excellence in der Pharmaindustrie. Pharm. Ind., 66 (2): 148-155.

Walton, M. 1986. The Deming Management Method. New York: The Berkeley Publishing Group.

Ward, P. T., Leong, G. K. 1995. The six Ps of Manufacturing Strategy. International Journal of Operations & Production Management, 15 (12): 32-45.

Warren McFarlan, F., DeLacey, B. J. 2004. Pfizer's Virtual CIO. Harvard Business School Cases: 16.

Wernerfelt, B. 1984. A Resource-Based View of the Firm. Strategic Management Journal, 5 (2): 171-180.

Wheelwright, S. C., Hayes, R. H. 1985. Competing through manufacturing. Harvard Business Review, 63 (1): 99-109.

Wheelwright, S. C., Clark, K. 1992. Competing Through Development Capability in a Manufacturing-Based Organization. Business Horizons, 35 (4): 29.

Wise, R., Baumgartner, P. 1999. Go Downstream; The New Profit Imperative in Manufacturing. Harvard Business Review, 77 (5): 133-142.

Womack, J. P., Jones, D. T., Roos, D. 1990. The Machine That Changed the World. New York: Rawson.